Mr. Kelley

lab 306

2d tues   Feb. 7

6th thurs   1:00 - 3:00   406

May 31   1:00 - 2:50

            Rm 209   5&6

B · R% = P

Base · Rate

INTERMEDIATE
ALGEBRA

alternate edition

William Wooton

Irving Drooyan

Los Angeles Pierce College

INTERMEDIATE
ALGEBRA

alternate edition

**WADSWORTH PUBLISHING COMPANY, INC.
BELMONT, CALIFORNIA**

Fourth printing: August 1966

L.C. Cat. Card No.: 65-12158

Printed in the United States of America

PREFACE

This alternate edition of *Intermediate Algebra* is designed—as is the regular edition—for a one-semester course. The material covered remains substantially the same as that incorporated in the original, although a few new topics have been added. Nevertheless, this book differs significantly from the regular edition.

We have reviewed all the exercise sets carefully in the light of classroom experience and have revised them accordingly. In particular, the exercises in the early part of the book have been strengthened by the addition of problems of somewhat greater difficulty. Increased attention has been given to the restrictions on variables in fractions, exponents and bases in rational powers, and radical expressions. Although both this and the regular edition are transitional books in the sense that they blend modern concepts and terminology with traditional topics, the changes made in this edition are toward modernization. Increased emphasis is given to structure, more material on inequalities is included, and new material dealing with Cartesian products and relations leads to a more precise formulation of the concept of a function.

As in the regular edition, the axioms for a field are stated very early in the book and are used consistently throughout the rest of the course. In addition, some assumptions that are not properly axiomatic have been stated in order to smooth the presentation; that is to say, the axiom system is deliberately far from minimal. Although there is more emphasis on proof in this alternate edition and the statement-reason form is employed at times, formal proofs do not play a significant role in the presentation. Informal deductive or inductive arguments lend plausibility to formally stated conclusions. The decision to rely on logical implication, but not on logical formalism, is a result of the authors' association with students who must begin their study of intermediate algebra at the college level. To such students the notion of a formal proof is generally profound and difficult. Our presentation is designed to give the student at least a general sense of what might constitute a formal argument, and should, in large measure, ease his passage into the more demanding climate of future courses in mathematics.

Chapters 1 through 6 review material normally encountered in some form in a beginning algebra course. The review, however, is conducted from an axiomatic standpoint, and is designed to present the material as a unified, related structure. The axioms for a field are explicitly listed in Chapter 1, and are used throughout Chapter 2 as a basis for the discussion of fundamental operations with polynomials. Operations with fractions are discussed in Chapter 3, and the definitions of the operations are shown to be consistent with the assumptions made concerning real numbers. The fundamental principle of fractions is always invoked when writing equal fractions. Chapter 4 acquaints the student with the properties of expressions involving rational number exponents. Chapter 5 introduces linear equations and inequalities as open sentences; their solution is approached through the concept of equivalent sentences. Chapter 6 is a treatment of quadratic equations and inequalities in one variable. Chapters 7 through 11 include material that is generally new to the student at this level. The presentation centers around the function concept, and heavy emphasis is placed on graphing. In particular, linear and quadratic relations and functions and their graphs are explored in some detail, variation is treated from the function standpoint, function concepts are employed in the discussion of sequences and series, and logarithms are developed from a consideration of the inverse of the exponential function.

Exercises are provided in each section, with the answers to most odd-numbered problems given in the Appendix. Although the topics in the text are those usually covered in an intermediate algebra course, Chapters 9, 10, and 11 are independent of each other and any of these may be omitted in a short course. Review exercise sets follow each chapter, and the answers to all problems in the reviews are included in the answer section.

The authors wish to thank Dr. Ernest Kuljian of the Chemistry Department of Los Angeles Pierce College for his help in formulating some of the exercises in Chapter 11, Professor Walter Hadel of the Mathematics Department for his careful reading of the manuscript, and Mrs. Doris Wooton for typing the manuscript and for extremely helpful editorial assistance.

Appreciation is also expressed to Professors E. M. Beesley of the University of Nevada, John N. Fujii of Oakland City College, C. Louise Gillespie of Los Angeles Valley College, James L. Jackson of the College of San Mateo, Joyce Shana'a of the University of Oklahoma, and Lee A. Stevens of Foothill College for their helpful comments and suggestions on the manuscript.

William Wooton
Irving Drooyan

CONTENTS

x   **Contents**

10

SEQUENCES AND SERIES   235

11

EXPONENTIAL AND LOGARITHMIC FUNCTIONS   257

INTERMEDIATE
ALGEBRA

alternate edition

I

PROPERTIES
OF REAL NUMBERS

Algebra is frequently called a generalization of arithmetic, and that is the viewpoint maintained throughout this book. Our study is concerned, basically, with numbers and the properties associated with them. It is sometimes easy to lose sight of this fact in the midst of the seemingly complicated manipulations of symbols in which we engage, but we shall be better off if we strive to give meaning to everything we do in terms of numbers.

The names used for counting numbers (one, two, etc.) should, of course, be familiar to us all. We should also be familiar with the symbols, called **numerals** (1, 2, etc.), used to represent them. In addition, we should know that numerals such as $\frac{1}{2}$, $\frac{3}{4}$, -3, $-\frac{2}{3}$, π, $\sqrt{2}$, and 4^3 also represent numbers.

The point of this discussion is that the names and symbols used to talk about numbers are not the numbers themselves. There are places in algebra where confusing the two ideas—the number itself and the symbol used to represent it—can lead to misunderstanding. In this book, however, we propose to discuss such things as the number 2 or the number 5 or the number 8234. We do so simply as a matter of convenience. We do not wish to have always to say "the number represented by the numeral 2," partly because of the seeming circumlocution, but primarily because this intent should be clear from context.

1.1   Sets and Symbolism—The Real Numbers

A **set** is simply a collection of some kind. It may be a collection of people, or books, or colors, or almost anything else; however, in algebra we are interested primarily in sets of numbers. Any one of the collection of things in a set is called a **member** or **element** of the set. For example, the counting numbers 1, 2, 3, $\cdots$ are the elements of a set we call the set of **natural numbers.** Because there exists no last counting number, we refer to this set as an **infinite set.** A set whose elements can be arranged in some fashion and counted one by one until a last element is arrived at is called a **finite set.** For example, the set of numbers represented by the symbols on a die, 1, 2, 3, 4, 5, 6, is a finite set. The finite set containing no members is called the **empty set** or **null set.**

Sets are designated symbolically by means of capital letters—A, I, R, etc.— or by means of braces, { }, used in conjunction with words or symbols. Thus, when we write

$$\{\text{counting numbers less than 7}\}$$

or

$$\{1, 2, 3, 4, 5, 6\},$$

we mean the set whose members are the numbers 1, 2, 3, 4, 5, and 6. We say that two sets are equal if they have the same members; thus

$$\{2, 3, 4\} = \{\text{counting numbers between 1 and 5}\},$$

where on the left-hand side of the equality symbol the elements are *listed* and on the right-hand side the elements are *described by a rule.* We represent the empty set by the symbol $\emptyset$.

If every member of a given set A is also a member of another set B, we say that A is a **subset** of B. Thus $\{1, 2, 3\}$ is a subset of $\{1, 2, 3, 4, 5\}$. The symbol "$\subseteq$" (read "is a subset of" or "is contained in") will be used to denote the subset relationship. If A is a subset of B and, in addition, B contains at least one member not in A, then A is called a **proper subset** of B. The symbol "$\subset$" (read "is a proper subset of" or "is properly contained in") will be used to denote proper subsets. Thus

$$\{1, 2, 3\} \subseteq \{1, 2, 3, 4\}$$

and

$$\{1, 2, 3\} \subseteq \{1, 2, 3\},$$

in which both statements make valid use of $\subseteq$, but $\subset$ is valid also for the first of these pairs of sets. That is,

$$\{1, 2, 3\} \subset \{1, 2, 3, 4\}.$$

Of course, by definition, every set is a subset of itself.

When discussing an individual element in a set, we generally denote the element by means of a lower-case letter, such as a, b, c, x, y, or z. When symbols are used in this way they are called *variables*. More formally:

*A **variable** is a symbol representing an unspecified element of a set containing more than one member.*

If the given set, called the **replacement set** of the variable, is a set of numbers (as it will be throughout this book), then the variable represents a number. That is, when we use the variable x, it is to be understood that x represents a number. We use the Greek letter $\in$ (epsilon) to denote membership in a set, and write

$$x \in R$$

to indicate that x is an element of the set R. A symbol used to denote the member of a set containing only one member is called a **constant**.

The set of numbers with which you first become acquainted is the set N of natural numbers (the counting numbers):

$$N = \{1, 2, 3, \cdots\}.$$

You learn to add, subtract, multiply, and divide such numbers, and to use them in simple quantitative problems. By the end of a first-year course in algebra, you are working with the set R of real numbers. In particular, you should be familiar with the following sets:

1. The set N of **natural numbers**, among whose elements are such numbers as 1, 2, 7, and 235.
2. The set W of **whole numbers**, whose elements consist of the natural numbers and zero.
3. The set J of **integers**, whose elements consist of the natural numbers, their negatives, and zero. Among the integers are such numbers as -7, -3, 0, 5, and 11.
4. The set Q of **rational numbers**, whose elements are all those numbers that can be represented in the form a/b, where a and b are integers and b is not zero. Among the elements of Q are such numbers as $-3/4$, $18/27$, 3, and -6.
5. The set H of **irrational numbers**, whose elements are those numbers whose representations are nonterminating, nonrepeating decimal numerals. Among the elements of this set are such numbers as $\sqrt{2}$, π, and $-\sqrt{7}$. An irrational number cannot be represented in the form a/b where a and b are integers.
6. The set R of **real numbers**, which is the set of all rational and all irrational numbers (see Figure 1.1).

Observe that $J \subset Q$, $Q \subset R$, and $H \subset R$.

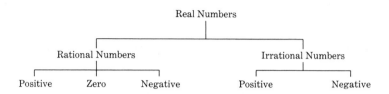

Fig. 1.1

It is with the real numbers or subsets of the real numbers that we shall be most concerned in this book.

EXERCISE 1.1

Specify each set by listing the members.

Examples:

    a. {natural numbers between 7 and 10}

    Ans.   {8, 9}

    b. {natural-number multiples of 4}

    Ans.   {4, 8, 12, $\cdots$}

1. {first five natural numbers}   **2.** {even natural numbers}

3. {odd natural numbers}   **4.** {first six odd natural numbers}

5. {odd natural numbers between 4 and 12}

6. {even natural numbers between 3 and 15}

7. {first four natural-number multiples of 3}

8. {first four natural-number multiples of 5}

In each of Problems 9–14, let

$$A = \{6, -3, \tfrac{3}{5}, \sqrt{7}, 0, \tfrac{1}{5}, -\sqrt{3}, -5, -\tfrac{2}{3}, \sqrt{5}\}.$$

Example:

What is the set whose members are the natural numbers contained in A?

Ans.   {6}

9. What is the set whose members are the integers contained in A?

10. What is the set whose members are the rational numbers contained in A?

11. What is the set whose members are the irrational numbers contained in A?

12. What is the set whose members are the odd natural numbers contained in A?

13. What is the set whose members are the positive even integers contained in A?

14. What is the set whose members are the real numbers between 1 and 7 contained in A?

15. List all possible subsets of the set $\{1, 2, 3\}$.   *Hint:* $\emptyset$ is considered a subset of every set.

16. List all possible subsets of the set $\{0, 1, 2, 3\}$.   *Hint:* $\emptyset$ is not the same set as $\{0\}$.

In Problems 17–22, state whether the given set is finite or infinite.

17. The natural numbers whose numerals end in 2.

18. The people alive today.

19. The natural numbers whose numerals contain four digits.

20. The grains of sand in the world.

21. The odd natural numbers.

22. The rational numbers between 0 and 1.

Let $a \in A$. In each of the following cases, state whether a is a variable or a constant.

23. $A = \{3, 4, 5, 6\}$ **24.** $A = \{3\}$

25. $A = \{$real numbers$\}$ **26.** $A = \{$real numbers between 1 and 2$\}$

27. $A = \{$integers between 7 and 9$\}$ **28.** $A = \{$rational numbers less than 2$\}$

In Problems 29–34, replace the comma outside the braces with either $\subset$, $\subseteq$, or $\in$.

29. $5, \{4, 5, 6\}$ **30.** $\{5\}, \{4, 5, 6\}$ **31.** $\emptyset, \{4, 5, 6\}$

32. $\{4, 5, 6\}, \{4, 5, 6\}$ **33.** $\{3\}, \{2, 3\}$ **34.** $3, \{2, 3\}$

In Problems 35–38, replace the comma with either $\subset$ or $\not\subset$ (read "is not a proper subset of").

35. $\{3, 4\}, R$ **36.** $\{\frac{3}{4}, 2\}, J$ **37.** $\{0\}, N$ **38.** $\emptyset, Q$

In Problems 39–42, replace the comma with either $\in$ or $\notin$ (read "is not an element of").

39. $3, R$ **40.** $0, J$ **41.** $\frac{2}{3}, N$ **42.** $1000, Q$

43. Without looking at Figure 1.1, draw a schematic diagram of the set of real numbers and its subsets.

In Problems 44–48, use the subset symbol "$\subseteq$" to express the relationship between the specified sets.

44. The set of natural numbers N, and the set of real numbers R.

45. The set of rational numbers Q, and the set of integers J.

46. The set of real numbers R, and the set of whole numbers W.

47. The set of irrational numbers H, and the set of real numbers R.

48. The set of rational numbers Q, and the set of whole numbers W.

1.2 Operations on Sets

Let us define some operations on two sets that we shall find useful in later sections of this book.   One such operation consists of forming the **union** of two sets, say A and B, and producing a third set which contains all of the elements that belong *either* to A or to B or to both.   The symbol $\cup$ is used to denote the operation.   Thus $A \cup B$ is read "the union of A and B" or, sometimes, "A cup B."   If $A = \{1, 2, 3, 4, 5\}$ and $B = \{3, 4, 5, 6, 7\}$, then

$$A \cup B = \{1, 2, 3, 4, 5, 6, 7\}.$$

Notice that each element in $A \cup B$ is listed only once in this example.   In general, the same symbol is not used twice in a given set notation.   We restrict each symbol to one referent in order to avoid redundancy.   The numeral "2" denotes just one number, and $\{2, 2\}$ contains only one member, even if we write its name twice.

A second operation on two sets A and B consists of forming the **intersection** of the sets and producing a third set which contains all the elements that belong to *both* A and B.   The symbol $\cap$ is used to denote this operation. Thus $A \cap B$ is read "the intersection of A and B" or, sometimes, "A cap B." For example, if $A = \{1, 2, 3, 4, 5\}$ and $B = \{3, 4, 5, 6, 7\}$, then

$$A \cap B = \{3, 4, 5\}.$$

EXERCISE 1.2

Let $A = \{2, 4, 6, 8, 10\}$, $B = \{1, 2, 3, 4, 5\}$, $C = \{1, 3, 5, 7, 9\}$, and $D = \{6, 7, 8, 9, 10\}$.   List each of the following.

Examples:

a. $A \cap B$

Ans. $A \cap B$ contains those members that are in both A and B.   Hence $A \cap B = \{2, 4\}$.

b. $(A \cap B) \cup C$

Ans.   Since $(A \cap B) = \{2, 4\}$ and $C = \{1, 3, 5, 7, 9\}$, $(A \cap B) \cup C = \{1, 2, 3, 4, 5, 7, 9\}$.

1. $B \cap C$	**2.** $C \cap D$	**3.** $A \cup D$	**4.** $B \cup C$
5. $A \cap D$	**6.** $B \cap D$	**7.** $A \cup C$	**8.** $B \cup D$
9. $A \cap A$	**10.** $C \cap C$	**11.** $B \cup B$	**12.** $D \cup D$

13. $A \cap \emptyset$ **14.** $B \cap \emptyset$ **15.** $C \cup \emptyset$ **16.** $D \cup \emptyset$

17. $(A \cap C) \cup B$ **18.** $(B \cap D) \cup A$ **19.** $(C \cup D) \cap A$ **20.** $(C \cup A) \cap D$

21. $(A \cup B) \cup C$ **22.** $(B \cap C) \cap D$

For the sets A, B, C, and D above, determine whether each of the following statements is true.

23. $(A \cap B) \cap C = A \cap (B \cap C)$

24. $(A \cup B) \cup C = A \cup (B \cup C)$

25. $A \cup (B \cap C) = (A \cup B) \cap (A \cup C)$

26. $A \cap (B \cup C) = (A \cap B) \cup (A \cap C)$

Consider two sets G and H. Under what conditions would each of the following be true?

27. $G \cup H = \emptyset$ **28.** $G \cup \emptyset = \emptyset$ **29.** $G \cap H = G$

30. $G \cup H = G$ **31.** $G \cap \emptyset = G$ **32.** $G \cup H = G \cap H$

33. Explain why, for any two sets A and B, $A \cup B = B \cup A$.

34. Explain why, for any two sets A and B, $A \cap B = B \cap A$.

35. If A contains 5 members, B contains 6 members, and $A \cap B = \emptyset$, how many members has $A \cup B$?

36. If A contains m members, B contains n members, and $A \cap B = \emptyset$, how many members has $A \cup B$?

37. If A contains 3 members, B contains 8 members, and $A \cap B$ contains 1 member, how many members has $A \cup B$?

38. If A contains m members, B contains n members, and $A \cap B$ contains k members, how many members has $A \cup B$?

1.3   Axioms of Equality and Order

In mathematics, when we make formal assumptions about numbers or their properties, we call the assumptions **axioms** or **postulates**. These assumptions may arise as a result of observing a number of specific instances, although this is not essential. They are simply formal statements about properties which we propose to assume as always valid. While we are free to formulate axioms in any way we please, it is clearly desirable that any axioms we adopt lead to useful consequences. In building a set of useful axioms, the consequences of the set must not be contradictory; that is, the axioms must not lead to contradictory conclusions.

The words *property*, *law*, and *principle* are sometimes used to denote assumptions, although these words may also be applied to certain consequences of axioms. In this book we shall use, in each situation, the word we believe to be the one most frequently encountered.   The first such assumptions to be considered have to do with equality.

An **equality**, or an "is equal to" assertion, is simply a mathematical statement that two symbols, or groups of symbols, are names for the same number.   A number has an infinite number of names.   Thus, 3, $\frac{6}{2}$, $4 - 1$, and $2 + 1$ are all names for the same number; hence the equality

$$4 - 1 = 2 + 1$$

is a statement that $4 - 1$ and $2 + 1$ are different names for the same number.

We shall assume that the "is equal to" ($=$) relationship has the following properties.

If a, b, c $\in$ R:

E–1 $a = a$ (reflexive law)

E–2 *If $a = b$, then $b = a$.*   (symmetric law)

E–3 *If $a = b$ and $b = c$, then $a = c$.*   (transitive law)

E–4 *If $a = b$ then b may be replaced by a or a by b in any*   (substitution law)
statement without altering the truth or falsity of the statement.

In writing an equality, we refer to the symbol or symbols to the left of the equals sign as the left member, and those to the right as the right member of the equality.

Because there exists a one-to-one correspondence between the *real numbers* and the *points* on a geometric line (for each real number there corresponds one and only one point on the line, and vice versa), a geometric line can be used to visualize relationships existing between real numbers.   For example, to represent $\{1, 3, 5\}$ on a line, we simply scale a straight line in convenient units with increasing positive direction indicated by an arrow, and indicate the required points with closed dots on the line.   This geometric representation is called a **line graph** or **number line** (Figure 1.2).

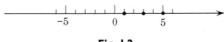

−5   0   5

Fig. 1.2

The real number corresponding to a point on a line graph is called the **coordinate** of the point, and the point is called the **graph** of the number.

A line graph can be used to separate the real numbers into three subsets—one set R_+ whose elements are associated with the points on the line to the right of 0, one set R_- whose elements are associated with the points on the line to the left of 0, and one set, the **origin**, whose only element is 0.   The elements of the set R_+ are called **positive numbers,** and in some cases we prefix their numerals with plus signs ($+1$, $+7$, $+\pi$) to denote the fact that they are positive. The elements of the set R_- are called **negative numbers,** and numerals representing such numbers are prefixed with minus signs (-2, $-\frac{1}{2}$, $-\pi$) to identify them as such. The number zero is neither positive nor negative and serves as a point of separation for the positive and negative numbers.

Because each real number is associated with a single point located a specific distance from the origin O, we can associate a distance with each real number. However, $-a$ and a are each located the same distance from the origin, and if we wish to refer simply to this distance and not to its direction to the left or right of 0, we can use the notation $|a|$ (read "the **absolute value** of a"). Thus $|a|$ is always non negative. For example, $|3| = 3$, $|-3| = 3$, $|-2| = 2$, and $|0| = 0$. A formal definition for absolute value will be given in Section 1.4.

The addition of the *positive* real number c to a real number b can be visualized as the process of locating the point corresponding to b on a line graph, and then locating the sum $b + c$ by moving along the line c units to the right of b (Figure 1.3).

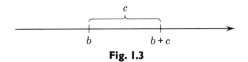

Fig. 1.3

We are now in a position to define the real number b to be **less than** the real number a if, for some *positive* real number c, $b + c = a$. Conversely, we say that if b is less than a, then there exists a *positive* $c \in R$ such that $b + c = a$. In symbols, we write $b < a$ (read "b is less than a") or, equivalently, $a > b$ (read "a is greater than b"). It is evident that, on a line graph, the point b will be found to the left of the point a (Figure 1.4). The number c is called the **difference** of a and b, and can be denoted by $a - b$.

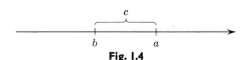

Fig. 1.4

The following symbols are used in connection with the property of order:

    $<$, read "is less than";
    $\leq$, read "is less than or equal to";
    $>$, read "is greater than";
    $\geq$, read "is greater than or equal to."

The slant bar, $/$, is used in conjunction with an order symbol to indicate the word "not"; thus $\neq$ means "is not equal to" and $\not<$ means "is not less than."

Inequalities such as
$$1 < 2 \quad \text{and} \quad 3 < 5$$
are said to be in the same sense, because the left-hand member is less than the right-hand member in each case.   Inequalities such as
$$1 < 2 \quad \text{and} \quad 5 > 3$$
are said to be of opposite sense, because in one case the left-hand member is less than the right-hand member but in the other case the left-hand member is greater than the right-hand member.

We adopt the following axioms with respect to the order of real numbers.

If $a, b, c \in R$:

0–1 *Exactly one of the following relationships holds:* **(trichotomy law)**

$$a < b, \qquad a = b, \qquad a > b.$$

0–2 *If $a < b$ and $b < c$, then $a < c$.*   **(transitive law of order)**

Line graphs can be used to display infinite sets of points as well as finite sets.   For example, Figure 1.5 is the graph of the set of all real numbers greater than or equal to 2 and less than 5.   The closed dot on the left-hand end of the shaded portion of the graph indicates that the end point is a part of the graph, while the open dot on the right indicates that the end point is not in the graph.

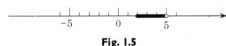

Fig. 1.5

A symbolism useful in describing sets of numbers, particularly when discussing inequalities, is
$$\{x \mid 2 \le x < 5\}$$
(read "the set of all x such that x is greater than or equal to two *and* less than five").   This symbolism, called **set-builder notation,** names a variable (in this case, x) and, at the same time, a condition on the variable (in this case, that x is greater than or equal to two and less than five).

EXERCISE 1.3

Each of the statements 1–10 is an application of one of the axioms E–1 through E–4. Justify each statement by quoting the appropriate axiom.   (There may be more than one correct answer.)

Example: If $3 = a$, and $a = b$, then $3 = b$.

   Ans.   Transitive law.

1. If $a = 2$, then $2 = a$.   2. If $a + 3 = b$, then $b = a + 3$.

3. If $x = 5$ and $5 = y$, then $x = y$.

4. If $x = 5$ and $y = x + 2$, then $y = 5 + 2$.

5. If $a = b$ and $b + 2 = 3$, then $a + 2 = 3$.

6. If $x = 4$ and $y = x + 1$, then $y = 4 + 1$.

7. $y = y$

8. If $m = n$ and $2m = 4$, then $2n = 4$.

9. If $a = 2c$ and $c = 6$, then $a = 2 \cdot 6$.

10. If $-6 = x$, then $x = -6$.

Plot the members of each of the following sets on a line graph. Use a separate line graph for each set. $N = \{\text{natural numbers}\}$ and $J = \{\text{integers}\}$.

Example: $\{x \mid -2 < x < 3, x \in J\}$

   Ans.

11. $\{x \mid x < 8, x \in N\}$ 12. $\{x \mid 2 \leq x < 8, x \in N\}$

13. $\{x \mid -5 < x < 5, x \in J\}$ 14. $\{x \mid -10 < x \leq 0, x \in J\}$

15. $\{x \mid 50 < x < 55, x \in J\}$ *Hint:* Show only an appropriate segment of the number line.

16. $\{x \mid -100 \leq x < -90, x \in J\}$

In Problems 17–28, consider $x \in R$, where $R = \{\text{real numbers}\}$, and graph each set on the number line.

Example: $\{x \mid -3 < x \leq 2\}$

   Ans.

17. $\{x \mid x > 2\}$ 18. $\{x \mid -2 \leq x < 6\}$

19. $\{x \mid x < -3 \text{ or } x > 3\}$ 20. $\{x \mid x \leq -5 \text{ or } x \geq 1\}$

21. $\{x \mid x < 5\} \cap \{x \mid x > 2\}$ 22. $\{x \mid x < 3\} \cap \{x \mid x \geq -2\}$

23. $\{x \mid x \leq 0\} \cap \{x \mid x > -5\}$ 24. $\{x \mid x > 3\} \cap \{x \mid x < -2\}$

25. $\{x \mid x > 2\} \cup \{x \mid x < -5\}$ 26. $\{x \mid x < 3\} \cup \{x \mid x \geq 3\}$

27. $\{x \mid x < 5\} \cup \{x \mid x \leq 0\}$ 28. $\{x \mid x > 1\} \cup \{x \mid x < -1\}$

Express each of the following relations by means of symbols.

Examples:

a. 5 is greater than -7.

Ans. $5 > -7$

b. x is between 5 and 8.

Ans. $5 < x < 8$

29. 7 is greater than 3.

30. 2 is less than 5.

31. -4 is less than -3.

32. -4 is greater than -7.

33. 0 is between -1 and 1.

34. 5 is greater than 4 and less than 6.

35. x is not less than y.

36. a is not greater than b.

37. x is between 3 and 5.

38. x is between -2 and 7.

39. $3x$ is not less than or equal to 5.

40. $2y$ is not less than or equal to 3.

Replace the commas with appropriate order symbols.

41. $-2, 5$

42. $3, 4$

43. $-7, -1$

44. $0, -1$

45. $-5, -2$

46. $\dfrac{-3}{2}, \dfrac{-3}{4}$

47. $1\dfrac{1}{2}, \dfrac{3}{2}$

48. $3, \dfrac{6}{2}$

49. $3, 5, 7$

50. $-3, 0, 3$

51. $3, \dfrac{12}{4}, 2$

52. $5, 5, 5$

Rewrite without using absolute-value notation.

53. $|5|$

54. $|-3|$

55. $-\left|-\dfrac{1}{2}\right|$

56. $-|\pi|$

57. $|0|$

58. $|-7|$

59. $|-2|$

60. $|-5|$

Write an equivalent relation without using the slant bar.

61. $2 \not> 5$

62. $-1 \not< -2$

63. $7 \not> 8$

64. $-3 \not> 0$

65. $x \not< y$

66. $x \not> z$

In Problems 67–70, write the relation in two ways—with the slant bar and without it.

67. x is positive.

68. x is negative.

69. x is nonnegative.

70. x is nonpositive.

1.4 Properties of the Real Numbers

In addition to the equality and order axioms, we take as axioms the following properties of the real numbers.

If $a, b, c \in R$:

R–1 $a + b$ *is a unique real number.*   **(closure for addition)**

R–2 $a + b = b + a$ **(commutative law of addition)**

R–3 $(a + b) + c = a + (b + c)$ (associative law of addition) *group*

R–4   *ab is a unique real number.*   (closure for multiplication)

R–5 $ab = ba$ (commutative law of multiplication)

R–6 $(ab)c = a(bc)$ (associative law of multiplication)

R–7 $a(b + c) = ab + ac$ (distributive law)

R–8   *There exists a unique number 0 with the property $a + 0 = 0 + a = a$.*   (identity element for addition)

R–9   *There exists a unique number 1 with the property $a \cdot 1 = 1 \cdot a = a$.*   (identity element for multiplication)

R–10   *For each real number a, there exists a unique real number $-a$ (called the negative of a) with the property $a + (-a) = (-a) + (a) = 0$.*   (negative or additive inverse axiom)

R–11   *For each real number a except zero, there exists a unique real number $1/a$ (called the reciprocal of a) with the property $a(1/a) = (1/a)a = 1$.*   (reciprocal or multiplicative inverse axiom)

Parentheses are used in some of the above relations (and hereafter) to indicate an order of operations. Operations enclosed in parentheses are performed before any other operations.

Axioms R–1 and R–4 assert that the sum or product of any two real numbers is always another real number, and that each product and each sum is unique. When the performance of an operation on two elements of some set of numbers always results in another element of the same set, we say that the set is **closed** with respect to that operation. Thus, we assume that the set of real numbers is closed with respect to addition and multiplication.

Axioms R–2 and R–5 state that the order in which we write two terms in a sum or two factors in a product does not alter the sum or product. Thus,

$$2 + 4 = 4 + 2$$

and

$$2 \cdot 4 = 4 \cdot 2.$$

Axioms R–3 and R–6 assert that three terms in a sum or three factors in a product may be associated in either of two ways, and give meaning to $a + b + c$ and $a \cdot b \cdot c$. Thus,

$$(2 + 3) + 4 = 2 + (3 + 4)$$

and

$$(2 \cdot 3)4 = 2(3 \cdot 4).$$

If both the associative and commutative laws are invoked, we can add any number of terms or multiply any number of factors in any order that we wish.

Axiom R–7 gives us a means of relating the operations of addition and multiplication. Thus,

$$2(3 + 4) = 2(3) + 2(4).$$

If we use this law with the associative law, we can show that

$$a(b + c + d) = ab + ac + ad,$$
$$a(b + c + d + e) = ab + ac + ad + ae, \quad \text{etc.}$$

We refer to this property as the generalized distributive law.

Axioms R–8 and R–9 simply state some basic properties of the numbers zero and one. The sum of zero and any real number a is a, and the product of one and any real number a is a.

R–10 asserts the existence of a negative for each real number, and tells us that the sum of any real number and its negative is zero. For example,

$$3 + (-3) = 0.$$

R–11 is another existence axiom. It guarantees the existence of a reciprocal for each nonzero number and tells us that the product of any such number a and its reciprocal, $1/a$, is 1. For example,

$$3 \cdot \frac{1}{3} = 1.$$

Axioms R–8 through R–11 state that the numbers 0, 1, $-a$, and $1/a$ $(a \neq 0)$ are unique; that is, there is only one such element for the property stated. Although it follows logically from the other axioms, we shall take this property of uniqueness as an assumption.

The axioms R–1 through R–11 together with axioms E–1 through E–4 imply other properties of the real numbers. (Uniqueness for the elements 0, 1, $-a$, and $1/a$ is among these.) Such implications are generally stated as **theorems,** which are simply assertions of facts that are logical consequences of the axioms and other theorems. Theorems generally consist of two parts: an "if" part, called the **hypothesis,** and a "then" part, called the **conclusion.** Proving a theorem consists of showing that if the hypothesis is true, then because of the axioms the conclusion must be true. Proofs are displayed in a variety of formats. We shall illustrate several cases of relatively formal proofs in this section and then, in general, use *informal arguments* through the remainder of the book. Consider the following theorems.

Addition Law of Equality

> *If a, b, and c $\in$ R, and a = b, then*
>
> $$a + c = b + c \quad \text{and} \quad c + a = c + b.$$

Proof

Statement	*Reason*
1. a, b, and $c \in R$ and $a = b$	1. Hypothesis.
2. $a + c \in R$	2. Closure law for addition.
3. $a + c = a + c$	3. Reflexive law of equality.
4. $a + c = b + c$	4. Substitution in (3) from (1), by substitution law.
5. $c + a = c + b$	5. Commutative law of addition.

Thus, if the hypothesis "a, b, and c are real numbers and $a = b$" is true, the conclusion "$a + c = b + c$ and $c + a = c + b$" follows logically.

The following theorem is closely analogous to the one above.

Multiplication Law of Equality

$$\textit{If } a, b, \textit{ and } c \in R, \textit{ and } a = b, \textit{ then}$$

$$ac = bc \quad \textit{and} \quad ca = cb.$$

The proof exactly parallels that of the previous theorem and is left as an exercise (Problem 45, Exercise 1.4).

Cancellation Law for Addition

$$\textit{If } a, b, \textit{ and } c \in R, \textit{ and } a + c = b + c, \textit{ then}$$

$$a = b.$$

Proof

Statement	*Reason*
1. $a + c = b + c$	1. Hypothesis.
2. $(a + c) + (-c) = (b + c) + (-c)$	2. Addition law of equality.
3. $a + [c + (-c)] = b + [c + (-c)]$	3. Associative law of addition.
4. $c + (-c) = 0$	4. Additive inverse.
5. $a + 0 = b + 0$	5. Substitution in (3) from (4), by substitution law.
6. $a + 0 = a;\ b + 0 = b$	6. Identity element for addition.
7. $a = b$	7. Substitution in (5) from (6), by substitution law.

Cancellation Law for Multiplication

$$\textit{If } a, b, \textit{ and } c \in R,\ c \neq 0, \textit{ and } ac = bc, \textit{ then}$$

$$a = b.$$

The proof exactly parallels that of the cancellation law for addition and is also left as an exercise (Problem 46, Exercise 1.4).

Zero Factor Law

$$\text{For every } a \in R, \ a \cdot 0 = 0.$$

Proof

Statement	*Reason*
1. $0 + 0 = 0$	1. Identity element for addition.
2. $a \cdot (0 + 0) = a \cdot 0$	2. Multiplication law of equality.
3. $a \cdot 0 + a \cdot 0 = a \cdot 0$	3. Distributive law.
4. $a \cdot 0 = 0 + a \cdot 0$	4. Identity element for addition.
5. $a \cdot 0 + a \cdot 0 = 0 + a \cdot 0$	5. Substitution in (3) from (4) by substitution law.
6. $a \cdot 0 = 0$	6. Cancellation law for addition.

Since the number $-a$ is assumed unique, it follows that, if $a + b = 0$, $b = -a$; that is, if the sum of two numbers is zero, each is the negative of the other. Thus, the negative of a negative number is a positive number; that is,

$$(-3) + [-(-3)] = 0$$

implies that

$$-(-3) = 3.$$

A formalization of this idea will be useful later.

Double Negative Law

$$\text{For each } a \in R, \ -(-a) = a.$$

As one application of this law, we can write a formal definition for absolute value:

$$|x| = \begin{array}{l} x, \quad \text{if} \quad x \geq 0, \\ -x, \quad \text{if} \quad x < 0. \end{array}$$

We have given names to the theorems above because they are used frequently throughout the book. In general, the laws we obtain as the result of our arguments are not named.

EXERCISE 1.4

Each of the statements 1–26 is an application of one of the axioms R–1 through R–11. Justify each statement by citing the appropriate axiom.

Example: $2(3 + 1) = 2 \cdot 3 + 2 \cdot 1$

    Ans. Distributive law.

1. $5 + 3 = 3 + 5$ 2. $7 + 0 = 7$

3. $3 \cdot 2 = 2 \cdot 3$ 4. $5 + (4 + 1) = (5 + 4) + 1$

5. $3 + (-3) = 0$ 6. $7 \cdot \frac{1}{7} = 1$

7. If x and y are real numbers and $xy = z$, then z is a real number.

8. If a and b are real numbers and $a + b = c$, then c is a real number.

9. $(2 \cdot 3)4 = 2(3 \cdot 4)$ 10. $3 \cdot 1 = 3$

11. $3(2 + 5) = 3 \cdot 2 + 3 \cdot 5$ 12. $5 + (-2) = (-2) + 5$

13. $3(-2) = (-2)3$ 14. $3 \cdot 0 = 0 \cdot 3$

15. $(-4 + 3) + 1 = -4 + (3 + 1)$ 16. $-2[1 + (-5)] = -2 \cdot 1 + (-2)(-5)$

17. $a\left(\frac{1}{a}\right) = \left(\frac{1}{a}\right)a \quad (a \neq 0)$ 18. $a(b + c) = (b + c)a$

19. $(a + b) + c = c + (a + b)$ 20. $a + (b + c) = a + (c + b)$

21. $a + (b + c)d = a + d(b + c)$ 22. $a + (b + c)d = (b + c)d + a$

23. $a + c(b + d) = a + cb + cd$ 24. $a[b + (c + d)] = ab + a(c + d)$

25. $(a + b) + [-(a + b)] = 0$ 26. $\frac{1}{c}(a + b) = \frac{1}{c} \cdot a + \frac{1}{c} \cdot b \quad (c \neq 0)$

27. If a is negative, what is $-a$?   28. If $-a$ is positive, what is a?

29. If $-a$ is negative, what is a?   30. If a is positive, what is $-a$?

Each of the statements 31–40 is an application of one of the six theorems $(a, b, c \in R)$:

I.   If $a = b$, then $a + c = b + c$ Addition law of equality.
II. If $a = b$, then $ca = cb$ Multiplication law of equality.
III. If $a + c = b + c$, then $a = b$ Cancellation law for addition.
IV. If $ca = cb$, then $a = b$ Cancellation law for multiplication.
V. $a \cdot 0 = 0$ Zero factor law.
VI. $-(-a) = a$ Double negative law.

Justify each statement by citing the appropriate theorem.

31. If $x = 2$, then $x + 3 = 2 + 3$.   32. $3 \cdot 0 = 0$

33. $-(-7) = 7$ 34. If $y = -3$, then $2y = 2(-3)$.

35. If $3r = 3s$, then $r = s$.   36. $-(-2) = 2$

37. $(-5)(0) = 0$ 38. If $-6m = -6n$, then $m = n$.

39. If $(x - y) + 3 = z + 3$, then $x - y = z$.

40. If $k(x + 2y) = kz$, then $x + 2y = z$.

41. Is the set $\{0, 1\}$ closed with respect to addition? With respect to multiplication?

42. Is the set $\{-1, 0, 1\}$ closed with respect to addition? With respect to multiplication?

43. Is the set {1, 2} closed with respect to addition? With respect to multiplication?

44. Which of the subsets of the real numbers N, W, J, Q, and H are closed with respect to addition? With respect to multiplication?

45. Use a proof similar to the one shown for the addition law of equality and prove the multiplication law of equality.

46. Use a proof similar to the one shown for the cancellation law for addition and prove the cancellation law for multiplication.

1.5 Addition

Addition is a binary operation that pairs two numbers $a \in R$ and $b \in R$ with a third number in the set R, $a + b$. The number $a + b$ is called the **sum** of a and b.

The assumptions we have made regarding the real numbers permit us to formulate some further statements (theorems) concerning sums and differences as logical consequences of these assumptions. The statements follow from the assumptions; however, it is preferable to be able to use these statements themselves to justify the routine manipulation of numbers in arithmetic without each time having to refer to the axioms and invoke the full logical machinery of the system. We should be aware, though, that the procedures developed here do not materialize out of thin air, but are consequences of the assumptions we have made.

In this section, let us see how the axioms we have adopted relate to rewriting sums. First, let us make an additional assumption:

0–3   *If a, $b \in R$, and if $a > 0$ and $b > 0$, then $a + b > 0$.*

This is an agreement that the sum of two positive numbers is positive.

Next, let us look at a property of the additive inverses of real numbers.

$$\text{If } a, b \in R, \text{ then } (-a) + (-b) = -(a + b).$$

Proof

Statement	*Reason*
1. $[(-a) + (a)] + [(-b) + (b)] = 0$	1. Additive inverse axiom and the identity axiom for addition.
2. $[(-a) + (-b)] + [(a) + (b)] = 0$	2. Associative and commutative laws of addition.
3. $[-(a) + (-b)] = -[(a) + (b)]$	3. Uniqueness of the additive inverse.

We have omitted some detail in this proof and condensed several steps. The degree of rigorous detail desirable in proofs of this kind is purely relative. What is important now is that you be able to follow and understand the argument.

Among other things, this theorem implies that the sum of two negative numbers is the negative of the sum of the absolute values of the numbers. For if $a > 0$ and $b > 0$, then $-a < 0$ and $-b < 0$, and $(-a) + (-b)$ is the sum of two negative numbers. Since 0–3 assures us that $a + b > 0$, then $-(a + b) < 0$. Now if a and b are positive, $|-a| = a$ and $|-b| = b$, so that

$$(-a) + (-b) = -(|-a| + |-b|),$$

as asserted. For example,

$$(-3) + (-7) = -(|-3| + |-7|) = -(3 + 7) = -10.$$

Now, what can be said about the sum of a positive and a negative number? We can begin by looking at a specific example. Observe that

$$7 = 2 + 5,$$

and, by the addition law of equality,

$$
\begin{aligned}
7 + (-5) &= (2 + 5) + (-5) \\
&= 2 + [5 + (-5)] \quad \text{(Why?)} \\
&= 2 + 0,
\end{aligned}
$$

or

$$7 + (-5) = 2.$$

We observe that the sum, 2, is the *difference* of the absolute values of 7 and -5, that is, $7 - |-5| = 2$.

We can show that if a and b are positive real numbers, such that $a > b$, it is always true that $a + (-b) = a - b$. Thus:

If a, $b \in R$, and $a > b > 0$, then $a + (-b) = a - b$.

The proof of this statement is quite short. By the definition of difference, if $a > b > 0$, then $a - b$ is the positive number c such that

$$a = b + c.$$

Adding $(-b)$ to each member of the latter equation, we have

$$a + (-b) = (b + c) + (-b),$$

where the right-hand member can be simplified to c. Since $c = a - b$, then, by the transitive law of equality,

$$a + (-b) = a - b.$$

A similar argument will establish the fact that, if $b > a > 0$, then

$$a + (-b) = -(b - a).$$

Summarizing what has been done, we see that the sum of a positive and a negative number is equal to the difference of their absolute values, and is positive or negative as the number of greater absolute value is positive or negative, and if the absolute values are equal, the sum is 0.

For example,

$$8 + (-6) = 8 - 6 = 2,$$

$$-3 + 5 = 5 - |-3| = 5 - 3 = 2,$$

$$-12 + 10 = -(|-12| - 10) = -(12 - 10) = -2,$$

$$5 + (-7) = -(|-7| - 5) = -(7 - 5) = -2,$$

$$-5 + 5 = |-5| - 5 = 5 - 5 = 0.$$

This process is easily accomplished mentally.

The definition given in Section 1.3 for the difference of two real numbers a and b, for $a < b$, can be generalized. Thus, for $a, b \in R$, we define the difference of any two real numbers

$$a - b$$

to be the real number c such that

$$b + c = a.$$

It follows that

$$(b + c) + (-b) = a + (-b)$$ Addition law of equality.
$$(c + b) + (-b) = a + (-b)$$ Commutative law of addition.
$$c + [b + (-b)] = a + (-b)$$ Associative law of addition.
$$c + 0 = a + (-b)$$ Additive inverse axiom.
$$c = a + (-b)$$ Identity element for addition.

This argument asserts that the difference, $a - b$, a, $b \in R$, is equal to the sum of a and the additive inverse of b, that is,

$$a - b = a + (-b).$$

For example,

$$8 - (-3) = 8 + [-(-3)] = |8| + |3| = 11,$$
$$(-7) - (4) = (-7) + (-4) = -(|-7| + |-4|) = -11,$$
$$(-5) - (-2) = (-5) + [-(-2)] = -(|-5| - |2|) = -3.$$

We have now used the signs $+$ and $-$ in two ways. In Section 1.3 we used these signs to denote positive and negative numbers. Here we have used them as signs of operation to indicate the sum or difference of two numbers. Since we have seen that the difference $a - b$ is given by $a + (-b)$, we may consider the symbols $a - b$ as representing either the difference of a and b or, preferably, the sum of a and $(-b)$.

Wed

To aid in discussing the results of operations, it is convenient to use the term "basic numeral." For example, while the numeral "3 + 5" names the sum of the real numbers 3 and 5, we shall refer to "8" as the basic numeral for this number. Similarly, the basic numeral for 2 − 8 is "− 6."

EXERCISE 1.5

1−19

Write each sum or difference using a basic numeral.

23, 25

Examples:

  a. $3 + (-7)$ b. $(-3) - (-7)$ c. $(-2) + (-3) - (4)$

  Ans. -4 $(-3) + [-(-7)]$ $(-2) + (-3) + (-4)$

                     $(-3) + (+7)$ **Ans.** -9

               Ans. 4

1. $2 + 3$	**2.** $3 + (-5)$	**3.** $(-5) + (-1)$
4. $25 + (-30)$	**5.** $(-8) + (-28)$	**6.** $(6) + (-6)$
7. $8 - 7$	**8.** $7 - 8$	**9.** $25 - (-2)$
10. $18 - (-18)$	**11.** $-18 - (-18)$	**12.** $(-12) - (-2)$
13. $3 + 2 - 4$	**14.** $8 - 2 + 1$	**15.** $8 - (+2) + (-3)$
16. $(-3) - (-5) - 6$	**17.** $8 + (-8) - (+1)$	**18.** $25 + 18 - 43$
19. $8 - 8 + 6$	**20.** $8 + 3 - 5$	

In Problems 21–26, use the number line to help visualize the relationship.

21. If $a < b < 0$, is $b - a > 0$ or is $b - a < 0$?

22. If $|a| < b$, and $a \neq 0$, is $b - a > 0$ or is $b - a < 0$?

23. If $a < |b|$, and $a > 0$, must $a + b$ be positive? Explain.

24. If $|a| < |b|$, and $a < 0$, must $a + b$ be less than $|b|$? Explain.

25. If $a - b < 0$, must $|a|$ be less than $|b|$? Explain.

26. If $a + b < a$, must $|a|$ be less than $|b|$? Explain.

27. Argue that the real numbers are closed with respect to subtraction.

28. Observe that, for a, b, and c positive,

$$a + (-b) = a + [c + (-c)] + (-b),$$

from which

$$a + (-b) = (a + c) + (-c) + (-b).$$

Argue from here that if $a + c = b$, that is, if $b > a$, then $a + (-b) = -c$.

1.6   Multiplication

Multiplication is a binary operation that pairs two numbers $a \in R$ and $b \in R$ with a third number in the set R, $a \cdot b$ or ab. The number ab is called the **product** of the **factors** a and b. In this section, we shall examine briefly some properties of products of real numbers. Let us begin by making another assumption:

0–4   *If a, b $\in$ R, and a > 0 and b > 0, then ab > 0.*

This is an agreement that the product of positive real numbers is positive.

Now, what can be said about the product of a positive and a negative number? Let us assume that a and b are positive and begin by considering the equality

$$b + (-b) = 0.$$

By the multiplication law of equality,

$$a[b + (-b)] = a \cdot 0,$$

and the distributive law and the zero factor law permit us to write

$$ab + a(-b) = 0.$$

Now, since $a(-b)$ must be a number that adds to ab to yield zero, it follows that

$$a(-b) = -(ab) = -ab$$

or, alternatively,

$$(-b)(a) = -(ab) = -ab.$$

Thus the product of two real numbers with unlike signs is always negative. By a similar argument (see Exercise 1.6, Problem 62), we can show that $(-a)(-b)$ is a number that adds to $-ab$ to give zero, so

$$(-a)(-b) = -(-ab)$$

or, from the double negative law,

$$(-a)(-b) = ab.$$

For example,

$$(3)(-2) = -6, \qquad (-3)(-2) = 6,$$
$$(-2)(3) = -6, \qquad (3)(2) = 6.$$

We define the **quotient** of two real numbers a and b to be the number q,

$$\frac{a}{b} = q \quad (b \neq 0),$$

such that

$$bq = a.$$

In general, a fraction bar is used to indicate that one algebraic expression is to be divided by another; the dividend is the numerator and the divisor is the denominator. Note that the denominator is restricted to nonzero numbers, for, if b is zero and a is not zero, then there exists no q such that

$$0 \cdot q = a.$$

Again, if b is zero and a is zero, then, for *any* q,

$$0 \cdot q = 0,$$

and the quotient is not unique. Thus we can state:

Division by zero is not defined.

Since the quotient of two numbers a/b is a number q such that $bq = a$, the sign of the quotient of two signed numbers must be consistent with the laws of signs for the product of two signed numbers. Therefore, for $a, b, q > 0$,

$$\frac{+a}{+b} = +q, \qquad \frac{-a}{-b} = +q,$$

$$\frac{+a}{-b} = -q, \qquad \frac{-a}{+b} = -q.$$

It follows from our definition of a quotient that a/b and $a(1/b)$ represent the same number. To see that this is true, assume that

$$a\left(\frac{1}{b}\right) = q \quad (b \neq 0). \tag{1}$$

Then multiply each member of this equality by b to obtain

$$a\left(\frac{1}{b}\right)b = qb; \tag{2}$$

since $(1/b)b = 1$, (2) becomes

$$a = qb.$$

But, by definition, $a = qb$ implies that $q = a/b$, and, by the transitive law of equality from (1) above,

$$\frac{a}{b} = a\left(\frac{1}{b}\right).$$

For convenient reference, we shall call this relationship the alternate definition of a quotient.

Recall that in discussing the product abc, we refer to the numbers a, b, and c as *factors* of the product. Thus 2 and 3 are factors of 6; 5 and 1 are factors of 5. If a natural number greater than 1 has no factors that are natural numbers other than itself and 1, it is said to be a **prime number.** Thus 2, 3, 5, 7, 11, etc. are prime numbers. A natural number greater than 1 that is not a prime number is said to be a **composite number.** Thus 4, 6, 8, 9, 10, etc. are composite numbers. When a composite number is exhibited as a product of prime factors only, it is said to be **completely factored.**

For example, although 30 may be factored into (5)(6), (10)(3), (15)(2), or (1)(30), if we continue the factorization, we arrive at the set of prime factors 2, 3, and 5 in each case. Although it is unnecessary to develop the argument here, it is a fact that, except for order, *each composite number has one and only one prime factorization.* This is known as the Fundamental Theorem of Arithmetic.

Notice again that the words "composite" and "prime" are used in reference to natural numbers only. Integers, rational numbers, and irrational numbers are not referred to as either prime or composite. Any negative integer can, however, be expressed as the product $(-1)a$, where a is a natural number. Hence, if we refer to the completely factored form of a negative integer, we refer to the product of (-1) and the prime factors of the associated natural number.

It is evident that there are infinitely many sets of factors for a natural number if *real numbers* are considered as factors. Thus 30 can also be expressed as $(\frac{1}{2})(60)$, $(\frac{1}{3})(90)$, $(\pi)(30/\pi)$, etc., where the possibilities are unlimited.

EXERCISE 1.6

Write each product or quotient using a basic numeral.

Examples:

a. $(-3)(2)$ b. $(-7)(-5)$ c. $(-2)(-3)(-5)$

Ans. -6 Ans. 35   Ans. -30

1. $(3)(-2)$ 2. $(-7)(6)$ 3. $(-12)(-4)$

4. $(8)(5)$ 5. $(-6)(-2)(-3)$ 6. $(8)(-1)(5)$

7. $(3)(-2)(0)$ 8. $(-75)(0)(-5)$ 9. $(-4)(4)(4)$

10. $(-3)(3)(-3)$ 11. $(-2)(-3)(-4)$ 12. $(-1)(-10)(-5)$

Examples:

a. $\dfrac{-18}{9}$ b. $\dfrac{-27}{-3}$ c. $\dfrac{6}{-2}$

Ans. -2 Ans. 9   Ans. -3

13. $\dfrac{24}{6}$ 14. $\dfrac{-50}{10}$ 15. $\dfrac{-18}{-2}$

16. $\dfrac{36}{-9}$ 17. $\dfrac{0}{-7}$ 18. $\dfrac{0}{27}$

19. $\dfrac{-32}{0}$ 20. $\dfrac{-63}{0}$

From the definition of a quotient, rewrite each of the following expressions in the form $a = bq$.

Examples:

a. $\dfrac{18}{-3} = -6$

    Ans. $18 = (-3)(-6)$

b. $\dfrac{-27}{-3} = 9$

    Ans. $-27 = (-3)(9)$

21. $\dfrac{-32}{-8} = 4$ 22. $\dfrac{-14}{2} = -7$ 23. $\dfrac{21}{-7} = -3$

24. $\dfrac{36}{18} = 2$ 25. $\dfrac{56}{-7} = -8$ 26. $\dfrac{-54}{-9} = 6$

Rewrite each of the following quotients as a product in which one factor is the reciprocal of a natural number.

Examples:

a. $\dfrac{3}{4}$

    Ans. $3\left(\dfrac{1}{4}\right)$

b. $\dfrac{16}{5}$

    Ans. $16\left(\dfrac{1}{5}\right)$

c. $\dfrac{7}{9}$

    Ans. $7\left(\dfrac{1}{9}\right)$

27. $\dfrac{7}{8}$ 28. $\dfrac{27}{7}$ 29. $\dfrac{3}{8}$ 30. $\dfrac{9}{17}$

31. $\dfrac{82}{11}$ 32. $\dfrac{3}{13}$ 33. $\dfrac{7}{100}$ 34. $\dfrac{3}{1000}$

Rewrite each of the following products as a quotient.

35. $3\left(\dfrac{1}{2}\right)$ 36. $8\left(\dfrac{1}{3}\right)$ 37. $2\left(\dfrac{1}{7}\right)$ 38. $\left(\dfrac{1}{100}\right)3$

39. $\left(\dfrac{1}{8}\right)5$ 40. $\left(\dfrac{1}{7}\right)6$ 41. $9\left(\dfrac{1}{2}\right)$ 42. $7\left(\dfrac{1}{10,000}\right)$

Express each of the following integers in completely factored form. If the integer is a prime number, so state.

Examples:

a. 36   b. 29   c. -51

  Ans. $(2)(2)(3)(3)$ Ans.   Prime   Ans. $-1(3)(17)$

43. 8   44. 26   45. 49   46. 18

47. 17   48. -64 49. -12 50. 23

51. 56   52. 65   53. -38 54. -47

55. 20   56. 39   57. 106   58. 117

59. What can be said about the sign on the product of an even number of negative numbers? An odd number of negative numbers?

60. Argue that the real numbers are closed with respect to division as long as the divisor is not zero.

61. Show that if $a \neq b$, $(a - b)(b - a) < 0$.

62. By observing that $b + (-b) = 0$, and that the multiplication law of equality permits us to write $-a[b + (-b)] = -a \cdot 0$, parallel the argument in the text to show that if a, $b > 0$, $(-a)(-b) = ab$.

63. Notice that 1 is not called a prime number. Considering the statement of the uniqueness of the prime factors of a composite number, can you tell why 1 is not included in the set of prime numbers?

CHAPTER REVIEW

1. Let $A = \{3, -2, \frac{1}{2}, \sqrt{3}, 0, -\frac{2}{3}, \sqrt{2}\}$.
   a. List the members of $S = \{x \mid x \in A \text{ and } x \text{ is an integer}\}$.
   b. List the members of $S = \{x \mid x \in A \text{ and } x \text{ is a natural number}\}$.

2. Let $A = \{3, 5, 7, 9\}$ and $B = \{-1, 3, 7, 11\}$.
   a. List the members of $A \cup B$.   b. List the members of $A \cap B$.

3. List the subsets of $\{1, 2, 3, 4, 5\}$ that have $\{1, 3, 5\}$ as a subset.

4. If A contains 7 members, B contains 13 members, and $A \cup B$ contains 15 members, how many members has $A \cap B$?

Each of the statements 5–8 is an application of one or more of the axioms on pages 12 and 13. Justify each statement.

5. $4 + 0 = 4$ 6. $4(\frac{1}{4}) = 1$

7. $6 \cdot 3 = 3 \cdot 6$ 8. $(5) + (-5) = 0$

Each of the statements 9–12 is a special case of a law that is a consequence of the axioms on pages 12 and 13. Assuming that each variable represents a real number, justify each statement.

9. If $x = 4$, then $x + 3 = 4 + 3$.   10. $5 \cdot 0 = 0$

11. If $5x = 5y$, then $x = y$.   12. $-(-3) = 3$

13. If $a \leq b$ and $b < c$, how is a related to c?

14. Use the symbols a, b, c, and $<$ to show that b is between a and c.

15. Express 96 in completely factored form.

16. What relationship must exist between a and b if $|a - b| = a - b$?

17. Write the quotient $2x/2y$ ($y \neq 0$) as a product in which one factor is $2x$.

18. Graph $\{x \mid -2 < x \leq 9, x \text{ an integer}\}$.

19. Let $A = \{x \mid x \leq 3, x \text{ a real number}\}$ and $B = \{x \mid x > 1, x \text{ a real number}\}$. Graph $A \cap B$.

20. Let $A = \{x \mid x > 7, x \text{ a real number}\}$ and $B = \{x \mid x < -2, x \text{ a real number}\}$ Graph $A \cup B$.

2

POLYNOMIALS

2.1 Definitions

In Section 1.1, "variable" was defined through the use of the terms "set" and "member of." Since we can define words only by using other words, we must have some terms with which to begin a chain of definitions. In algebra we necessarily take as undefined a small number of terms about which most of us have some intuitive notion. These include "set," "member of," "number," "addition," and "multiplication," among others. From these undefined terms we shall define others.

Some agreements should first be made about symbolism. As we have seen, the sum of two numbers is expressed by writing $a + b$, and their product by writing ab. In some cases, where the intent needs clarification, a raised dot is used to indicate multiplication—for example, $a \cdot b$, $x \cdot y$, $2 \cdot 3$. In other cases, parentheses are written around one or both of the symbols, as $(2)(3)$, $2(3)$, $(x)(x)$. If the factors in a product are identical, the multiplicity of factors is indicated by means of a natural number **exponent.** An exponent is a small numeral written to the right and above a given numeral to indicate the number of times the number represented by the given numeral appears as a factor in a product; thus $x \cdot x = x^2$, $y \cdot y \cdot y = y^3$, $3 \cdot 3 \cdot 3 \cdot 3 \cdot 3 = 3^5$. If no exponent appears, the exponent 1 is intended—that is, $x = x^1$. The number represented by the symbol to which the exponent is attached is called the **base,** and the product is said to be a **power** of the base.

Any collection of numerals, variables, and signs of operation is called an **expression.** In an expression of the form $A + B + C + \cdots$, A, B, and C are called **terms** of the expression. Any factor or group of factors in a term is said to be the **coefficient** of the remaining factors in the term. Thus, in the term $3xyz$, $3x$ is the coefficient of yz, y is the coefficient of $3xz$, 3 is the coefficient of xyz, and so on. Hereafter, the word "coefficient" will refer to a number unless otherwise indicated. For example, the coefficient of the term $4xy$ is 4; the coefficient of $-2a^2b$ is -2. If no coefficient appears in a term, the coefficient is understood to be 1. Thus x shall be viewed as $1x$.

An expression in which the operations involved consist solely of addition, subtraction, multiplication, and division, and in which all variables occur as natural number powers only, is called a **rational expression.** Thus, 5, $(x + y)/2$, $x - 1/x$, $(3x + 2y)/(x - y)$, and $x^2 + 2x + 1$ are rational expressions. Any rational expression in which no variable occurs in a denominator is called a **polynomial.** Thus, x^2, 5, $3x^2 - 2x + 1$, $\frac{1}{5}x - 2$, and $x^2y - 2x + y$ are polynomials. A polynomial consisting of only one term is called a **monomial.** If the polynomial contains two or three terms, we refer to it as a **binomial** or **trinomial,** respectively. For example,

$$3, \ x^2y, \text{ and } 5x^3 \text{ are monomials,}$$

$$x + y, \ 2x^2 - 3x, \text{ and } 4x + 3y \text{ are binomials,}$$

$$4x + 3y + 2z, \ x^2 + 2x + 1, \text{ and } 5xy + 2x - 3y \text{ are trinomials,}$$

and each of these examples is a polynomial.

The **degree** of a monomial is given by the exponent on the variable in the monomial. Thus $3x^4$ is of fourth degree, and $7x^5$ is of fifth degree. If the monomial contains more than one variable, the degree is given by the sum of the exponents on the variables. Thus the monomial $3x^2y^3z$ is of sixth degree in x, y, and z. It can also be described as being of second degree in x, or third degree in y, or of first degree in z. The degree of a polynomial is the same as the degree of its term of largest degree; $3x^2 + 2x + 1$ is a second-degree polynomial, $x^5 - x - 1$ is a fifth-degree polynomial, and $2x - 3$ is a first-degree polynomial.

If the constants in a polynomial are real numbers, then the polynomial is called a **polynomial over the field of real numbers.** If the variables are restricted to represent only real numbers, then the polynomial is said to be a **polynomial in the real variable** x. If both the coefficients and the variables are restricted to real values, we say that the polynomial is a **real polynomial.**

Polynomials are frequently represented by symbols such as

$$P(x), \qquad D(y), \qquad Q(z),$$

where the symbol in parentheses designates the variable. For example, we might write

$$P(x) = 2x^2 - 2x + 1,$$
$$D(y) = y^6 - 2y^2 + 3y - 2,$$
$$Q(z) = 8z^4 + 3z^3 - 2z^2 + z - 1.$$

The notation $P(x)$ can be used to denote values of the polynomial for specific values of x. Thus $P(2)$ means the value of the polynomial $P(x)$ when x is replaced by 2. For example, if

$$P(x) = x^2 - 2x + 1,$$

then

$$P(2) = 2^2 - 2(2) + 1 = 1,$$
$$P(3) = 3^2 - 2(3) + 1 = 4,$$

and

$$P(-4) = (-4)^2 - 2(-4) + 1 = 25.$$

EXERCISE 2.1

Write the given expression using exponents.

Examples:

a. $xx + xyyy$ b. $aac - abbbcc$

   Ans. $x^2 + xy^3$ **Ans.** $a^2c - ab^3c^2$

1. xxx	**2.** xxy	**3.** $-5abbb$
4. $-3aab$	**5.** $-2xxyyy$	**6.** $xyyyyz$
7. $-rr + rss$	**8.** $-2abb - aab$	**9.** $xxx + yyy$
10. $2bb - 3aab$	**11.** $3aac - abbcc$	**12.** $2aaab - 2bbcc$

Write the given expression without exponents.

Examples:

a. $-x^3(-y)^2$ b. $2x^3 - (2x)^3$

   Ans. $-xxx(-y)(-y)$ **Ans.** $2xxx - (2x)(2x)(2x)$

13. x^4y^3	**14.** x^2y^3	**15.** $-a^3b^2$
16. $-3ab^5$	**17.** $(-x)^3$	**18.** $(-y)^2x$
19. $-y^2x$	**20.** $(-xy)^2$	**21.** $-(x^3)(-y)^2$
22. $-(-x)^2y^3$	**23.** $a^2b^3 - ab^4$	**24.** $ab^3 - 4a^2(-b)^2$

Identify the given polynomial as a monomial, binomial, or trinomial. What is the degree of the polynomial?

Examples:

a. $2x^3 - x$

b. $x^2y^3 + y^4 + x^2$

Ans. Binomial; degree 3 in x

Ans. Trinomial; degree 5 in x and y; degree 2 in x; degree 4 in y

25. $3y^2 + 6y + 4$ **26.** $7z^2 - z$ **27.** $x^3y + xy^2$

28. $x^3 - x^2y^2 + y^4$ **29.** $xy^2z^2 + xy + yz^3$ **30.** $x^4y - yz^3 + x^2y^2z^2$

How many terms are there in each of the following expressions as written?

31. $a(b + c)$ **32.** $(x + y)^2 + 2$ **33.** $\dfrac{x + y}{3} - 2x$

34. $3 - \dfrac{2x + y^2}{x}$ **35.** $(x + y - 2z)^2$ **36.** $(x + y)^2 - (a + b)^2$

Find the values of the polynomial for the specified values of the variable.

Example: If $P(x) = 2x^2 - x + 3$, find $P(3)$, $P(-3)$, $P(0)$, $P(a)$.

Ans. $P(3) = 2(3)^2 - (3) + 3 = 18$

$P(-3) = 2(-3)^2 - (-3) + 3 = 24$

$P(0) = 2(0)^2 - (0) + 3 = 3$

$P(a) = 2(a)^2 - (a) + 3 = 2a^2 - a + 3$

37. If $P(x) = x^3 - 3x^2 + x + 1$, find $P(2)$, $P(-2)$, $P(0)$.

38. If $P(x) = 2x^3 + x^2 - 3x + 4$, find $P(3)$, $P(-3)$, $P(0)$.

39. If $Q(x) = x^{12}$, find $Q(1)$, $Q(-1)$, $Q(0)$.

40. If $Q(x) = x^{13}$, find $Q(1)$, $Q(-1)$, $Q(0)$.

41. If $D(x) = (2x - 4)^2 - x^2$, find $D(2)$, $D(-2)$, $D(0)$.

42. If $D(x) = (3x - 1)^2 + 2x^2$, find $D(4)$, $D(-4)$, $D(0)$.

43. If $P(x) = x^2 + 3x + 1$ and $Q(x) = x^3 - 1$, find $P(3)$, $Q(2)$.

44. If $P(x) = -3x^2 + 1$ and $Q(x) = 2x^2 - x + 1$, find $P(0)$, $Q(-1)$.

45. If $P(x) = x^5 + 3x - 1$ and $Q(x) = x^4 + 2x - 1$, find $P(2)$, $Q(-2)$.

46. If $P(x) = x^6 - x^5$ and $Q(x) = x^7 - x^6$, find $P(-1)$, $Q(-1)$.

Example: If $P(x) = x - 3$ and $Q(x) = x^3 + 2$, find $P[Q(2)]$, $Q[P(2)]$.

$Q(2) = (2)^3 + 2 = 10$. Therefore $P[Q(2)] = P(10) = 10 - 3 = 7$.

$P(2) = (2) - 3 = -1$. Therefore $Q[P(2)] = Q(-1) = (-1)^3 + 2 = 1$.

Ans. $P[Q(2)] = 7$; $Q[P(2)] = 1$

47. If $P(x) = x + 2$ and $Q(x) = x + 1$, find $P[Q(2)]$, $Q[P(2)]$.

48. If $P(x) = x^2 - 3$ and $Q(x) = x + 3$, find $P[Q(0)]$, $Q[P(0)]$.

49. If $P(x) = 3x^2 + x$ and $Q(x) = x^2 - 1$, find $P[Q(1)]$, $Q[P(1)]$.

50. If $P(x) = 4x^3 - x$ and $Q(x) = x^2 + 1$, find $P[Q(2)]$, $Q[P(2)]$.

51. Which axiom(s) from Chapter 1 can be invoked to justify the assertion that if the variables in a monomial represent real numbers, the monomial represents a real number? That the same is true of any polynomial with real coefficients?

52. Argue that, for each real $x > 0$, $(-x)^n = -x^n$ for n an odd natural number, and $(-x)^n = x^n$ for n an even natural number. *Hint:* Write $(-x)^n$ as

$$(-x)(-x)\cdots(-x) = (-1)(x)(-1)(x)\cdots(-1)(x).$$

2.2 Sums and Differences

By the symmetric law of equality, the distributive law can be written in the form

$$ab + ac = a(b + c),$$

and, by the commutative law, it can be written

$$ba + ca = (b + c)a.$$

This provides us with a means of simplifying certain polynomials. For example, if x and y are real numbers,

$$3x + 2x = (3 + 2)x$$
$$= 5x,$$
$$3y + 2y + 5y = (3 + 2 + 5)y$$
$$= 10y,$$
$$2x^2y + 6x^2y + x^2y = (2 + 6 + 1)x^2y$$
$$= 9x^2y.$$

Terms that differ only in their numeral coefficients are commonly called **like terms,** and the application of the distributive law to this form is referred to as *combining like terms.*

Because we have seen that $a - b$ is equal to $a + (-b)$, we shall view the signs in any polynomial as signs denoting positive or negative coefficients, and the operation involved shall be understood to be addition. Thus

$$3x - 5x + 4x = (3x) + (-5x) + (4x)$$
$$= (3 - 5 + 4)x$$
$$= 2x.$$

We have been using grouping devices such as parentheses to indicate that various expressions are to be viewed as a single number.   The expression

$$3x + (2x + 5x)$$

tells us to add $3x$ to the sum of $2x$ and $5x$, while the expression

$$(3x + 2x) + 5x$$

tells us to add $5x$ to the sum of $3x$ and $2x$.   But the associative law asserts that these expressions are identical.   Hence, the order in which we group terms in expressions of addition is immaterial.   We can consider

$$3x + 2x + 5x$$

equal to either of the grouped expressions above.

An expression such as

$$a - (b + c),$$

in which a set of parentheses is preceded by a negative sign, can first be written

$$a - (b + c) = a + [-(b + c)];$$

and then, since

$$-(b + c) = -1(b + c) = -b - c,$$

we have

$$a - (b + c) = a + [-b - c]$$

$$= a - b - c.$$

For example,

$$(x^2 + 2x) - (2x^2 - 3x + 2) = x^2 + 2x - 2x^2 + 3x - 2$$

$$= -x^2 + 5x - 2.$$

In any expression where grouping devices are nested—that is, where groups occur within groups—a great deal of difficulty can be avoided by removing the inner devices first and working outward.   Thus

$$3x - [2 - (3x + 1)] = 3x - [2 - 3x - 1]$$

$$= 3x - 2 + 3x + 1$$

$$= 6x - 1.$$

The rewriting of a polynomial by combining like terms is a process that might be called "simplifying" the polynomial, since the result is a polynomial with fewer terms than the original.   Indeed, if a polynomial is one in which no two terms contain identical variable factors, we shall say the polynomial is in **simple form.**   Thus, the polynomial in simple form that is equal to $3x - [2 - (3x + 1)]$ in the example above is $6x - 1$.

EXERCISE 2.2

Simplify by writing each expression as a polynomial in simple form.

Examples:

a. $2x - 3x + 7x$ b. $(a - a^2) + (5a - 3a^2)$

Ans. $6x$ $a - a^2 + 5a - 3a^2$

Ans. $-4a^2 + 6a$

1. $2a + 3a$ 2. $4a^2 - 7a^2$ 3. $3x - 2x$

4. $-5x - 7x$ 5. $2x - x - 4x$ 6. $3a^2 - a^2 + a^2$

7. $b - 2a + b$ 8. $b^2 - 5b^2 + a^2$ 9. $2xy + x^2y + xy$

10. $ab^2 + a^2b + 3a^2b$ 11. $x + (2x + 3y)$ 12. $4y + (2x - 3y)$

13. $(3x + 2) - (-x + 3)$ 14. $(a + 2b) - (2a - 3b)$

15. $(x^2 + 3x - 2) - (2x^2 - 2x - 1)$ 16. $(2x^2 - x + 4) - (x^2 - x - 1)$

17. $(a - b + c) - (a + b + c)$ 18. $-(a + 3b + c) + (a - b + c)$

19. Subtract $x^2 - 3x + 4$ from $-2x^2 + x - 2$.

20. Subtract $x^2 - 3x + 1$ from $x - 1$. $3\text{-}35$

21. Subtract $a + b - 2c$ from $2a - 3$.

22. Subtract $a^2 + 2a$ from 0.

23. Subtract $x^2 - 2x$ from the sum of $x^2 + 2x$ and $2x^2 - x + 2$.

24. Subtract $2y^2 - y + 1$ from the sum of $y + 2$ and $y^2 - 4y + 3$.

Examples:

a. $x - [2x + (3 - x)]$ b. $[x^2 - (2x + 1)] - [2x^2 - (x - 3)]$

$x - [2x + 3 - x]$ $[x^2 - 2x - 1] - [2x^2 - x + 3]$

$x - 2x - 3 + x$ $x^2 - 2x - 1 - 2x^2 + x - 3$

Ans. -3 Ans. $-x^2 - x - 4$

25. $y - [2y + (y + 1)]$ 26. $3a + [2a - (a + 4)]$

27. $3 - [2x - (x + 1) + 2]$ 28. $5 - [3y + (y - 4) - 1]$

29. $(3x + 2) - [x + (2 + x) + 1]$ 30. $-(x - 3) + [2x - (3 + x) - 2]$

31. $[x^2 - (2x + 3)] - [2x^2 + (x - 2)]$

32. $[2y^2 - (4 - y)] - [-y^2 + (2 + y)]$

33. $2x - \{3y - [x - (x - y)] + x\}$

34. $x - (x + y) - \{y - [x - (2x + y)] - 2y\}$

35. $3y - (2x - y) - \{y - [2x - (y - 2x)] + 3y\}$

36. $[x - (y + x)] - \{2x - [3x - (x - y)] + y\}$

37. If x and $y \in R$ in Problems 33–36, which of the axioms justifies saying that the polynomials represent real numbers?

38. Which axiom justifies writing $2x^2y + 5x^2y$ as $7x^2y$?

2.3 Products and Quotients

Consider the product

$$x^m x^n,$$

where m and n are natural numbers. Since

$$x^m = xxx\cdots x \; (m \text{ factors}),$$

and

$$x^n = xxx\cdots x \; (n \text{ factors}),$$

it follows that

$$
x^m x^n = \overbrace{(xxx\cdots x)}^{m \text{ factors}}\overbrace{(xxx\cdots x)}^{n \text{ factors}}
$$

$$
= \overbrace{(xxx\cdots x)}^{m+n \text{ factors}},
$$

$$x^m x^n = x^{m+n}. \tag{1}$$

Equation (1) is referred to as the **first law of exponents.** Thus we can multiply two natural number powers of the same base simply by adding the exponents and writing the sum as an exponent on the same base. For example,

$$x^2 x^3 = x^5,$$

$$xx^3 x^4 = x^8,$$

$$y^3 y^4 y^2 = y^9.$$

In multiplying two monomials, say

$$(3x^2y)(2xy^2),$$

we use the commutative and associative laws to write

$$3 \cdot 2 \cdot x^2 \cdot x \cdot y \cdot y^2,$$

which can be written

$$6x^3 y^3.$$

The generalized distributive law justifies writing the product of a monomial and a polynomial containing more than one term as a polynomial. For example,

$$3x(x + y + z) = 3x^2 + 3xy + 3xz.$$

The distributive law can be applied successively to write products of polynomials containing more than one term as polynomials. For example,

$$(3x + 2y)(x - y) = 3x(x - y) + 2y(x - y)$$
$$= 3x^2 - 3xy + 2xy - 2y^2$$
$$= 3x^2 - xy - 2y^2.$$

The following list of binomial products represents types so frequently encountered hereafter that you should learn to recognize them on sight:

$$(x + a)(x + b) = x^2 + (a + b)x + ab,$$
$$(x + a)^2 = x^2 + 2ax + a^2,$$
$$(x + a)(x - a) = x^2 - a^2,$$
$$(ax + by)(cx + dy) = acx^2 + (ad + bc)xy + bdy^2.$$

Turning now to division, we note that in dividing x^5 by x^3, we can write

$$\frac{x^5}{x^3} = x^5 \left(\frac{1}{x^3} \right) \quad (x \neq 0)$$
$$= x^2 \cdot x^3 \left(\frac{1}{x^3} \right)$$
$$= x^2 \left(x^3 \cdot \frac{1}{x^3} \right).$$

Then, because $x^3 \cdot 1/x^3$ equals 1 for all values of $x \neq 0$, we have

$$\frac{x^5}{x^3} = x^2 \quad (x \neq 0).$$

We can make the same argument for

$$\frac{x^m}{x^n} \quad (x \neq 0),$$

where m and n are natural numbers and $m > n$. Thus

$$\frac{x^m}{x^n} = x^m \left(\frac{1}{x^n} \right)$$
$$= x^{m-n} \cdot x^n \left(\frac{1}{x^n} \right)$$
$$= x^{m-n} \left(x^n \cdot \frac{1}{x^n} \right),$$

$$\frac{x^m}{x^n} = x^{m-n} \quad (x \neq 0). \tag{2}$$

Equation (2) is called the **second law of exponents**.

For example, using the second law of exponents,

$$\frac{18x^3y^2z^4}{6x^2yz^2} = \left(\frac{18}{6}\right)(x^{3-2}y^{2-1}z^{4-2})$$

$$= 3xyz^2 \quad (x, y, z \neq 0).$$

In multiplying and dividing monomials, we are doing a great deal of work with symbols rather than with numbers.   The fact that we can multiply and divide powers by operating on their exponents is a property of the symbolism we have adopted and not a property of the numbers these symbols represent. We are interested in multiplying or dividing numbers whose representations are x^m and x^n.   We perform these operations by adding or subtracting the numbers m and n, which are simply parts of the representations.   It is very important in manipulations of this kind to keep clearly in mind the operations we are performing on the numbers themselves.

19-33

1-13

EXERCISE 2.3

Write each product as a polynomial in simple form.   (Assume that all variables in exponents represent natural numbers.)

Examples:

a. $(-2x^2)(3xy)(y^2)$ b. $a^n \cdot a^{n+1}$
   By the first law of exponents,
   $-6x^{2+1}y^{1+2}$ a^{n+n+1}

Ans. $-6x^3y^3$ Ans. a^{2n+1}

1. $(a)(5a)$ 2. $(3a)(a^2b)$ 3. $(3)(-5a)(a^2)$

4. $(2)(-3b)(4ab)$ 5. $(-2x)(xy)(y^2)$ 6. $(-3x^2)(-2xy)(-y^3)$

7. $(-a)(-b)(c^2)$ 8. $(a^3)(-2ab^2)(-b^3)$ 9. $x^n \cdot x^n$

10. $x^n \cdot x^{2n}$ 11. $a^{n+1} \cdot a^{n-1}$ 12. $a^{2n-1} \cdot a^{n+3}$

13. $x^{n-1} \cdot x^{3n+1}$ 14. $a^{n^2-n} \cdot a^{n+1} \cdot a$

Examples:

a. $-(a + b - c)$ b. $(2x - 3)^2$ c. $x^{2n}(x^n - 1)$
   $-1(a + b - c)$ $(2x - 3)(2x - 3)$ By the distributive law and
                                                     first law of exponents,
Ans. $-a - b + c$ Ans. $4x^2 - 12x + 9$
                                                  Ans. $x^{3n} - x^{2n}$

15. $-2a(a - b)$ 16. $-3a^2(a + a^2)$ 17. $-(x^2 + x - 2)$

18. $-(x^2 - x + 5)$ 19. $abc(a - b + c)$ 20. $-ab(2a - b + 3c)$

21. $ab(a^2 - ab + b^2)$ 22. $2ab(ab^2 - ab + a^2b)$ 23. $a^n(a^n - 1)$

47+48 Wed.

24. $3a^{2n}(2 - a^{n+1})$ **25.** $a^{n-1}(a + a^n)$ **26.** $a^{n+1}(a^{2n} - a)$

27. $(x - 1)(x + 3)$ **28.** $(x - 5)(x - 7)$ **29.** $(x - 2a)(x + a)$

30. $(x - 3a)(x + 2a)$ **31.** $(x + y)^2$ $(x+y)$ **32.** $(x - 2y)^2$

33. $(5x + 1)(2x + 3)$ **34.** $(2x + 3)(x - 5)$ **35.** $(3a - 1)^2$ $3a-1$

36. $(2a + 3)^2$ **37.** $(2x - 5)(2x + 5)$ **38.** $(3x - 2)(3x + 2)$

39. $(2x - a)(x + 2a)$ **40.** $(3x + a)(x + 5a)$ **41.** $(2a + 3b)^2$ $(2a+3b)$

42. $(3a - 5b)^2$ **43.** $(x + 4)(x^2 + 2x - 1)$ **44.** $(x - 2)(x^2 - x + 3)$

45. $(\frac{1}{2}x - y)(\frac{1}{4}x + 2y)$ **46.** $(x - \frac{2}{3}y)(\frac{1}{2}x + y)$

47. $(\frac{3}{4}x + \frac{1}{2}y)(x - \frac{1}{2}y)$ **48.** $(\frac{2}{3}x - \frac{1}{4}y)(\frac{2}{3}x + \frac{1}{4}y)$

49. $(2x + 4)(3x^2 + 2x - 1)$ **50.** $(3x - 2)(2x^2 - x + 3)$

51. $(1 + a^n)(1 - a^n)$ **52.** $(2a^n + 1)(a^n - 2)$

53. $(a^{3n} + 2)(a^{2n} - 1)$ **54.** $(a^{2n} - 3)(a^{2n} + 3)$

55. $(2a^n - b^n)(a^n + 3b^n)$ **56.** $(a^{2n} - 2b^n)(a^{3n} + b^{2n})$

61-73   81-99

Examples:

  a. $3(x - 1)(x + 2)$
    $3(x^2 + x - 2)$

    Ans. $3x^2 + 3x - 6$

  b. $a(a - [3 - (a + 1)] + 4)$
    $a(a - [3 - a - 1] + 4)$
    $a(a - 3 + a + 1 + 4)$
    $a(2a + 2)$

    Ans. $2a^2 + 2a$

57. $-2x(x + 3)^2$ **58.** $-2x(x - 4)^2$

59. $3x^2(x - 2)(3x - 5)$ **60.** $2x^2(2x + 1)(x - 3)$

61. $-(2a + b)(c - 3d)$ **62.** $-(3a - b)(c + 2d)$

63. $(a - b)(a^2 + ab + b^2)$ **64.** $(a + b)(a^2 - ab + b^2)$

65. $2[a - (a - 1) + 2]$ **66.** $3[2a - (a + 1) + 3]$

67. $a[a - (2a + 3) - (a - 1)]$ **68.** $-2a[3a + (a - 3) - (2a + 1)]$

69. $-[a - 3(a + 1) - (2a + 1)]$ **70.** $-[(a + 1) - 2(3a - 1) + 4]$

71. $2(a - [a - 2(a + 1) + 1] + 1)$ **72.** $-(4 - [3 - 2(a - 1) + a] + a)$

73. $-x(x - 3[2x - 3(x + 1)] + 2)$ **74.** $x(4 - 2[3 - 4(x + 1)] - x)$

75. $2x(x + 3[2(2x - 1) - (x - 1)] + 5)$

76. $-x(4 - 2[(x + 1) - 3(x + 2)] - x)$

77. Develop a rule to write directly the square of a binomial expression of the form $(ax + by)^2$.

78. Develop a rule to write directly the square of a binomial expression of the form $(ax - by)^2$.

79. Develop a rule to write directly the product of two binomial expressions of the form $(ax + by)(ax - by)$.

80. Find the difference between $(a + b)^2$ and $a^2 + b^2$. What are the conditions on a and b for $a^2 + b^2$ to be greater than $(a + b)^2$?

Write each quotient as a polynomial. (Assume that all variables in exponents represent natural numbers.)

Examples:

a. $\dfrac{6x^2y^3}{-2xy}$ b. $\dfrac{x^{2n+3}}{x^{n+1}}$

By the second law of exponents,

$\left(\dfrac{6}{-2}\right)x^{2-1}y^{3-1}$ $(x, y \neq 0)$ $x^{(2n+3)-(n+1)}$ $(x \neq 0)$

Ans. $-3xy^2$ $(x, y \neq 0)$ **Ans.** x^{n+2} $(x \neq 0)$

81. $\dfrac{-a^2b}{ab}$ **82.** $\dfrac{-a^3b^2}{ab}$ **83.** $\dfrac{6a^3b}{3a}$ **84.** $\dfrac{12a^2bc^2}{3abc}$

85. $\dfrac{4(x-2)^3}{2(x-2)^2}$ **86.** $\dfrac{3(a-b)^2}{(a-b)}$ **87.** $\dfrac{-6x^2y^2z}{-3xz}$ **88.** $\dfrac{a^2bc^3}{-abc}$

89. $\dfrac{x^{2n}}{x^n}$ **90.** $\dfrac{x^{5n}}{x^{2n}}$ **91.** $\dfrac{a^{n+1}}{a}$ **92.** $\dfrac{a^{3n+1}}{a^{2n}}$

93. $\dfrac{x^{3n+5}}{x^{n+1}}$ **94.** $\dfrac{x^{n+1}}{x^n}$ **95.** $\dfrac{x^n y^{n+1}}{xy}$ **96.** $\dfrac{x^{2n}y^{3n+1}}{x^n y^{2n}}$

97. $\dfrac{a^{2n}b^{n+1}}{a^n b}$ **98.** $\dfrac{a^{2n}b^{n+5}}{a^n b^{n+3}}$ **99.** $\dfrac{a^{n^2+n+1}}{a^{n+1}}$ **100.** $\dfrac{a^{n^2-n+2}}{a^{n^2-n}}$

101. Assuming we could apply the second law of exponents in dividing x^n/x^n, we would obtain x^{n-n} or x^0. What meaning must we assign to the symbol x^0 so that this result is consistent with the definition of a quotient? What restriction must be placed on x in this case?

102. We have stated two laws of exponents in this chapter. Argue that, for natural numbers m and n, $(x^m)^n = (x^m)(x^m)\cdots(n$ factors$)$, and go from here to the third law of exponents, $(x^m)^n = x^{mn}$.

103. Argue that, for any natural number n, $(xy)^n = x^n y^n$, and hence develop the fourth law of exponents.

2.4 Factoring Monomials from Polynomials

The distributive law in the form

$$ax + bx + cx + dx = x(a + b + c + d)$$

furnishes a means of writing a polynomial as a single term comprised of two or more factors. This process is called **factoring.** Thus, by the distributive law,

$$3x^2 + 6x = 3x(x + 2).$$

Of course, we can also write

$$3x^2 + 6x = 3(x^2 + 2x)$$

or

$$3x^2 + 6x = 3x^2\left(1 + \frac{2}{x}\right) \quad (x \neq 0)$$

or any other of an infinite number of such expressions. We are, however, primarily interested in factoring a polynomial into a unique (except for signs and order of factors) form referred to as the **completely factored form.** A polynomial with integral coefficients is in completely factored form if:

1. it is written as a product of polynomials with integral coefficients;
2. no polynomial—other than a monomial—in the factored form contains a polynomial factor with integral coefficients.

The restriction that the factors be polynomials means that all of the variables involved have exponents from the set $\{1, 2, 3, \cdots\}$. Restricting the coefficients to integers prohibits such factorizations as

$$x + 3 = 3(\tfrac{1}{3}x + 1).$$

Notice that complete factorization of monomial factors is not required. Thus it is not necessary that the form

$$6x^2(x - 2)$$

be written

$$2 \cdot 3 \cdot x \cdot x \cdot (x - 2)$$

in order for the expression to be considered completely factored.

The earlier observation that the completely factored form is unique *except for signs and order of factors* stems from the fact that

$$-ab = (-a)(b) = a(-b)$$

or

$$ab = (-a)(-b) = (a)(b)$$

and

$$ab = ba.$$

The choice of signs and order of factors being arbitrary, the form that seems most "natural" should be used, although this is admittedly not always easy to determine. For instance, the forms $a(1 - x - x^2)$ and $-a(x^2 + x - 1)$ are equivalent, but it is difficult to affirm one as more "natural" than the other.

Common monomial factors can be factored from a polynomial by first identifying such common factors and then writing the resultant factored expression. For example, observe that the polynomial

$$6x^3 + 9x^2 - 3x$$

contains the monomial $3x$ as a factor of each term. We therefore write

$$6x^3 + 9x^2 - 3x = 3x(\qquad)$$

and insert within the parentheses the appropriate polynomial factor. This factor can be determined by inspection. We ask ourselves for the monomials that multiply $3x$ to yield $6x^3$, $9x^2$, and $-3x$ in turn. The final result appears

$$6x^3 + 9x^2 - 3x = 3x(2x^2 + 3x - 1).$$

EXERCISE 2.4

Factor completely. (Assume that all variables in exponents represent natural numbers.)

Examples:

a. $6x - 18$
   $6(? - ?)$

   Ans. $6(x - 3)$

b. $18x^2y - 24xy^2$
   $6xy(? - ?)$

   Ans. $6xy(3x - 4y)$

1. $2x + 6$ **2.** $3x - 9$ **3.** $4x^2 + 8x$

4. $3x^2y + 6xy$ **5.** $3x^2 - 3xy + 3x$ **6.** $x^3 - x^2 + x$

7. $24a^2 + 12a - 6$ **8.** $15r^2s + 18rs^2 - 3rs$ **9.** $2x^4 - 4x^2 + 8x$

10. $ay^2 + aby + ab$ **11.** $x^2y^2z^2 + 2xyz - xz$ **12.** $3m^2n - 6mn^2 + 12mn$

Examples:

a. $x^{2n} + x^n$
   $x^n(? + ?)$

   Ans. $x^n(x^n + 1)$

b. $x^{a+2} - 2x^2$
   $x^a \cdot x^2 - 2x^2$
   $x^2(? - ?)$

   Ans. $x^2(x^a - 2)$

13. $x^{3n} + x^n$ **14.** $x^{4n} - x^{2n}$ **15.** $a^{3n} - a^{2n} - a^n$

16. $y^{4n} + y^{3n} + y^{2n}$ **17.** $x^{n+2} + x^n$ **18.** $x^{n+2} + x^{n+1} + x^n$

Supply the missing factors and hence, in each case, write the expression on the left in completely factored form.

Examples:

a. $-5x + 10 = -5(\ ?\ )$

   Ans. $-5(x - 2)$

b. $-x^{3n} + x^{2n} = ?(x^n - 1)$

   Ans. $-x^{2n}(x^n - 1)$

19. $-2x + 2 = -2(\ ?\ )$ **20.** $-6x - 9 = -3(\ ?\ )$

21. $-ab - ac = ?(b + c)$ **22.** $-a^2 + ab = ?(a - b)$

23. $-xy - x^2y = -xy(\ ?\ )$ **24.** $-x^3y + y^3x = -xy(\ ?\ )$

25. $-x + x^2 - x^3 = -x(\ ?\ )$ **26.** $-y + 2xy + xy^2 = -y(\ ?\ )$

27. $-x^{2n} - x^n = ?(x^n + 1)$ **28.** $-x^{5n} + x^{2n} = ?(x^{3n} - 1)$

29. $x^{a+1} + x^a = x^a(\ ?\ )$ **30.** $y^{a+2} + y^2 = y^2(\ ?\ )$

31. Suppose that a, b, and c are natural numbers such that $a + b = c$. Show that $x^c + x^b = x^b(x^a + 1)$.

2.5 Factoring Quadratic Polynomials

One very common type of factoring is that involving quadratic (second-degree) binomials or trinomials. From Section 2.3, we recall that

(1) $(x + a)(x + b) = x^2 + (a + b)x + ab$;

(2) $(x + a)^2 = x^2 + 2ax + a^2$;

(3) $(x + a)(x - a) = x^2 - a^2$;

(4) $(ax + by)(cx + dy) = acx^2 + (ad + bc)xy + bdy^2$.

These four forms are those most commonly encountered in the chapters that follow. In this section, we are interested in viewing these relationships from right to left—that is, from polynomial to factored form. Again, we shall require integral coefficients and positive integral exponents on the variables.

As an example of the application of form (1), consider the trinomial

$$x^2 + 6x - 16.$$

We desire, if possible, to find two binomial factors of the form.

$$(x + a)(x + b)$$

whose product is the given trinomial. We see from form (1) that a and b are two integers such that $a + b = 6$ and $ab = -16$; that is, their sum must be the coefficient of the linear term $6x$ and their product must be -16. By inspection, or by trial and error, we determine that the two numbers are 8 and -2, so that

$$(x^2 + 6x - 16) = (x + 8)(x - 2).$$

Form (2) is simply a special case of (1), the square of a binomial. Thus

$$x^2 + 8x + 16 = (x + 4)(x + 4)$$

$$= (x + 4)^2.$$

Form (3) is another special case of (1), in which the coefficient of the first-degree term in x is zero. For example,

$$x^2 - 25 = (x - 5)(x + 5).$$

In particular, form (3) states that the difference of the squares of two numbers is equal to the product of the sum and the difference of the two numbers.

Form (4) is a generalization of (1)—that is, in (4) we are confronted with a quadratic trinomial where the coefficient of the term of second degree in x is other than 1.   We illustrate the factoring of such a trinomial by example:

$8x^2 - 9 - 21x$

1. Write in decreasing powers of x.

$8x^2 - 21x - 9$

2. Consider possible combinations of first-degree factors of the first term.

$(8x\quad)(x\quad)$
$(4x\quad)(2x\quad)$

3. Consider combinations of the factors of the last term.

$(8x\quad9)(x\quad1)$
$(8x\quad1)(x\quad9)$
$(8x\quad3)(x\quad3)$
$(4x\quad9)(2x\quad1)$
$(4x\quad1)(2x\quad9)$
$(4x\quad3)(2x\quad3)$

4. Select the combination(s) of products (2) and (3) whose sum(s) could be the second term $(-21x)$.

$(8x\quad3)(x\quad3)$

5. Insert the proper signs.

$(8x + 3)(x - 3)$

This process can normally by accomplished mentally, and is written out in detail here for the purposes of illustration only.

If a polynomial of more than one term contains a common monomial factor in each of its terms, this monomial should be factored from the polynomial before seeking other factors.   Thus

$$32x^2 - 84x - 36 = 4(8x^2 - 21x - 9)$$
$$= 4(8x + 3)(x - 3).$$

EXERCISE 2.5

Factor completely.   (Assume that all variables in exponents represent natural numbers.)

Examples:

a. $x^2 - 2x - 3$ b. $x^2 - 9y^2$ c. $5x^2 - 9x - 2$

Ans. $(x - 3)(x + 1)$ $x^2 - (3y)^2$ **Ans.** $(5x + 1)(x - 2)$

Ans. $(x - 3y)(x + 3y)$

1. $x^2 - 8x + 12$
2. $x^2 + 5x + 6$
3. $6 - a - a^2$
4. $15 - 2a - a^2$
5. $x^2 + 6xy + 5y^2$
6. $x^2 - 9xy + 20y^2$
7. $x^2 - 1$
8. $x^2 - 25$
9. $4 - b^2$
10. $9 - a^2$
11. $(ab)^2 - 1$
12. $(a^2b)^2 - 4$
13. $x^4 - 9$
14. $25 - y^4$
15. $a^2 - 16b^2$
16. $x^2 - 4y^2$
17. $a^{2n} - 4$
18. $9 - a^{2n}$
19. $x^{2n} - y^{2n}$
20. $x^{4n} - y^{2n}$
21. $(ab)^{2n} - 1$
22. $(ab)^{2n} - c^{4n}$
23. $3x^2 + 4x + 1$
24. $4a^2 - 5a + 1$
25. $9x^2 - 21x - 8$
26. $10x^2 - 3x - 18$
27. $3x^2 - 7ax + 2a^2$
28. $9x^2 + 9ax - 10a^2$
29. $9x^2 - y^2$
30. $4x^2 - 9y^2$
31. $4x^2 + 12x + 9$
32. $4y^2 + 4y + 1$
33. $1 - 16x^2y^2$
34. $64x^2y^2 - 1$

Examples:

a. $4a^3 - 5a^2 + a$

   $a(4a^2 - 5a + 1)$

  Ans. $a(4a - 1)(a - 1)$

b. $8x^5 - 2x^3$

   $2x^3(4x^2 - 1)$

  Ans. $2x^3(2x - 1)(2x + 1)$

35. $3x^2 + 12x + 12$
36. $2x^2 + 6x - 20$
37. $2a^3 - 8a^2 - 10a$
38. $2a^3 + 15a^2 + 7a$
39. $4a^2 - 8ab + 4b^2$
40. $20a^2 + 60ab + 45b^2$
41. $4x^2y - 36y$
42. $x^2 - 4x^2y^2$
43. $12x - x^2 - x^3$
44. $x^2 - 2x^3 + x^4$
45. $x^4y^2 - x^2y^2$
46. $x^3y - xy^3$

Examples:

a. $x^4 + 2x^2 + 1$ $43\text{-}61$

  Ans. $(x^2 + 1)^2$

b. $x^4 - 3x^2 - 4$

   $(x^2 - 4)(x^2 + 1)$

  Ans. $(x - 2)(x + 2)(x^2 + 1)$

47. $y^4 + 3y^2 + 2$ $(y^2+2)(y^2+1)$
48. $a^4 + 5a^2 + 6$ $(a^2+3)(a^2+2)$
49. $3x^4 + 7x^2 + 2$ $(3x^2+2)(y^2+1)$
50. $4x^4 - 11x^2 - 3$ $(x^2-3)(2y^2+1)$
51. $x^4 + 3x^2 - 4$ $(x^2+4)(x^2-1)$
52. $x^4 - 6x^2 - 27$
53. $x^4 - 5x^2 + 4$ (x^2+1)
54. $y^4 - 13y^2 + 36$ $(y^2-9)(y^2-4)$
55. $2a^4 - a^2 - 1$
56. $3x^4 - 11x^2 - 4$
57. $x^4 + a^2x^2 - 2a^4$ $(y^2-a^2)(y^2+2a^2)$
58. $4x^4 - 33a^2x^2 - 27a^4$
59. $x^{4n} - 1$
60. $16 - y^{4n}$ $(4-y^{2n})(4+y^2)$
61. $x^{4n} - y^{4n}$
62. $x^{4n} - 2x^{2n} + 1$
63. $3x^{4n} - 10x^{2n} + 3$
64. $6y^{2n} + 30y^n - 900$

65. For what value(s) of the variable is $x(x - 2)$ equal to 0?
66. For what value(s) of the variable is $(x - 3)(x + 2)$ equal to 0?
67. For what value(s) of the variable is $x^2 - 3x + 2$ equal to 0? *Hint:* Factor the polynomial.

68. For what value(s) of the variable is $x^3 + x^2 - 12x$ equal to 0?

69. Show that $a^2 - b^2 = -(b + a)(b - a)$.

70. Show that $x^2 - 2x + 1 = (1 - x)^2$.

71. Show that $(a - b)(c - d) = (b - a)(d - c)$.

2.6 Factoring Other Polynomials

There are a few other polynomials that occur frequently enough to justify a study of their factorization. In particular, the forms

(1) $(a + b)(x + y) = ax + ay + bx + by$,

(2) $(x + a)(x^2 - ax + a^2) = x^3 + a^3$,   and

(3) $(x - a)(x^2 + ax + a^2) = x^3 - a^3$

are often encountered in one or another area of mathematics. We are again interested in viewing these relationships from right to left. Expressions such as the right-hand member of form (1) are factorable by grouping. For example, to factor

$$3x^2y + 2y + 3xy^2 + 2x,$$

we rewrite it in the form

$$3x^2y + 2x + 3xy^2 + 2y$$

and factor the common monomials x and y from the first group of two terms and the second group of two terms, respectively, yielding

$$x(3xy + 2) + y(3xy + 2).$$

If now we factor the common binomial $(3xy + 2)$ from each term, we have

$$(3xy + 2)(x + y).$$

The application of forms (2) and (3) is direct. Thus

$$(8a^3 + b^3) = [(2a)^3 + b^3]$$
$$= (2a + b)[(2a)^2 - 2ab + b^2]$$
$$= (2a + b)[4a^2 - 2ab + b^2].$$

EXERCISE 2.6

Factor.

Examples:

a. $yb - ya + xb - xa$
    $y(b - a) + x(b - a)$
Ans. $(b - a)(y + x)$

b. $x^2 + xb - ax - ab$
    $x(x + b) - a(x + b)$
Ans. $(x + b)(x - a)$

1. $ax^2 + x + ax + 1$

2. $5a + ab + 5b + b^2$

3. $ax^2 + x + a^2x + a$

4. $a + ab + b + b^2$

6. $x^3 - x^2y + xy - y^2$

5. $x^2 + ax + xy + ay$

7. $3ab - cb - 3ad + cd$

8. $1 - x - y + xy$

9. $3x + y - 6x^2 - 2xy$

10. $5xz - 5yz - x + y$

11. $a^3 + 2ab^2 - 4b^3 - 2a^2b$

12. $6x^3 - 4x^2 + 3x - 2$

13. $x^2 - x + 2xy - 2y$

14. $2a^2 + 3a - 2ab - 3b$

15. $2a^2b + 6a^2 - b - 3$

16. $2ab^2 + 5a - 8b^2 - 20$

17. $x^3y^2 + x^3 - 3y^2 - 3$

18. $12 - 4y^3 - 3x^2 + x^2y^3$

Examples:

a. $x^3 + 8$
   $x^3 + (2)^3$
   $(x + 2)(x^2 - 2x + 2^2)$

   Ans. $(x + 2)(x^2 - 2x + 4)$

b. $8x^3 - y^3$
   $(2x)^3 - y^3$
   $(2x - y)[(2x)^2 + 2xy + y^2]$

   Ans. $(2x - y)(4x^2 + 2xy + y^2)$

19. $x^3 - 1$

20. $y^3 + 27$

21. $(2x)^3 + y^3$

22. $y^3 - (3x)^3$

23. $a^3 - 8b^3$

24. $8a^3 + b^3$

25. $(xy)^3 - 1$

26. $8 + x^3y^3$

27. $27a^3 + 64b^3$

28. $8a^3 - 125b^3$

29. $x^3 + (x - y)^3$

30. $(x + y)^3 - z^3$

31. $x^6 - y^6$

32. $x^6 + (x - 2y)^3$

33. $(x + 1)^3 - (x - 1)^3$

34. $(2y - 1)^3 + (y - 1)^3$

35. $\dfrac{1}{y^3} - \dfrac{x^6}{8}$

36. $\dfrac{1}{8x^3y^3} + \dfrac{x^3}{y^6}$

37. Show that $ac - ad + bd - bc$ can be factored both as $(a - b)(c - d)$ and as $(b - a)(d - c)$.

38. Show that $a^2 - b^2 - c^2 + 2bc$ can be factored as $(a - b + c)(a + b - c)$.

39. Consider the polynomial $x^2 + 10xy + 16y^2$. If $9y^2$ is both added to and subtracted from this expression (thus producing an equal expression), we have

$$x^2 + 10xy + 16y^2 + 9y^2 - 9y^2$$

$$(x^2 + 10xy + 25y^2) - 9y^2$$

$$(x + 5y)^2 - 9y^2$$

$$(x + 5y - 3y)(x + 5y + 3y).$$

By adding and subtracting an appropriate monomial, factor $x^2 + 6xy + 5y^2$.

40. Use the method of Problem 39 to factor $x^2 - 4xy + 3y^2$.

CHAPTER REVIEW

Write as a polynomial in simple form.

1. a. $(a - 2b) - (a - b + 2c)$ b. $2x - [x - (x - 1) + 2]$

2. a. $(3xy)(-2x^2y)(-3xy^3)$ b. $3[(3x - 2)(x + 1) - (x - 2)^2]$

3. a. $\dfrac{24x^2yz}{-3xy}$ $(x, y \neq 0)$ b. $\dfrac{4xy^3 \cdot x^2y}{xy^2}$ $(x, y \neq 0)$

4. a. $a^{2n} \cdot a^{n+1}$ b. $\dfrac{x^{2n+1}y^n}{x^ny}$ $(x, y \neq 0)$

In Problems 5–8, factor completely.

5. a. $2x^2 + 11x - 21$ b. $2x^3 - 4x^2 + 6x$

6. a. $a^2 - 7ab + 12b^2$ b. $x^3 - 8a^3$

7. a. $2xy + 2x^2 + y + x$ b. $9x^4 - y^2z^2$

8. a. $6x^{3n} + 3x^n$ b. $x^{2n+1} + 2x^{n+1}$

9. If $P(x) = 3x^2 - 4x + 2$, find a. $P(-2)$, b. $P(x + 1)$

10. If $P(x) = x^2 - 3x + 1$ and $Q(x) = x^3 + x^2$, find a. $Q(2)$, b. $P[Q(2)]$

If x and y are real numbers, which axiom or axioms on pages 12 and 13 justify each of the following?

11. $(x + 2)(x + 3) = (x + 2)x + (x + 2)3$

12. $3x^2y$ represents a real number.

13. $3x + 2x = (3 + 2)x$ 14. $(x + y) + [-(x + y)] + z = z$

15. $x + (x + y)$ represents a real number.

3

FRACTIONS

A fraction is an expression denoting a quotient. If the numerator (dividend) and the denominator (divisor) are polynomials, then the fraction is said to be a **rational expression.** Trivially, any polynomial can be considered a rational expression, since it is the quotient of itself and 1. For each replacement of the variable(s) for which the numerator and denominator of a fraction represent real numbers and for which the denominator is not zero, a rational expression represents a real number. Of course, for any value of the variable(s) for which the denominator vanishes (is equal to zero), the fraction does not represent a real number and is said to be undefined.

We recall from Chapter 1 that $a/b = a(1/b)$; with this in mind, we observe that if two fractions represent the same number, that is, if

$$\frac{a}{b} = \frac{c}{d} \quad (b, d \neq 0),$$

then we can argue

$$bd\left(\frac{a}{b}\right) = bd\left(\frac{c}{d}\right),$$

$$bda\left(\frac{1}{b}\right) = bdc\left(\frac{1}{d}\right),$$

$$adb\left(\frac{1}{b}\right) = bcd\left(\frac{1}{d}\right),$$

and, since $b(1/b)$ is equal to 1 and $d(1/d)$ is equal to 1, we have

$$ad(1) = bc(1),$$

$$ad = bc.$$

Since each step in this argument is reversible, we can say that:

If a, b, c, and d $\in$ R, and b, d $\neq$ 0, then

$$\frac{a}{b} = \frac{c}{d} \quad \textit{if and only if} \quad \textbf{ad = bc.} \tag{1}$$

Assertions in mathematics involving the phrase "if and only if" are really dual assertions. If we say that a statement p is true "if" a statement q is true, we mean that the truth of q implies the truth of p, whereas if we say p is true "only if" q is true, we mean that the truth of p implies the truth of q. Therefore, the foregoing assertion means that, if $a/b = c/d$, then $ad = bc$ $(b, d \neq 0)$ and, if $ad = bc$ $(b, d \neq 0)$, then $a/b = c/d$, with both of these implications being made in a single statement.

Assertion (1) establishes a means by which we can identify fractions that represent the same number. For example,

$$\frac{2}{3} = \frac{4}{6} \quad \text{because} \quad 2 \cdot 6 = 3 \cdot 4,$$

$$\frac{6}{9} = \frac{8}{12} \quad \text{because} \quad 6 \cdot 12 = 9 \cdot 8,$$

$$\frac{2}{3} \neq \frac{3}{4} \quad \text{because} \quad 2 \cdot 4 \neq 3 \cdot 3.$$

There are numerous places in algebra where, for one reason or another, we wish to replace a given fraction with an equal fraction. We can write any number of fractions equal to a given fraction. For example, 4/6, 6/9, and 8/12 are all equal to 2/3. In general we have the following:

If a, b, and c $\in$ R, and b, c $\neq$ 0, then

$$\frac{a}{b} = \frac{ac}{bc}.$$

This law is called the **fundamental principle of fractions** and asserts that an equal fraction is obtained if the numerator and the denominator of a fraction are each multiplied by the same nonzero number. The validity of the fundamental principle follows from our criteria for the equality of two fractions (1) above; that is,

$$\frac{a}{b} = \frac{ac}{bc} \quad (b, c \neq 0)$$

because

$$a(bc) = b(ac).$$

3.1 Signs of Fractions

There are three signs associated with a fraction: a sign for the numerator, a sign for the denominator, and a sign for the fraction itself. Although there are eight different possible symbols associated with the symbol "a/b" and the two signs "$+$" and "$-$," these symbols represent only two real numbers, a/b and its additive inverse $-(a/b)$. It follows from the definition of a quotient and the fundamental principle of fractions that

$$\frac{-a}{b} = \frac{a}{-b} = -\frac{a}{b} = -\frac{-a}{-b}. \tag{1}$$

Also

$$\frac{a}{b} = \frac{-a}{-b}, \quad \text{and} \quad -\left(\frac{a}{-b}\right) = -\left(\frac{-a}{b}\right) = -\left(-\frac{a}{b}\right).$$

From the double-negative law, $-(-a/b) = a/b$. Therefore

$$\frac{a}{b} = \frac{-a}{-b} = -\frac{a}{-b} = -\frac{-a}{b}. \tag{2}$$

The forms a/b and $-a/b$, which have the sign of the fraction and the sign of the denominator both positive, are generally the most convenient representations and will be referred to as **standard forms.** Thus,

$$\frac{-3}{5}, \quad \frac{3}{5}, \quad \text{and} \quad \frac{7}{10}$$

are in standard form, while

$$\frac{3}{-5}, \quad -\frac{-3}{5}, \quad \text{and} \quad -\frac{7}{-10}$$

are not.

If the denominator of a fraction is an expression containing more than one term, there are two possibilities for standard form. Since $-(a - b) = b - a$, we have

$$\frac{-b}{a - b} = \frac{-b(-1)}{(a - b)(-1)}$$

$$= \frac{b}{-(a - b)}$$

$$= \frac{b}{b - a},$$

and either $\dfrac{-b}{a - b}$ or $\dfrac{b}{b - a}$ may be taken as standard form, as convenience dictates.

EXERCISE 3.1

Write in standard form and specify any real values of the variables for which the fraction is undefined.

Examples:

a. $-\dfrac{5}{-y}$ b. $-\dfrac{a}{a-2}$ c. $-\dfrac{x-1}{3}$

Ans. $\dfrac{5}{y}\,(y \neq 0)$ **Ans.** $\dfrac{-a}{a-2}$ or $\dfrac{a}{2-a}\,(a \neq 2)$ **Ans.** $\dfrac{-(x-1)}{3}$ or $\dfrac{1-x}{3}$

1. $-\dfrac{3}{5}$ 2. $-\dfrac{-5}{-6}$ 3. $\dfrac{-4}{-7}$ 4. $\dfrac{3}{-8}$

5. $\dfrac{-4x}{y}$ 6. $\dfrac{2y}{-3z}$ 7. $-\dfrac{-2}{x}$ 8. $-\dfrac{-6}{-xy}$

9. $-\dfrac{-3x}{-2y^2}$ 10. $\dfrac{8xy^2}{-3z}$ 11. $\dfrac{2+x}{-x}$ 12. $-\dfrac{-a+b}{b}$

Write each fraction on the left as an equal fraction in standard form with the denominator shown on the right. Specify any real values of the variables for which the fraction is undefined.

Examples:

a. $\dfrac{-1}{2-x}, \dfrac{}{x-2}$ b. $-\dfrac{a}{b-a}, \dfrac{}{a-b}$

$\dfrac{-1\;(-1)}{(2-x)(-1)}$ $-\dfrac{a}{-(a-b)}$

Ans. $\dfrac{1}{x-2}\,(x \neq 2)$ **Ans.** $\dfrac{a}{a-b}\,(a \neq b)$

13. $-\dfrac{4}{3-y}, \dfrac{}{y-3}$ 14. $\dfrac{-3}{2-x}, \dfrac{}{x-2}$ 15. $\dfrac{1}{x-y}, \dfrac{}{y-x}$

16. $\dfrac{-6}{x-y}, \dfrac{}{y-x}$ 17. $\dfrac{x-2}{3-x}, \dfrac{}{x-3}$ 18. $\dfrac{2x-5}{3-y}, \dfrac{}{y-3}$

19. $\dfrac{-x}{x-y}, \dfrac{}{y-x}$ 20. $\dfrac{x-3}{y-x}, \dfrac{}{x-y}$ 21. $-\dfrac{1}{x-y}, \dfrac{}{y-x}$

22. $-\dfrac{x}{x-2y}, \dfrac{}{2y-x}$ 23. $\dfrac{-a}{-3a-b}, \dfrac{}{3a+b}$ 24. $\dfrac{-a}{2b-3a}, \dfrac{}{3b-2a}$

25. Do all fractions represent rational numbers? Support your answer with examples.

3.2   Changing Fractions to Lowest Terms

A fraction is said to be in lowest terms when the numerator and denominator do not contain certain types of factors in common. The arithmetic fraction a/b, where a and b are integers and $b \neq 0$, is in lowest terms providing a and b are relatively prime—that is, providing they contain no common integral factors other than 1. If the numerator and denominator of a fraction are polynomials with integral coefficients, then the fraction is said to be in lowest terms if the numerator and denominator do not contain a common polynomial factor with integral coefficients.

To express a given fraction in lowest terms (called *reducing* the fraction), we can factor the numerator and denominator, and then apply the fundamental principle of fractions. For example,

$$\frac{8x^3y}{6x^2y^3} = \frac{4x \cdot 2x^2y}{3y^2 \cdot 2x^2y}$$

$$= \frac{4x}{3y^2} \quad (x, y \neq 0).$$

If binomial factors are involved, the process is the same. Thus

$$\frac{12(x + y)(x - y)^2}{15(x + y)^2(x - y)} = \frac{4(x - y) \cdot [3(x + y)(x - y)]}{5(x + y) \cdot [3(x + y)(x - y)]}$$

$$= \frac{4(x - y)}{5(x + y)} \quad (x \neq y, -y).$$

Diagonal lines are sometimes used to abbreviate this procedure. Instead of writing

$$\frac{y}{y^2} = \frac{1 \cdot y}{y \cdot y} = \frac{1}{y} \quad (y \neq 0),$$

we may write

$$\frac{y}{y^2} = \frac{\overset{1}{\cancel{y}}}{\underset{y}{\cancel{y^2}}} = \frac{1}{y} \quad (y \neq 0).$$

Reducing a fraction to lowest terms should be accomplished mentally whenever possible.

Observe that the process of reducing fractions is consistent with the second law of exponents wherever this law is applicable. Thus we can write

$$\frac{x^3}{x} = \frac{x^2 \cdot x}{1 \cdot x} = x^2 \quad (x \neq 0)$$

from the fundamental principle of fractions, or

$$\frac{x^3}{x} = x^{3-1} = x^2 \quad (x \neq 0)$$

directly from the second law of exponents.

The division of a polynomial containing more than one term by a monomial may also be considered a special case of changing a fraction to lowest terms, providing the monomial is contained as a factor in each term in the polynomial. For example, we may write

$$\frac{9x^3 - 6x^2 + 3x}{3x} = \frac{3x(3x^2 - 2x + 1)}{3x}$$

$$= \frac{(3x^2 - 2x + 1) \cdot (3x)}{1 \cdot (3x)}$$

$$= 3x^2 - 2x + 1 \quad (x \neq 0).$$

Alternatively, we may utilize an approach based on the representation of the sum of two or more fractions, which is developed at length in Section 3.5; namely,

$$\frac{a}{g} + \frac{b}{g} + \frac{c}{g} = \frac{a + b + c}{g},$$

and by the symmetric law of equality,

$$\frac{a + b + c}{g} = \frac{a}{g} + \frac{b}{g} + \frac{c}{g}.$$

As an illustration, we have

$$\frac{9x^3 - 6x^2 + 3x}{3x} = \frac{9x^3}{3x} - \frac{6x^2}{3x} + \frac{3x}{3x}$$

$$= \frac{3x^2 \cdot 3x}{1 \cdot 3x} - \frac{2x \cdot 3x}{1 \cdot 3x} + \frac{3x}{3x}$$

$$= 3x^2 - 2x + 1 \quad (x \neq 0).$$

This second approach has the advantage of being applicable even though the denominator is not a factor of the numerator, but in this case it cannot be looked upon as a matter of reducing a fraction to lowest terms.

If the denominator is contained as a factor in the numerator, the division of one polynomial by another polynomial, where each contains more than one term, may also be considered as an example of reducing a fraction to lowest terms. Thus

$$\frac{2x^2 + x - 15}{x + 3} = \frac{(2x - 5)(x + 3)}{1 \cdot (x + 3)}$$

$$= 2x - 5 \quad (x \neq -3).$$

The preceding result may also be obtained through a method similar to the long division process used in arithmetic. For example:

$$x + 3\overline{\smash{\big)}2x^2 + x - 15}$$

> Divide $2x^2$ by x. Subtract product of $2x$ and $x + 3$ from $2x^2 + x$, and "bring down" -15.

$$
\begin{array}{r}
2x \\
x + 3\overline{\smash{\big)}2x^2 + x - 15} \\
\underline{2x^2 + 6x } \\
-5x - 15
\end{array}
$$

> Divide $-5x$ by x. Subtract product of -5 and $x + 3$ from $-5x - 15$.

$$
\begin{array}{r}
2x - 5 \\
x + 3\overline{\smash{\big)}2x^2 + x - 15} \\
\underline{2x^2 + 6x } \\
-5x - 15 \\
\underline{-5x - 15}
\end{array}
$$

This latter procedure is most useful when the divisor is not a factor of the dividend. If such is the case, the division process will produce a remainder that may be expressed by a fraction. For example, in dividing

$$(x^2 + 2x + 2) \quad \text{by} \quad (x + 1) \quad (x \neq -1),$$

we have

$$
\begin{array}{r}
x + 1 \\
x + 1\overline{\smash{\big)}x^2 + 2x + 2} \\
\underline{x^2 + x } \\
x + 2 \\
\underline{x + 1} \\
1
\end{array}
$$

and the result may be expressed as

$$x + 1 + \frac{1}{x + 1} \quad (x \neq -1).$$

The foregoing example illustrates an important relationship between the dividend and the divisor of a quotient $P(x)/(x - a)$, where $P(x)$ is a real polynomial of degree $n \geq 1$. This relationship can be expressed in the form

$$\frac{P(x)}{x - a} = Q(x) + \frac{r}{x - a}$$

or

$$P(x) = (x - a)Q(x) + r,$$

where $Q(x)$ is a real polynomial of degree $n - 1$ and r is a real number. Illustrating this form, we have

$$\frac{x^2 + 2x + 2}{x + 1} = x + 1 + \frac{1}{x + 1} \quad (x \neq -1)$$

or

$$x^2 + 2x + 2 = (x + 1)(x + 1) + 1.$$

Observe that, although

$$\frac{P(x)}{x - a} = Q(x) + \frac{r}{x - a}$$

is not defined if $x = a$, the expression obtained from this, namely,

$$P(x) = (x - a)Q(x) + r,$$

is defined for every value of x, including a.

EXERCISE 3.2

Reduce to lowest terms.

Examples:

a. $\dfrac{2y + xy}{2y}$ b. $\dfrac{a - b}{b^2 - a^2}$

$\dfrac{(2 + x)y}{2y}$ $\dfrac{-1(b - a)}{(b + a)(b - a)}$

By the fundamental principle of fractions,

Ans. $\dfrac{2 + x}{2} \quad (y \neq 0)$ **Ans.** $\dfrac{-1}{b + a} \quad (b \neq -a, a)$

1. $\dfrac{-a^2bc}{-ab^2c}$ 2. $\dfrac{96x^4y^2z}{-16x^3y^2z^2}$ 3. $\dfrac{2a(-b)(-c)^2}{6a^3b^3(-c)^3}$

4. $\dfrac{3r(-s)^2(-t)^2}{7r^2s^2t^2}$ 5. $\dfrac{2x + 2y}{x + y}$ 6. $\dfrac{x^2 + x}{x + 1}$

7. $\dfrac{a - b}{b - a}$ 8. $\dfrac{x^2 - xy}{y - x}$ 9. $\dfrac{(a - b)^2}{b - a}$

10. $\dfrac{9(x - y)^3}{3(y - x)}$ 11. $\dfrac{x^2 - 1}{1 - x}$ 12. $\dfrac{x^2 - 16}{4 - x}$

Write each quotient as a polynomial.

Examples:

a. $\dfrac{2y^3 - 6y^2 + 10y}{2y}$ b. $\dfrac{y^2 + y - 6}{y - 2}$

$\dfrac{2y(y^2 - 3y + 5)}{2y}$ $\dfrac{(y + 3)(y - 2)}{1 \cdot (y - 2)}$

By the fundamental principle of fractions,

Ans. $y^2 - 3y + 5 \quad (y \neq 0)$ **Ans.** $y + 3 \quad (y \neq 2)$

13. $\dfrac{4x - 6}{2}$ **14.** $\dfrac{6x - 9}{3}$ **15.** $\dfrac{ay - a}{a}$

16. $\dfrac{bx^2 - bx}{bx}$ **17.** $\dfrac{a^3 - 3a^2 + 2a}{a}$ **18.** $\dfrac{3x^3 - 6x^2 + 3x}{-3x}$

19. $\dfrac{y^2 + 5y - 14}{y - 2}$ **20.** $\dfrac{x^2 + 5x + 6}{x + 3}$ **21.** $\dfrac{y^2 - y - 2}{y + 1}$

22. $\dfrac{6x^2 + 11x - 35}{3x - 5}$ **23.** $\dfrac{8y^3 - 27}{2y - 3}$ **24.** $\dfrac{(x + y)^3 - 8z^3}{(x + y - 2z)}$

25. $\dfrac{x^2 + ax + xy + ay}{x + a}$ **26.** $\dfrac{2x^2 + 6x - xy - 3y}{2x - y}$

Write each quotient $P(x)/D(x)$ in the form $Q(x) + r/D(x)$, where r is a constant. State values of the variable for which the result is not defined.

Examples:

a. $\dfrac{2y^3 - 6y^2 + 4}{y}$ b. $\dfrac{y^2 + y - 5}{y - 2}$

$\dfrac{2y^3}{y} - \dfrac{6y^2}{y} + \dfrac{4}{y}$

$$\begin{array}{r} y + 3 \\ y - 2 \overline{\smash{)}\, y^2 + y - 5} \\ \underline{y^2 - 2y} \\ 3y - 5 \\ \underline{3y - 6} \\ 1 \end{array}$$

Ans. $2y^2 - 6y + \dfrac{4}{y}$ $(y \neq 0)$

Ans. $y + 3 + \dfrac{1}{y - 2}$ $(y \neq 2)$

27. $\dfrac{8a^2 + 4a + 1}{2}$ **28.** $\dfrac{12x^3 - 8x^2 + 3x}{4x}$

29. $\dfrac{2x^3 - 4x^2 - 3x}{2x}$ **30.** $\dfrac{8a^2x^2 - 4ax + ax}{2ax}$

31. $\dfrac{4y^2 + 12y + 5}{2y + 1}$ **32.** $\dfrac{2x^2 + 13x - 7}{2x - 1}$

33. $\dfrac{4y^2 - 4y - 5}{2y + 1}$ **34.** $\dfrac{2r^2 - 3r - 15}{2r + 5}$

3.3 Synthetic Division

If the divisor in a quotient of two polynomials is of the form $x - c$, the division algorithm can be simplified by a procedure known as **synthetic division.** Consider the quotient

$$\dfrac{x^4 + x^2 + 2x - 1}{x + 3}.$$

The division can be accomplished as follows:

$$
\begin{array}{r}
x^3 - 3x^2 + 10x - 28 \\
\hline
\end{array}
$$

$$
x + 3 \,\big|\, x^4 \qquad\quad + x^2 + 2x - 1
$$

$$
\begin{array}{r}
\underline{x^4 + 3x^3} \\
-3x^3 + x^2 \\
\underline{-3x^3 - 9x^2} \\
10x^2 + 2x \\
10x^2 + 30x \\
\underline{} \\
-28x - 1 \\
\underline{-28x - 84} \\
83 \text{ (remainder).}
\end{array}
$$

We see that

$$
\frac{x^4 + x^2 + 2x - 1}{x + 3} = x^3 - 3x^2 + 10x - 28 + \frac{83}{x + 3} \quad (x \neq -3).
$$

If we omit writing the variables and write only the coefficients of the terms, and use zero for the coefficient of any missing power, we have

$$
\begin{array}{r}
1 - 3 + 10 - 28 \\
\hline
\end{array}
$$

$$
1 + 3 \,\big|\, 1 + 0 + 1 + 2 - 1
$$

$$
\begin{array}{r}
\underline{[1] + 3} \\
-3 + (1) \\
\underline{[-3] - 9} \\
10 + (2) \\
\underline{[10] + 30} \\
-28 - (1) \\
\underline{[-28] - 84} \\
83 \text{ (remainder).}
\end{array}
$$

Now, observe that the numbers in brackets, [ ], are repetitions of the numbers written immediately above and are also repetitions of the coefficients of the associated variable in the quotient; the numbers in parentheses, ( ), are repetitions of the coefficients of the dividend. Therefore, the whole process can be written in compact form as

$$
\begin{array}{llrrrrr}
(1) & 3\,|\ 1 & 0 & 1 & 2 & -1 \\
(2) & & 3 & -9 & 30 & -84 \\
\hline
(3) & 1 & -3 & 10 & -28 & 83 \text{ (remainder: 83),}
\end{array}
$$

where the repetitions are omitted and where 1, the coefficient of x in the divisor, has also been omitted.

The numbers in line (3), which are the coefficients of the variables in the quotient and the remainder, have been obtained by *subtracting* the **detached**

coefficients in line (2) from the detached coefficients of terms of the same degree in line (1). We could obtain the same result by replacing 3 with -3 in the divisor and *adding* instead of subtracting at each step, and this is what is done in the *synthetic division* process. The final form then appears:

$$\begin{array}{lrrrrr}
(1) & -3\,|\,1 & 0 & 1 & 2 & -1 \\
(2) & & -3 & 9 & -30 & 84 \\
\hline
(3) & 1 & -3 & 10 & -28 & 83 \text{ (remainder: 83).}
\end{array}$$

Comparing the results of using synthetic division with the same process using long division, we observe that the numbers in line (3) are the coefficients of the polynomial $x^3 - 3x^2 + 10x - 28$, and that there is a remainder of 83.

As another example, let us write $\dfrac{3x^3 - 4x - 1}{x - 2}$ in the form $Q + \dfrac{r}{D}$.

Using synthetic division, we begin by writing

$$2\,|\,3 \quad 0 \quad -4 \quad -1$$

where 0 has been inserted in the position that would be occupied by the coefficient of a second-degree term if such a term were present in the dividend. The divisor is the negative of -2, or 2. Then, we have

$$\begin{array}{lrrrr}
(1) & 2\,|\,3 & 0 & -4 & -1 \\
(2) & & 6 & 12 & 16 \\
\hline
(3) & 3 & 6 & 8 & 15 \text{ (remainder: 15).}
\end{array}$$

This process employs these steps:

1. 3 is "brought down" from line (1) to line (3).
2. 6, the product of 2 and 3, is written in the next position on line (2).
3. 6, the sum of 0 and 6, is written on line (3).
4. 12, the product of 2 and 6, is written in the next position on line (2).
5. 8, the sum of -4 and 12, is written on line (3).
6. 16, the product of 2 and 8, is written in the next position on line (2).
7. 15, the sum of -1 and 16, is written on line (3).

We can use the first three numbers on line (3) as coefficients to write a polynomial of degree one less than the degree of the dividend. This polynomial is the quotient lacking the remainder. The last number is the remainder. Thus, for $x - 2 \neq 0$, the quotient when $3x^3 - 4x - 1$ is divided by $x - 2$ is $3x^2 + 6x + 8$ with a remainder of 15; that is,

$$\frac{3x^3 - 4x - 1}{x - 2} = 3x^2 + 6x + 8 + \frac{15}{x - 2} \quad (x \neq 2).$$

EXERCISE 3.3

Use synthetic division to write each quotient $P(x)/D(x)$ in the form $Q(x) + r/D(x)$, where r is a constant.

Examples:

a. $\dfrac{2x^4 + x^3 - 1}{x + 2}$

$$\underline{-2\,|}\ \ \begin{array}{rrrrr} 2 & 1 & 0 & 0 & -1 \\ & -4 & 6 & -12 & 24 \\ \hline 2 & -3 & 6 & -12 & 23 \end{array}$$

Ans. $2x^3 - 3x^2 + 6x - 12 + \dfrac{23}{x + 2}$

$$(x \neq -2)$$

b. $\dfrac{x^3 - 1}{x - 1}$

$$\underline{1\,|}\ \ \begin{array}{rrrr} 1 & 0 & 0 & -1 \\ & 1 & 1 & 1 \\ \hline 1 & 1 & 1 & 0 \end{array}$$

Ans. $x^2 + x + 1 \quad (x \neq 1)$

1. $\dfrac{x^2 - 8x + 12}{x - 6}$

2. $\dfrac{a^2 + a - 6}{a + 3}$

3. $\dfrac{x^2 + 4x + 4}{x + 2}$

4. $\dfrac{x^2 + 6x + 9}{x + 3}$

5. $\dfrac{x^4 - 3x^3 + 2x^2 - 1}{x - 2}$

6. $\dfrac{x^4 + 2x^2 - 3x + 5}{x - 3}$

7. $\dfrac{2x^3 + x - 5}{x + 1}$

8. $\dfrac{3x^3 + x^2 - 7}{x + 2}$

9. $\dfrac{2x^4 - x + 6}{x - 5}$

10. $\dfrac{3x^4 - x^2 + 1}{x - 4}$

11. $\dfrac{x^3 + 4x^2 + x - 2}{x + 2}$

12. $\dfrac{x^3 - 7x^2 - x + 3}{x + 3}$

13. $\dfrac{x^6 + x^4 - x}{x - 1}$

14. $\dfrac{x^6 + 3x^3 - 2x - 1}{x - 2}$

15. $\dfrac{x^5 - 1}{x - 1}$

16. $\dfrac{x^5 + 1}{x + 1}$

17. $\dfrac{x^6 - 1}{x - 1}$

18. $\dfrac{x^6 + 1}{x + 1}$

3.4 Building Fractions

In a preceding section, we changed fractions to equal fractions in lowest terms by applying the fundamental principle in the form

$$\frac{ac}{bc} = \frac{a}{b} \quad (b,\ c \neq 0).$$

In this section, we shall change fractions to equal fractions by applying the fundamental principle in the form

$$\frac{a}{b} = \frac{ac}{bc} \quad (b, c \neq 0).$$

For example, $1/2$ can be changed to an equal fraction with a denominator of 8 by multiplying the numerator by 4 and the denominator by 4. Thus

$$\frac{1}{2} = \frac{1 \cdot 4}{2 \cdot 4} = \frac{4}{8}.$$

This process is called "building a fraction," and the number 4 is said to be a building factor.

In general, to build a fraction a/b to an equal fraction with bc as a denominator (i.e., $a/b = ?/bc$), we can usually determine the building factor c by inspection, and then multiply the numerator and the denominator of the original fraction by this building factor. If the building factor cannot be obtained by inspection, the desired denominator (bc) can be divided by the denominator of the given fraction (b) to determine the building factor (c).

EXERCISE 3.4

Express each of the given fractions as an equal fraction with the given denominator.

Examples:

a. $\dfrac{3}{4xy}; \dfrac{}{8x^2y^2}$ b. $\dfrac{a+1}{3}; \dfrac{}{6(a-3)}$

Obtain the building factor.

$(8x^2y^2 \div 4xy = 2xy)$ $[6(a-3) \div 3 = 2(a-3)]$

Multiply the numerator and the denominator of the given fraction by the building factor.

$\dfrac{3(2xy)}{4xy(2xy)}$ $\dfrac{(a+1)(2)(a-3)}{3(2)(a-3)}$

Ans. $\dfrac{6xy}{8x^2y^2} \quad (x, y \neq 0)$ **Ans.** $\dfrac{2a^2 - 4a - 6}{6(a-3)} \quad (a \neq 3)$

1. $\dfrac{3}{4}; \dfrac{}{12}$ 2. $\dfrac{1}{5}; \dfrac{}{10}$ 3. $\dfrac{16}{-5}; \dfrac{}{15}$

4. $\dfrac{7}{-6}; \dfrac{}{18}$ 5. $4; \dfrac{}{12}$ 6. $6; \dfrac{}{3}$

7. $\dfrac{2}{6x}; \dfrac{}{12x}$ 8. $\dfrac{5}{3y}; \dfrac{}{18y}$ 9. $\dfrac{-a^2}{b^2}; \dfrac{}{3b^3}$

10. $-\dfrac{r^2}{s^2}; \dfrac{}{6s^3}$ **11.** $y; \dfrac{}{xy}$ **12.** $b; \dfrac{}{a^2b}$

13. $\dfrac{1}{3}; \dfrac{}{3(x+y)}$ **14.** $\dfrac{1}{5}; \dfrac{}{10(a-b)}$ **15.** $\dfrac{x-1}{3}; \dfrac{}{9(x+1)}$

16. $\dfrac{a-2}{2}; \dfrac{}{6(a+1)}$ **17.** $3a; \dfrac{}{9(a+1)}$ **18.** $5x^2; \dfrac{}{3(x+2)}$

Example:

$$\frac{3}{2a-2b}; \frac{}{4a^2-4b^2}$$

Factor denominators.

$$\frac{3}{2(a-b)}; \frac{}{4(a-b)(a+b)}$$

Obtain the building factor.

$$[4(a-b)(a+b) \div 2(a-b) = 2(a+b)]$$

Multiply the numerator and the denominator of the given fraction by the building factor $2(a+b)$.

$$\frac{3 \cdot 2(a+b)}{2(a-b) \cdot 2(a+b)}$$

Ans. $\dfrac{6(a+b)}{4a^2-4b^2}$ $(a \neq b, -b)$

19. $\dfrac{3}{a-b}; \dfrac{}{a^2-b^2}$ **20.** $\dfrac{5}{2a+b}; \dfrac{}{4a^2-b^2}$

21. $\dfrac{3x}{y+2}; \dfrac{}{y^2-y-6}$ **22.** $\dfrac{5r}{s+3}; \dfrac{}{s^2+s-6}$

23. $\dfrac{-2}{x+1}; \dfrac{}{x^2+3x+2}$ **24.** $\dfrac{-3}{a+2}; \dfrac{}{a^2+3a+2}$

25. $\dfrac{2}{a-b}; \dfrac{}{b^2-a^2}$ **26.** $\dfrac{7}{x-y}; \dfrac{}{y^2-x^2}$

27. $\dfrac{x}{2-x}; \dfrac{}{x^2-3x+2}$ **28.** $\dfrac{y}{3-2y}; \dfrac{}{2y^2-y-3}$

29. $\dfrac{3}{a+3}; \dfrac{}{a^3+27}$ **30.** $\dfrac{2}{2x-3y}; \dfrac{}{8x^3-27y^3}$

31. $\dfrac{-2}{x^2+y^2}; \dfrac{}{x^4-y^4}$ **32.** $\dfrac{-1}{x+y}; \dfrac{}{x^4-y^4}$

33. $\dfrac{x}{x-2}; \dfrac{}{xy+3x-2y-6}$ **34.** $\dfrac{y}{x+1}; \dfrac{}{xy-x+y-1}$

3.5   Sums and Differences

Although we have defined fractions as symbols, for permissible real-number replacements of any variables involved they represent real numbers.

Therefore, we can use the properties of real numbers to rewrite sums involving fractions in simpler form. For example, by applying the alternative definition of a quotient, the sum

$$\frac{a}{c} + \frac{b}{c} \quad (c \neq 0)$$

can be rewritten as

$$a\left(\frac{1}{c}\right) + b\left(\frac{1}{c}\right),$$

and then, by the distributive law, as

$$(a + b)\frac{1}{c}.$$

This is, again by the alternative definition of a quotient, equal to

$$\frac{a + b}{c},$$

so that:

If a, b, and $c \in R$, and $c \neq 0$, then

$$\frac{a}{c} + \frac{b}{c} = \frac{a + b}{c}.$$

If the fractions in a sum have unlike denominators, we can build the fractions to equal fractions having common denominators and then rewrite the sum as above.

In rewriting sums by building the terms in the sum into fractions with common denominators, any such denominator can be used. By using the **least common multiple** (L.C.M.) of the denominators (called the **least common denominator**), however, we can obtain a simpler form for the sum than if any other common denominator is used. The least common multiple of two or more natural numbers is the smallest natural number that is exactly divisible by each of the given numbers. Thus 24 is the L.C.M. of 3 and 8, because 24 is the smallest natural number each will divide into without remainder. To find the L.C.M. of a set of natural numbers, we:

1. express each number in completely factored form;
2. write as factors of a product each *different* prime factor occurring in any of the numbers, including each factor the greatest number of times it occurs in any one of the given numbers.

For example, the L.C.M. of 12, 15, and 18 is found in the following manner:

1. 12   15   18
    2·2·3   3·5   3·3·2

2. The L.C.M. is $2^2 \cdot 3^2 \cdot 5$ or 180.

The notion of a least number among several polynomial expressions is, in general, meaningless. We can, however, define the least common multiple of a set of polynomials in a manner analogous to that described above—namely, the polynomial of lowest degree yielding a polynomial quotient upon division by each of the given polynomials.

We can find the L.C.M. of a set of polynomials with integral coefficients in a manner comparable to that used with a set of natural numbers. The L.C.M. of x^2, $x^2 - 9$, and $x^3 - x^2 - 6x$ is found in the following manner:

1. x^2 $x^2 - 9$ $x^3 - x^2 - 6x$

    $x \cdot x$ $(x - 3)(x + 3)$ $x(x - 3)(x + 2)$

2. The L.C.M. is $x^2(x - 3)(x + 3)(x + 2)$.

Since polynomials are easier to work with in factored form, it is usually advantageous to leave the L.C.M. of a set of polynomials in a factored form rather than actually to carry out the indicated multiplication.

Now, in order to rewrite sums containing fractions having different denominators, we can ascertain the least common denominator of the fractions, determine the factor necessary to express each of the fractions as a fraction having this common denominator, write the fraction accordingly, and then rewrite the sum as a single fraction.

A difference

$$\frac{a}{b} - \frac{c}{d} \quad (b, d \neq 0),$$

may be viewed as the sum

$$\frac{a}{b} + \frac{-c}{d},$$

and written

$$\frac{a}{b}\left(\frac{d}{d}\right) + \frac{-c}{d}\left(\frac{b}{b}\right) = \frac{ad - cb}{bd} \quad (b, d \neq 0).$$

EXERCISE 3.5

Find the least common multiple.

Examples:

   a.   24,   30,   20   b. $2a$, $4b$, $6ab^2$

      $2 \cdot 2 \cdot 2 \cdot 3$ $2 \cdot 3 \cdot 5$ $2 \cdot 2 \cdot 5$ $2 \cdot a$ $2 \cdot 2 \cdot b$ $2 \cdot 3 \cdot a \cdot b \cdot b$

   Ans. $2^3 \cdot 3 \cdot 5$ or 120   **Ans.** $2^2 \cdot 3ab^2$ or $12ab^2$

   1. 4, 6, 10   **2.** 3, 4, 5   **3.** 6, 8, 15

   4. 4, 15, 18   **5.** 14, 21, 36   **6.** 4, 11, 22

   7. $2ab$, $6b^2$ **8.** $12xy$, $24x^3y^2$ **9.** $6xy$, $8x^2$, $3xy^2$

   10. $7x$, $8y$, $6z$ **11.** $(a - b)$, $a(a - b)^2$ **12.** $6(x + y)^2$, $4xy^2$

Examples:

a. $2a - 2$, $a - 1$
    $2(a - 1)$, $(a - 1)$

   Ans. $2(a - 1)$

b. $x^2 - 1$, $2(x - 1)^2$
    $(x - 1)(x + 1)$, $2(x - 1)(x - 1)$

   Ans. $2(x - 1)^2(x + 1)$

13. $a^2 - b^2$, $a - b$

14. $x + 2$, $x^2 - 4$

15. $a^2 + 5a + 4$, $(a + 1)^2$

16. $x^2 - 3x + 2$, $(x - 1)^2$

17. $x^2 + 3x - 4$, $(x - 1)^2$

18. $x^2 - x - 2$, $(x - 2)^2$

19. $x^2 - x$, $(x - 1)^3$

20. $y^2 + 2y$, $(y + 2)^2$

21. $4a^2 - 4$, $(a - 1)^2$, 2

22. $3x^2 - 3$, $(x + 1)^2$, 4

23. x^3, $x^2 - x$, $(x - 1)^2$

24. y, $y^3 - y$, $(y - 1)^3$

Write each sum or difference as a single fraction in lowest terms.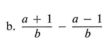

Examples:

a. $\dfrac{a}{3x} + \dfrac{b}{3x}$

   Ans. $\dfrac{a + b}{3x}$ $(x \neq 0)$

b. $\dfrac{a + 1}{b} - \dfrac{a - 1}{b}$

Write fraction in standard form.

$$\frac{a + 1}{b} + \frac{-(a - 1)}{b}$$

Write as a single fraction.

$$\frac{a + 1 - (a - 1)}{b}$$

$$\frac{a + 1 - a + 1}{b}$$

   Ans. $\dfrac{2}{b}$ $(b \neq 0)$

25. $\dfrac{x}{2} - \dfrac{3}{2}$

26. $\dfrac{y}{7} - \dfrac{5}{7}$

27. $\dfrac{a}{6} + \dfrac{b}{6} - \dfrac{c}{6}$

28. $\dfrac{x}{3} - \dfrac{2y}{3} + \dfrac{z}{3}$

29. $\dfrac{x - 1}{2y} + \dfrac{x}{2y}$

30. $\dfrac{y + 1}{b} + \dfrac{y - 1}{b}$

31. $\dfrac{3}{x + 2y} - \dfrac{x + 3}{x + 2y} - \dfrac{x + 1}{x + 2y}$

32. $\dfrac{2}{a - 3b} - \dfrac{b - 2}{a - 3b} + \dfrac{b}{a - 3b}$

33. $\dfrac{a + 1}{a^2 - 2a + 1} + \dfrac{5 - 3a}{a^2 - 2a + 1}$

34. $\dfrac{x + 4}{x^2 - x + 2} + \dfrac{2x - 3}{x^2 - x + 2}$

Example: $\dfrac{5}{a^2 - 9} - \dfrac{1}{a - 3}$

Factor denominators and write in standard form.

$$\frac{5}{(a - 3)(a + 3)} + \frac{-1}{(a - 3)}$$

Build each fraction to a fraction with the denominator $(a - 3)(a + 3)$.

$$\frac{5}{(a-3)(a+3)} + \frac{-1(a+3)}{(a-3)(a+3)}$$

Write as a single fraction and simplify.

$$\frac{5-(a+3)}{(a-3)(a+3)}$$

Ans. $\dfrac{2-a}{(a-3)(a+3)}$ $(a \neq 3, -3)$

35. $\dfrac{2}{ax} - \dfrac{2}{x}$ **36.** $\dfrac{3}{by} - \dfrac{2}{b}$ **37.** $\dfrac{a-2}{6} - \dfrac{a+1}{3}$

38. $\dfrac{x-3}{4} + \dfrac{5-x}{10}$ **39.** $\dfrac{2x-y}{2y} + \dfrac{x+y}{x}$ **40.** $\dfrac{3a+2b}{3b} - \dfrac{a+2b}{6a}$

41. $\dfrac{7}{5x-10} - \dfrac{5}{3x-6}$ **42.** $\dfrac{2}{y+2} - \dfrac{3}{y+3}$ **43.** $\dfrac{5}{2x-6} - \dfrac{3}{x+3}$

44. $\dfrac{2}{3-x} - \dfrac{1}{x-3}$ **45.** $\dfrac{7}{r-3} + \dfrac{3}{3-r}$ **46.** $\dfrac{1}{2x+1} - \dfrac{3}{x-2}$

47. $\dfrac{a}{3x+2} - \dfrac{a}{x-1}$ **48.** $\dfrac{a+1}{a+2} - \dfrac{a+2}{a+3}$ **49.** $\dfrac{5x-y}{3x+y} - \dfrac{6x-5y}{2x-y}$

50. $\dfrac{x+2y}{2x-y} - \dfrac{2x+y}{x-2y}$ **51.** $\dfrac{r-2s}{r+s} - \dfrac{2r-s}{r-s}$

52. $\dfrac{1}{b^2-1} - \dfrac{1}{b^2+2b+1}$ **53.** $\dfrac{y}{y^2-16} - \dfrac{y+1}{y^2-5y+4}$

54. $\dfrac{8}{a^2-4b^2} - \dfrac{2}{a^2-5ab+6b^2}$ **55.** $x + \dfrac{1}{x-1} - \dfrac{1}{(x-1)^2}$

56. $y - \dfrac{2y}{y^2-1} + \dfrac{3}{y+1}$

57. $\dfrac{1}{(a-b)(b-c)} + \dfrac{1}{(b-c)(c-a)} + \dfrac{1}{(c-a)(a-b)}$

58. A set of fractions has an infinite number of common denominators. Why is it convenient to use the least common denominator in finding sums or differences of fractions?

3.6   Products and Quotients

To discover how to rewrite products involving fractions, let us examine the product

$$\frac{a}{b} \cdot \frac{c}{d} = p \quad (b, d \neq 0)$$

and inquire into the nature of p. We have

$$\frac{a}{b} \cdot \frac{c}{d} = p \qquad \text{Given.}$$

$$bd\left(\frac{a}{b}\right)\left(\frac{c}{d}\right) = bdp \qquad \text{Multiplication axiom of equality.}$$

$$(b)(d)(a)\left(\frac{1}{b}\right)(c)\left(\frac{1}{d}\right) = bdp \qquad \text{Alternate definition of a quotient.}$$

$$(a)(c)(b)\left(\frac{1}{b}\right)(d)\left(\frac{1}{d}\right) = bdp \qquad \begin{array}{l}\text{Associative and commutative laws}\\ \text{of multiplication.}\end{array}$$

$$(a)(c)(1)(1) = bdp \qquad \text{Reciprocal property.}$$

$$ac = bdp \qquad \text{Multiplicative property of 1.}$$

$$p = \frac{ac}{bd} \qquad \text{Definition of a quotient.}$$

$$\frac{a}{b} \cdot \frac{c}{d} = \frac{ac}{bd} \qquad \text{Substitution for } p.$$

Therefore:

If a, b, c, and $d \in R$, and b, $d \neq 0$, then

$$\frac{a}{b} \cdot \frac{c}{d} = \frac{ac}{bd}.$$

For example,

$$\frac{6x^2}{y} \cdot \frac{xy}{2} = \frac{6x^3y}{2y}$$

$$= \frac{3x^3 \cdot 2y}{1 \cdot 2y}$$

$$= 3x^3 \quad (y \neq 0).$$

If any of the fractions, or any of the factors of the numerators or denominators of the fractions, have negative signs attached, it is advisable to proceed as if all of the signs were positive and then attach the appropriate sign to the simplified product. If there is an even number of negative signs involved, the result has a positive sign; if there is an odd number of negative signs involved, the result has a negative sign. For example,

$$\frac{-4x^2(y-x)}{9y} \cdot \frac{6y^2}{x(y-x)} = \frac{-8xy \cdot 3xy(y-x)}{3 \cdot 3xy(y-x)}$$

$$= \frac{-8xy}{3} \quad (x, y \neq 0, \ x \neq y)$$

When rewriting quotients

$$\frac{a}{b} \div \frac{c}{d} \quad (b, c, d \neq 0),$$

we seek a quotient q such that

$$\left(\frac{c}{d}\right)q = \frac{a}{b} \quad (b, c, d \neq 0).$$

To obtain q in terms of the other variables, we use the multiplication law of equality and multiply each member of this equality by d/c,

$$\left(\frac{d}{c}\right)\left(\frac{c}{d}\right)q = \left(\frac{d}{c}\right)\left(\frac{a}{b}\right),$$

from which

$$q = \left(\frac{d}{c}\right)\left(\frac{a}{b}\right) = \frac{da}{cb}.$$

Therefore it follows that:

If a, b, c, and $d \in R$, and b, c, $d \neq 0$, then

$$\frac{a}{b} \div \frac{c}{d} = \frac{a}{b} \cdot \frac{d}{c},$$

or, more directly,

$$\frac{a}{b} \div \frac{c}{d} = \frac{ad}{bc}.$$

For example,

$$\frac{2x^3}{3y} \div \frac{4x}{5y^2} = \frac{2x^3}{3y} \cdot \frac{5y^2}{4x}$$

$$= \frac{5x^2y \cdot 2xy}{6 \cdot 2xy}$$

$$= \frac{5x^2y}{6} \quad (x, y \neq 0).$$

|-37

EXERCISE 3.6

Write each product as a single fraction in lowest terms.

Examples:

a. $\dfrac{-3c^2}{5ab} \cdot \dfrac{10a^2b}{9c}$

$\dfrac{-2ac \cdot 15abc}{3 \cdot 15abc}$

Ans. $\dfrac{-2ac}{3} \quad (a, b, c \neq 0)$

b. $\dfrac{4a^2 - 1}{a^2 - 4} \cdot \dfrac{a^2 + 2a}{4a + 2}$

$\dfrac{(2a - 1)(2a + 1)}{(a - 2)(a + 2)} \cdot \dfrac{a(a + 2)}{2(2a + 1)}$

$\dfrac{a(2a - 1)(2a + 1)(a + 2)}{2(a - 2)(2a + 1)(a + 2)}$

Ans. $\dfrac{a(2a - 1)}{2(a - 2)} \quad (a \neq -2, -\tfrac{1}{2}, 2)$

1. $\dfrac{16}{38} \cdot \dfrac{19}{12}$

2. $\dfrac{4}{15} \cdot \dfrac{3}{16}$

3. $\dfrac{21}{4} \cdot \dfrac{2}{15}$

4. $\dfrac{7}{8} \cdot \dfrac{48}{64}$

5. $\dfrac{24}{3} \cdot \dfrac{20}{36} \cdot \dfrac{3}{4}$

6. $\dfrac{3}{10} \cdot \dfrac{16}{27} \cdot \dfrac{30}{36}$

7. $\dfrac{-12a^2b}{5c} \cdot \dfrac{10b^2c}{24a^3b}$

8. $\dfrac{a^2}{xy} \cdot \dfrac{3x^3y}{4a}$

9. $\dfrac{-2ab}{7c} \cdot \dfrac{3c^2}{4a^3} \cdot \dfrac{-6a}{15b^2}$

10. $\dfrac{10x}{12y} \cdot \dfrac{3x^2z}{5x^3z} \cdot \dfrac{6y^2x}{3yz}$

11. $5a^2b^2 \cdot \dfrac{1}{a^3b^3}$

12. $15x^2y \cdot \dfrac{3}{45xy^2}$

13. $\dfrac{5x + 25}{2x} \cdot \dfrac{4x}{2x + 10}$

14. $\dfrac{3y}{4xy - 6y^2} \cdot \dfrac{2x - 3y}{12x}$

15. $\dfrac{4a^2 - 1}{a^2 - 16} \cdot \dfrac{a^2 - 4a}{2a + 1}$

16. $\dfrac{9x^2 - 25}{2x - 2} \cdot \dfrac{x^2 - 1}{6x - 10}$

17. $\dfrac{x^2 - x - 20}{x^2 + 7x + 12} \cdot \dfrac{(x + 3)^2}{(x - 5)^2}$

18. $\dfrac{4x^2 + 8x + 3}{2x^2 - 5x + 3} \cdot \dfrac{6x^2 - 9x}{1 - 4x^2}$

19. $\dfrac{7a + 14}{14a - 28} \cdot \dfrac{4 - 2a}{a + 2} \cdot \dfrac{a - 3}{a + 1}$

20. $\dfrac{5x^2 - 5x}{3} \cdot \dfrac{x^2 - 9x - 10}{4x - 40} \cdot \dfrac{y^2}{2 - 2x^2}$

Write each quotient as a single fraction in lowest terms.

Examples:

a. $\dfrac{a^2b}{c} \div \dfrac{ab^3}{c^2}$

   $\dfrac{a^2b}{c} \cdot \dfrac{c^2}{ab^3}$

   $\dfrac{ac \cdot abc}{b^2 \cdot abc}$

  Ans. $\dfrac{ac}{b^2}$ $(a, b, c \neq 0)$

b. $\dfrac{3a^2 - 3}{2a + 2} \div \dfrac{3a - 3}{2}$

   $\dfrac{3(a - 1)(a + 1)}{2(a + 1)} \cdot \dfrac{2}{3(a - 1)}$

   $\dfrac{2 \cdot 3(a - 1)(a + 1)}{2 \cdot 3(a - 1)(a + 1)}$

  Ans. 1 $(a \neq 1, -1)$

21. $\dfrac{3}{4} \div \dfrac{9}{16}$

22. $\dfrac{2}{3} \div \dfrac{9}{15}$

23. $\dfrac{xy}{a^2b} \div \dfrac{x^3y^2}{ab}$

24. $\dfrac{9ab^3}{x} \div \dfrac{3}{2x^3}$

25. $\dfrac{-28x^2y^3}{15a^2b} \div \dfrac{-21x^2y^2}{35ab}$

26. $\dfrac{24a^3b}{-6xy^2} \div \dfrac{3a^2b}{12x}$

27. $\dfrac{x^2 - xy}{xy} \div \dfrac{2x - 2y}{xy}$

28. $\dfrac{r^2 + 2rs}{r} \div \dfrac{r + 2s}{s}$

29. $\dfrac{12 - 6x}{3x + 9} \div \dfrac{4x - 8}{-(5x + 15)}$

30. $\dfrac{18 - 4y}{3y + 2} \div \dfrac{6y - 27}{-(6y + 4)}$

31. $\dfrac{a^2 - a - 6}{a^2 + 2a - 15} \div \dfrac{a^2 - 4}{a^2 - 25}$

32. $\dfrac{x^2 + x - 2}{x^2 + 2x - 3} \div \dfrac{x^2 + 7x + 10}{x^2 - 2x - 15}$

33. $\dfrac{x^3 + y^3}{x} \div \dfrac{x + y}{3x}$

34. $\dfrac{8a^3 - b^3}{a + b} \div \dfrac{2a - b}{a^2 - b^2}$

35. $\dfrac{b^3 - 1}{b + 3} \div \dfrac{b^2 + b + 1}{b^2 + 4b + 3}$

36. $\dfrac{8y^3 - 1}{y - 2} \div \dfrac{4y^2 + 2y + 1}{y^2 - 4y + 4}$

37. $\dfrac{xy - 3x + y - 3}{x - 2} \div \dfrac{x + 1}{x^2 - 4}$

38. $\dfrac{2xy + 4x + 3y + 6}{2x + 3} \div \dfrac{y + 2}{y - 1}$

39. $\dfrac{a^2 - a}{a^2 - 2a - 3} \cdot \dfrac{a^2 + 2a + 1}{a^2 + 4a} \div \dfrac{a^2 - 3a - 4}{a^2 - 16}$

40. $\dfrac{y^2 - 4y + 3}{y^2} \cdot \dfrac{y^2 + y}{y^2 - 6y + 9} \div \dfrac{y^2 - 2y - 3}{y^2 - y - 6}$

41. Argue that the quotient $\dfrac{a}{b} \div c$ can be written $\dfrac{a}{bc}$ $(b, c \neq 0)$.

42. Argue that the quotient $a \div \dfrac{b}{c}$ can be written $\dfrac{ac}{b}$ $(b, c \neq 0)$.

3.7 Complex Fractions

A fraction that contains a fraction or fractions in either the numerator or denominator or both is called a **complex fraction.**

In simplifying complex fractions, it is helpful to remember that fraction bars serve as grouping devices in the same sense as parentheses or brackets. Thus the complex fraction

$$\frac{x + \dfrac{3}{4}}{x - \dfrac{1}{2}}$$

means

$$\left(x + \frac{3}{4}\right) \div \left(x - \frac{1}{2}\right).$$

Complex fractions may be simplified in either of two ways. In simple examples, it is easier to apply the fundamental principle of fractions and multiply the numerator and the denominator of the complex fraction by the L.C.D. of all of the fractions appearing therein. Thus, in the preceding example,

$$\frac{4\left(x + \dfrac{3}{4}\right)}{4\left(x - \dfrac{1}{2}\right)} = \frac{4x + 3}{4x - 2} \quad \left(x \neq \frac{1}{2}\right).$$

Alternatively, this fraction may be simplified by first representing the numerator as a single fraction and the denominator as a single fraction, and then writing the quotient as the product of the numerator and the reciprocal of the denominator:

$$\frac{x + \dfrac{3}{4}}{x - \dfrac{1}{2}} = \frac{\dfrac{4x + 3}{4}}{\dfrac{2x - 1}{2}}$$

$$= \frac{4x + 3}{4} \cdot \frac{2}{2x - 1}$$

$$= \frac{(4x + 3) \cdot 2}{2(2x - 1) \cdot 2}$$

$$= \frac{4x + 3}{2(2x - 1)} \quad \left(x \neq \frac{1}{2}\right).$$

The second method is generally more convenient in working with complicated fractions.

EXERCISE 3.7

Write each of the following complex fractions as a single fraction in lowest terms.

Example: $\dfrac{\dfrac{3}{a} - \dfrac{1}{2a}}{\dfrac{1}{3a} + \dfrac{5}{6a}}$

Find the L.C.D. for all fractions in numerator and denominator ($6a$); multiply each term in the numerator and each term in the denominator by $6a$ and simplify.

$$\frac{(6a)\dfrac{3}{a} - (6a)\dfrac{1}{2a}}{(6a)\dfrac{1}{3a} + (6a)\dfrac{5}{6a}} = \frac{18 - 3}{2 + 5} \qquad 1-15$$

Ans. $\dfrac{15}{7}$ $(a \neq 0)$

1. $\dfrac{\frac{3}{7}}{\frac{2}{7}}$ **2.** $\dfrac{\frac{3}{5}}{6}$ **3.** $\dfrac{14}{\frac{7}{10}}$ **4.** $\dfrac{\frac{5}{2}}{\frac{21}{4}}$

5. $\dfrac{\frac{b}{c}}{\frac{b^2}{a}}$ **6.** $\dfrac{\frac{5x}{6y}}{\frac{4x}{5y}}$ **7.** $\dfrac{\frac{2x}{5y}}{\frac{3x}{10y^2}}$ **8.** $\dfrac{\frac{3ab}{4}}{\frac{3b}{8a^2}}$

9. $\dfrac{\frac{3}{4}}{4 - \frac{1}{4}}$ **10.** $\dfrac{3}{4 + \frac{2}{3}}$ **11.** $\dfrac{1 - \frac{2}{3}}{3 + \frac{1}{3}}$ **12.** $\dfrac{\frac{1}{2} + \frac{3}{4}}{\frac{1}{2} - \frac{3}{4}}$

13. $\dfrac{\frac{2}{a} + \frac{3}{2a}}{5 + \frac{1}{a}}$ **14.** $\dfrac{x - 2}{1 - \frac{4}{x^2}}$ **15.** $\dfrac{x + \frac{x}{y}}{1 + \frac{1}{y}}$ **16.** $\dfrac{1 + \frac{1}{x}}{1 - \frac{1}{x}}$

Example:
$$\frac{a}{a + \dfrac{3}{3 + \frac{1}{2}}}$$

Combine $(3 + \frac{1}{2})$.

$$\frac{a}{a + \dfrac{3}{\frac{7}{2}}}$$

Write $\dfrac{3}{\frac{7}{2}}$ as $3 \cdot \dfrac{2}{7}$ or $\dfrac{6}{7}$; combine $\left(a + \dfrac{6}{7}\right)$.

$$\frac{a}{\dfrac{7a + 6}{7}}$$

Write $\dfrac{a}{\dfrac{7a + 6}{7}}$ as $a \cdot \dfrac{7}{7a + 6}$.

Ans. $\dfrac{7a}{7a + 6}$ $\left(a \neq -\dfrac{6}{7}\right)$

17. $2 - \dfrac{2}{3 + \frac{1}{2}}$

18. $1 - \dfrac{1}{1 - \frac{1}{3}}$

19. $a - \dfrac{a}{a + \frac{1}{4}}$

20. $x - \dfrac{x}{1 - \dfrac{x}{1 - x}}$

21. $1 - \dfrac{1}{1 - \dfrac{1}{y - 2}}$

22. $2y + \dfrac{3}{3 - \dfrac{2y}{y - 1}}$

23. $\dfrac{1 + \dfrac{1}{1 - \frac{a}{b}}}{1 - \dfrac{3}{1 - \frac{a}{b}}}$

24. $\dfrac{1 - \dfrac{1}{\frac{a}{b} + 2}}{1 + \dfrac{3}{\frac{a}{2b} + 1}}$

25. $\dfrac{a + 2 - \dfrac{12}{a + 3}}{a - 5 + \dfrac{16}{a + 3}}$

26. $\dfrac{a + 4 - \dfrac{7}{a - 2}}{a - 1 + \dfrac{2}{a - 2}}$

27. $\dfrac{\dfrac{1}{ab} + \dfrac{2}{bc} + \dfrac{3}{ac}}{\dfrac{2a + 3b + c}{abc}}$

28. $\dfrac{\dfrac{a}{bc} - \dfrac{b}{ac} + \dfrac{c}{ab}}{\dfrac{1}{a^2b^2} - \dfrac{1}{a^2c^2} + \dfrac{1}{b^2c^2}}$

29. $\dfrac{\dfrac{a^2 + b^2}{a^2 - b^2}}{\dfrac{a - b}{a + b} - \dfrac{a + b}{a - b}}$

30. $\dfrac{\dfrac{a + 1}{a - 1} + \dfrac{a - 1}{a + 1}}{\dfrac{a + 1}{a - 1} - \dfrac{a - 1}{a + 1}}$

31. $2 + \dfrac{1}{2 + \dfrac{1}{2 + \dfrac{1}{2 + \frac{1}{2}}}}$

32. $3 - \dfrac{1}{3 - \dfrac{1}{3 - \dfrac{1}{3 - \frac{1}{3}}}}$

CHAPTER REVIEW

1. a. Write six fractions equal to $\dfrac{1}{a - b}$ by changing the sign or signs of the numerator, denominator, or fraction itself.

   b. What are the conditions on a and b for the fraction to represent a positive number? A negative number?

2. a. Is $(x - 2)/(1 + x^2)$ defined for all real values of x?

   b. For what value(s) of x does the fraction equal 0?

3. Reduce to lowest terms.

   a. $\dfrac{8x^2 - 4x^3}{x(2 - x)}$

   b. $\dfrac{8x^3 + y^3}{4x^2 - y^2}$

   1,3,7,8,9ab

4. Write $\dfrac{6x^2 + x + 13}{2x + 3}$ in the form $[Q(x)] + \dfrac{R}{2x + 3}$.

5. Use synthetic division to write the quotient $\dfrac{y^3 + 3y^2 - 2y - 4}{y + 1}$ as a polynomial in simple form.

6. Use synthetic division to write the quotient $\dfrac{y^7 - 1}{y - 1}$ as a polynomial in simple form.

Write each expression as a single fraction in lowest terms.

7. a. $\dfrac{x^2 - 3x}{x^3 - x} \cdot \dfrac{x^2 + 2x - 3}{x^2 + 6x + 9}$

   b. $\dfrac{2x^2 - x}{3y - y^2} \cdot \dfrac{3xy^2(9 - 6y + y^2)}{4x^2 - 1}$

8. a. $\dfrac{2y - 6}{y + 2x} \div \dfrac{4y - 12}{2y + 4x}$

   b. $\dfrac{a^2}{b - a} \div \dfrac{a^3 - a^2}{a - b}$

9. a. $\dfrac{2}{5x} - \dfrac{3}{4y} + \dfrac{7y}{20xy}$

   b. $\dfrac{y}{y^2 - 16} - \dfrac{y + 1}{y^2 - 5y + 4}$

10. a. $\dfrac{a^2 - \dfrac{1}{a}}{a^3 - \dfrac{1}{a^3}}$

    b. $\dfrac{\dfrac{x}{x + y} + \dfrac{y}{x - y}}{\dfrac{x^2 + y^2}{x^2 - y^2}}$

11. a. $1 - \dfrac{a^2}{(a - b)^2}$

    b. $\dfrac{a + b}{b^2} + \dfrac{1 - \dfrac{a^2}{b^2}}{a - b}$

12. Simplify $\dfrac{x + \dfrac{1}{x}}{1 - \dfrac{1}{1 + \dfrac{1}{x - 1}}}$.

13. For what value of k will
$$\frac{x - 1}{x + 2} \div \frac{k - 3}{x + 3}$$
be undefined?

14. For what value(s) of x will $\dfrac{2x}{x^2 - y^2}$ be undefined?

The following laws developed in this chapter were shown to be consequences of axioms and laws previously developed. If a, b, c, and $d \in R$,

a. $\dfrac{ac}{bc} = \dfrac{a}{b}$ and $\dfrac{a}{b} = \dfrac{ac}{bc}$ $(b, c \neq 0)$ b. $\dfrac{a}{c} + \dfrac{b}{c} = \dfrac{a + b}{c}$ $(c \neq 0)$

c. $\dfrac{a}{b} \cdot \dfrac{c}{d} = \dfrac{a \cdot c}{b \cdot d}$ $(b, d \neq 0)$ d. $\dfrac{a}{b} \div \dfrac{c}{d} = \dfrac{a}{b} \cdot \dfrac{d}{c}$ $(b, c, d \neq 0)$

Which one or more of these laws justifies each of the following statements?

15. $\dfrac{x - y}{6} + \dfrac{z}{3} = \dfrac{x - y + 2z}{6}$ **16.** $\dfrac{x(x - 3)}{(x - 2)(x - 3)} = \dfrac{x}{x - 2}$ $(x \neq 2, 3)$

17. $\dfrac{x}{3} \div \dfrac{y}{5} = \dfrac{5x}{3y}$ $(y \neq 0)$ **18.** $\dfrac{x}{2} + \dfrac{y}{3} = \dfrac{3x + 2y}{6}$

19. $\dfrac{3x}{4y} = \dfrac{3xy}{4y^2}$ $(y \neq 0)$ **20.** $\dfrac{\dfrac{2x}{y}}{\dfrac{6x}{5y}} = \dfrac{5}{3}$ $(x, y \neq 0)$

4

EXPONENTS, ROOTS, AND RADICALS

know 6 laws

4.1 Laws for Positive Integral Exponents

In Chapter 2 the expression a^n, where a is any real number and n is a positive integer, was defined by

$$a^n = a \cdot a \cdot a \cdot a \cdots (n \text{ factors}).$$

The following laws were developed from this definition:

I. $a^m \cdot a^n = a^{m+n}$.

II. $\dfrac{a^m}{a^n} = a^{m-n}$ $(m > n, a \neq 0)$.

The following four laws are also very useful in simplifying expressions involving positive integral exponents.

IIa. $\dfrac{a^m}{a^n} = \dfrac{1}{a^{n-m}}$ $(m < n, a \neq 0)$, since

$$\frac{a^m}{a^n} = \frac{a \cdot a \cdots (m \text{ factors})}{a \cdot a \cdot a \cdots (n \text{ factors})}$$

$$= \frac{a \cdot a \cdots (m \text{ factors})}{[a \cdot a \cdots (m \text{ factors})][a \cdot a \cdots (n - m) \text{ factors}]}$$

$$= \frac{1}{a^{n-m}}.$$

For example, $\dfrac{x^5}{x^8} = \dfrac{1}{x^3}$; $\dfrac{x^2 y}{x^3 y^2} = \dfrac{1}{xy}$ $(x, y \neq 0)$.

III. $(a^m)^n = a^{mn}$,

since

$$(a^m)^n = a^m \cdot a^m \cdot a^m \cdots (n \text{ factors})$$

$$= a^{m + m + m \cdots (n \text{ terms})}$$

$$= a^{mn}.$$

For example, $(x^2)^3 = x^6$; $(x^5)^2 = x^{10}$.

IV. $(ab)^n = a^n b^n$,

since

$$(ab)^n = (ab)(ab)(ab) \cdots (n \text{ factors})$$

$$= [a \cdot a \cdot a \cdots (n \text{ factors})][b \cdot b \cdot b \cdots (n \text{ factors})]$$

$$= a^n b^n.$$

For example, $(xy)^3 = x^3 y^3$; $(2x^2 y^3)^3 = 8x^6 y^9$.

V. $\left(\dfrac{a}{b}\right)^n = \dfrac{a^n}{b^n}$ $(b \neq 0)$,

since

$$\left(\frac{a}{b}\right)^n = \left(\frac{a}{b}\right) \cdot \left(\frac{a}{b}\right) \cdot \left(\frac{a}{b}\right) \cdots (n \text{ factors})$$

$$= \frac{a \cdot a \cdot a \cdots (n \text{ factors})}{b \cdot b \cdot b \cdots (n \text{ factors})}$$

$$= \frac{a^n}{b^n}.$$

For example, $\left(\dfrac{x}{y}\right)^3 = \dfrac{x^3}{y^3}$; $\left(\dfrac{2x^2}{y}\right)^4 = \dfrac{(2x^2)^4}{y^4}$ $(y \neq 0)$.

EXERCISE 4.1

State which of the Laws (I–V) pertaining to exponents justifies writing the given statement.

Examples:

a. $\dfrac{x^3y^2}{xy} = x^2y \quad (x, y \neq 0)$

   Ans. Law II

b. $\left(\dfrac{2x^2}{y}\right)^3 = \dfrac{(2x^2)^3}{y^3} \quad (y \neq 0)$

   Ans. Law V

1. $(xy^2)^3 = x^3(y^2)^3$

2. $\left(\dfrac{x}{y^3}\right)^2 = \dfrac{x^2}{(y^3)^2} \quad (y \neq 0)$

3. $\dfrac{xy}{x^2y^3} = \dfrac{1}{xy^2} \quad (x, y \neq 0)$

4. $x^4(y^3)^2 = x^4y^6$

5. $\dfrac{x^3y}{x^2} = xy \quad (x \neq 0)$

6. $\left(\dfrac{x^3y^3}{xy^2}\right)^3 = (x^2y)^3 \quad (x, y \neq 0)$

7. $\dfrac{x^5y^2}{x^3y} = x^2y \quad (x, y \neq 0)$

8. $\left(\dfrac{2x^2}{y}\right)^3 = \dfrac{(2x^2)^3}{y^3} \quad (y \neq 0)$

9. $\left(\dfrac{x^2 \cdot x^3}{y^2}\right)^2 = \left(\dfrac{x^5}{y^2}\right)^2 \quad (y \neq 0)$

10. $\left(\dfrac{x}{x^3y}\right)^3 = \left(\dfrac{1}{x^2y}\right)^3 \quad (x, y \neq 0)$

11. $(x^2y^3)^3 = (x^2)^3(y^3)^3$

12. $(x^2)^3(y^3)^3 = x^6y^9$

State which of the Laws (I–V) pertaining to exponents justifies each step in the given sequence.

Example: **Ans.**

$\left(\dfrac{x^3y^2}{xy}\right)^4 = (x^2y)^4 \quad (x, y \neq 0)$ Law II

$(x^2y)^4 = (x^2)^4y^4$ Law IV

$(x^2)^4y^4 = x^8y^4$ Law III

13. $\left(\dfrac{xy^3}{y^4}\right)^2 = \left(\dfrac{x}{y}\right)^2 \quad (y \neq 0)$

$\left(\dfrac{x}{y}\right)^2 = \dfrac{x^2}{y^2} \quad (y \neq 0)$

14. $\left(\dfrac{x^4}{y}\right)^2 = \dfrac{(x^4)^2}{y^2} \quad (y \neq 0)$

$\dfrac{(x^4)^2}{y^2} = \dfrac{x^8}{y^2} \quad (y \neq 0)$

15. $(x^2y^3)^2 = (x^2)^2(y^3)^2$

$(x^2)^2(y^3)^2 = x^4y^6$

16. $\left(\dfrac{x^2y^2}{xy}\right)^3 = (xy)^3 \quad (x, y \neq 0)$

$(xy)^3 = x^3y^3$

17. $(x^2 \cdot x^3y^3)^2 = (x^5y^3)^2$

$(x^5y^3)^2 = (x^5)^2(y^3)^2$

$(x^5)^2(y^3)^2 = x^{10}y^6$

18. $\left(\dfrac{2x^2y^3}{z}\right)^2 = \dfrac{(2x^2y^3)^2}{z^2} \quad (z \neq 0)$

$\dfrac{(2x^2y^3)^2}{z^2} = \dfrac{2^2(x^2)^2(y^3)^2}{z^2} \quad (z \neq 0)$

$\dfrac{2^2(x^2)^2(y^3)^2}{z^2} = \dfrac{2^2x^4y^6}{z^2} \quad (z \neq 0)$

Using one or more of Laws I–V pertaining to exponents, write each of the following as a product or quotient in which each variable occurs, at most, once in each term and involves positive exponents only.

Examples:

a. $\dfrac{x^3 y^2}{x y^5}$

Ans. $\dfrac{x^2}{y^3}$ $(x, y \neq 0)$

b. $\left(\dfrac{2x^3}{y}\right)^2$

$\dfrac{2^2 \cdot x^6}{y^2}$

Ans. $\dfrac{4x^6}{y^2}$ $(y \neq 0)$

c. $\dfrac{(-xy^2)^3}{(-x^2 y)^2}$

$\dfrac{-x^3 y^6}{x^4 y^2}$

Ans. $\dfrac{-y^4}{x}$ $(x, y \neq 0)$

19. $x^2 \cdot x^3$

20. $a^5 \cdot a$

21. $y^3 \cdot y^4$

22. $b^5 \cdot b^5$

23. $\dfrac{x^5}{x^2}$

24. $\dfrac{y^3}{y^5}$

25. $\dfrac{x^3 y^5}{x y^2}$

26. $\dfrac{a^2 y^2}{a y}$

27. $(x^2)^4$

28. $(y^3)^2$

29. $(-x^2)^4$

30. $(-x^4)^3$

31. $(x^2 y^3)^3$

32. $(rst^2)^4$

33. $(x^3 y^2 z)^2$

34. $(a^2 b^2 c^2)^{10}$

35. $\left(\dfrac{x^2}{y^3}\right)^3$

36. $\left(\dfrac{a^3}{b^3}\right)^2$

37. $\left(\dfrac{3y}{x^2}\right)^4$

38. $\left(\dfrac{4x}{y}\right)^3$

39. $\left(-\dfrac{2x}{5y^2}\right)^3$

40. $\left(-\dfrac{3a}{7b^2}\right)^2$

41. $(2x^2)^2 (3x)^3$

42. $(4a^2)^3 (2a^4)^2$

43. $(xy^2)^3 (-2x^2)^2$

44. $(m^2 n^2)^3 (-mn^2)^3$

45. $\dfrac{(4x)^3}{(2x^2)^2}$

46. $\dfrac{(5x)^2}{(3x^2)^3}$

47. $\dfrac{(xy^2)^3}{(x^2 y)^2}$

48. $\dfrac{(-xy^2)^2}{(x^2 y)^3}$

49. $\dfrac{(xy)^2 (x^2 y)^3}{(x^2 y^2)^2}$

50. $\dfrac{(-x)^2 (-x^2)^4}{(x^2)^3}$

51. $\left(\dfrac{2x}{y^2}\right)^3 \left(\dfrac{y^2}{3x}\right)^2$

52. $\left(\dfrac{x^2 z}{2}\right)^2 \left(-\dfrac{2}{x^2 z}\right)^3$

53. $\left(\dfrac{-3}{y^2}\right)^2 (2y^3)^2$

54. $\left(\dfrac{y}{x}\right)^2 \left(-\dfrac{3}{4xy}\right)^3 \left(-\dfrac{x^2}{9y}\right)^2$

Examples:

a. $\dfrac{x^n \cdot x^{n+1}}{x^{n-1}}$

$x^{n + (n+1) - (n-1)}$

Ans. x^{n+2} $(x \neq 0)$

b. $\dfrac{(y^{n-1})^2}{y^{n-2}}$

$y^{(2n-2) - (n-2)}$

Ans. y^n $(y \neq 0)$

c. $(x^{n+1} \cdot x^{2n+3})^2$

$(x^{3n+4})^2$

Ans. x^{6n+8}

55. $x^n \cdot x^n$

56. $\dfrac{x^{2n} x^n}{x^{n+1}}$

57. $\dfrac{(x^{n+1} x^{2n-1})^2}{x^{3n}}$

58. $\left(\dfrac{y^2 \cdot y^3}{y}\right)^{2n}$

59. $\left(\dfrac{x^{3n} x^{2n}}{x^{4n}}\right)^2$

60. $\dfrac{(y^{n+1})^n}{y^n}$

4.2 Positive Rational Exponents

If the laws developed in the preceding section are to hold for rational exponents, meanings consistent with these laws must be assigned to powers with rational exponents.

Let us examine exponents that are the reciprocals of natural numbers, that is, exponents of the form $1/n$, where n is a natural number. We first assume that there exists a power of a, $a^{1/n}$, where a is positive. If the third law of exponents is to hold for these new powers, we have

$$(a^{1/n})^n = a^{n/n} = a,$$

and $a^{1/n}$ *must be defined as one of n equal factors of a.* $a^{1/n}$ is called an nth root of a. When n is 2 or 3, $a^{1/n}$ is called a square root or a cube root of a, respectively. Any positive number has both a positive and a negative nth root when n is an even number; however, we shall refer only to the positive nth root when using $a^{1/n}$ and $a > 0$. Thus $81^{1/4} = 3$, $81^{1/2} = 9$, etc. If we wish to refer to the negative nth root, we shall write $-a^{1/n}$.

If a is negative and n is a natural number, there are two possibilities to be considered for the power $a^{1/n}$.

1. If n is even, we can have no real root, for an even power of either a positive or a negative real number is always positive.
2. If n is odd, there will be one negative root, since an odd power of a negative real number is negative.

Thus

$$(-8)^{1/3} = -2 \quad \text{since} \quad (-2)(-2)(-2) = -8.$$

However,

$$(-4)^{1/2} \neq 2 \quad \text{since} \quad (2)(2) = 4$$

and

$$(-4)^{1/2} \neq -2 \quad \text{since} \quad (-2)(-2) = 4.$$

There is no square root of -4 in the real numbers.

We define the general rational exponent to obey the third law of exponents. Thus, for nonnegative real numbers a, $a^{m/n}$ is defined by

$$a^{m/n} = (a^{1/n})^m.$$

It can be shown that $(a^m)^{1/n}$ is also equal to $a^{m/n}$ so that

$$a^{m/n} = (a^{1/n})^m = (a^m)^{1/n},$$

and we may look at $a^{m/n}$ in two ways, either as the mth power of the nth root of a, or as the nth root of the mth power of a. For example,

$$8^{2/3} = (8^{1/3})^2 = (2)^2 = 4$$

or

$$8^{2/3} = (8^2)^{1/3} = (64)^{1/3} = 4.$$

Hereafter, we shall use whichever viewpoint is most convenient for the purpose at hand.

Because we defined $a^{1/n}$ to be the positive nth root of a for positive a and n an even natural number and a^m to be negative for a negative and m an odd natural number, we must also agree that, for m and n *even* natural numbers, and a any real number,

$$(a^m)^{1/n} = |a|^{m/n},$$

or, for the special case of *even m* and *n* where $m = n$,

$$(a^n)^{1/n} = |a|$$

for each real number a.   For example,

$$(a^2)^{1/2} = |a|.$$

If the absolute-value notation were not used, we would have the inconsistent result

$$[(-4)^2]^{1/2} = (-4)^{2(1/2)},$$

$$(16)^{1/2} = (-4)^1,$$

and

$$4 = -4.$$

Let us agree that in the exercises that follow *all bases are positive unless otherwise specified.*

We have defined powers with rational exponents so that they obey the third law for positive integral exponents.   However, they can also be shown to obey the other laws pertaining to positive integral exponents, so that Laws I–V for exponents are valid for all positive rational exponents.

Recall that any number that can be expressed as the quotient of two integers is called a rational number.   Any real number that cannot be so expressed is called an irrational number; any expression such as $a^{1/n}$ represents a rational number if and only if a is the nth power of a rational number.   Thus $4^{1/2}$, $(-27)^{1/3}$, and $(81)^{1/4}$ are rational numbers equal to 2, -3, and 3, while $2^{1/2}$, $5^{1/3}$, and $7^{1/4}$ are irrational numbers.   In Section 4.6 we will discuss ways of obtaining rational numbers that are approximations to some irrational numbers.

EXERCISE 4.2

Write each of the following as a basic numeral or basic fraction.

Examples:

a. $64^{1/2}$	b. $(\frac{8}{27})^{2/3}$	c. $(-27)^{4/3}$
Ans. 8	$[(\frac{8}{27})^{1/3}]^2$	$[(-27)^{1/3}]^4$
	$(\frac{2}{3})^2$	$(-3)^4$
	Ans. $\frac{4}{9}$	**Ans.** 81

1. $9^{1/2}$ 2. $(25)^{1/2}$ 3. $(32)^{1/5}$ 4. $(27)^{1/3}$

5. $(-27)^{1/3}$ 6. $(64)^{1/3}$ 7. $(27)^{2/3}$ 8. $(32)^{3/5}$

9. $(81)^{3/4}$ 10. $(125)^{2/3}$ 11. $(-8)^{4/3}$ 12. $(-64)^{2/3}$

13. $(\frac{1}{8})^{5/3}$ 14. $(\frac{1}{16})^{3/4}$ 15. $(\frac{4}{9})^{3/2}$ 16. $(\frac{25}{16})^{3/2}$

State which of the Laws I–V pertaining to exponents justifies each step in the given sequence. (Note: Remember that all bases are assumed to be positive real numbers.)

Example: **Ans.**

$$\left(\frac{y^3 z}{x^{1/2}}\right)^{2/3} = \frac{(y^3 z)^{2/3}}{(x^{1/2})^{2/3}}$$ Law V

$$\frac{(y^3 z)^{2/3}}{(x^{1/2})^{2/3}} = \frac{(y^3)^{2/3} z^{2/3}}{(x^{1/2})^{2/3}}$$ Law IV

$$\frac{(y^3)^{2/3} z^{2/3}}{(x^{1/2})^{2/3}} = \frac{y^2 z^{2/3}}{x^{1/3}}$$ Law III

17. $\left(\dfrac{x^{3/2}}{x}\right)^{2/3} = (x^{1/2})^{2/3}$

$(x^{1/2})^{2/3} = x^{1/3}$

18. $(x^{1/2} x^{3/4})^{2/5} = (x^{5/4})^{2/5}$

$(x^{5/4})^{2/5} = x^{1/2}$

19. $\left(\dfrac{x^{1/2}}{y^{3/2}}\right)^{2/3} = \dfrac{(x^{1/2})^{2/3}}{(y^{3/2})^{2/3}}$

$\dfrac{(x^{1/2})^{2/3}}{(y^{3/2})^{2/3}} = \dfrac{x^{1/3}}{y}$

20. $(x^{2/3} y^{1/2})^6 = (x^{2/3})^6 (y^{1/2})^6$

$(x^{2/3})^6 (y^{1/2})^6 = x^4 y^3$

21. $\left(\dfrac{x^{1/2} y^{2/3}}{z^{1/3}}\right)^6 = \dfrac{(x^{1/2} y^{2/3})^6}{(z^{1/3})^6}$

$\dfrac{(x^{1/2} y^{2/3})^6}{(z^{1/3})^6} = \dfrac{(x^{1/2})^6 (y^{2/3})^6}{(z^{1/3})^6}$

$\dfrac{(x^{1/2})^6 (y^{2/3})^6}{(z^{1/3})^6} = \dfrac{x^3 y^4}{z^2}$

22. $\left(\dfrac{x^{3/4} y}{x}\right)^{2/3} = \left(\dfrac{y}{x^{1/4}}\right)^{2/3}$

$\left(\dfrac{y}{x^{1/4}}\right)^{2/3} = \dfrac{y^{2/3}}{(x^{1/4})^{2/3}}$

$\dfrac{y^{2/3}}{(x^{1/4})^{2/3}} = \dfrac{y^{2/3}}{x^{1/6}}$

Write each of the following as a product or quotient of powers in which each variable occurs but once, and all exponents are positive.

Examples:

a. $x^{1/4} \cdot x^{1/2}$

Ans. $x^{3/4}$

b. $\dfrac{x^{5/6}}{x^{2/3}}$

$\dfrac{x^{5/6}}{x^{4/6}}$

Ans. $x^{1/6}$

c. $\dfrac{(x^{1/2} y^2)^2}{(x^{2/3} \cdot y)^3}$

$\dfrac{x y^4}{x^2 y^3}$

Ans. $\dfrac{y}{x}$

23. $x^{1/3} \cdot x^{1/3}$ **24.** $y^{1/2} \cdot y^{3/2}$ **25.** $\dfrac{x^{2/3}}{x^{1/3}}$ **26.** $\dfrac{x^{3/4}}{x^{1/4}}$

27. $(n^{1/2})^3$ **28.** $(x^6)^{2/3}$ **29.** $(m^4)^{1/8}$ **30.** $(x^{1/2}y^{1/3})^6$

31. $(a^{2/3}b)^{1/2}$ **32.** $\left(\dfrac{y^4}{x^2}\right)^{1/2}$ **33.** $\left(\dfrac{a^6}{c^3}\right)^{2/3}$ **34.** $\left(\dfrac{x^{1/2}}{y^2}\right)^2\left(\dfrac{y^4}{x^2}\right)^{1/2}$

Simplify.   Assume that $m, n > 0$.

Examples:

a. $\dfrac{(x^n)^{3/2}}{x^{n/2}}$

$x^{3n/2 - n/2}$

Ans. x^n

b. $(y^{2n} \cdot y^{n/2})^4$

$y^{8n} \cdot y^{2n}$

Ans. y^{10n}

c. $\left(\dfrac{a^{n+2} \cdot b^{n/2}}{a^n}\right)^2$

$(a^2 \cdot b^{n/2})^2$

Ans. $a^4 b^n$

35. $x^n \cdot x^{n/2}$ **36.** $(a^2)^{n/2} \cdot (b^{2n})^{2/n}$ **37.** $\dfrac{x^{2n}}{x^{n/2}}$

38. $\left(\dfrac{a^n}{b}\right)^{1/2}\left(\dfrac{b}{a^{2n}}\right)^{3/2}$ **39.** $\dfrac{x^{3n}y^{2m+1}}{(x^n y^m)^{1/2}}$ **40.** $\left(\dfrac{m^a n^{2a}}{n^{4a}}\right)^{1/a}$

41. $\left(\dfrac{x^{2n} \cdot y^{3n}}{x^n}\right)^{1/3}$ **42.** $\left(\dfrac{x^{n+1} \cdot y^{n+2}}{xy^2}\right)^{1/n}$

43. $\left[\left(\dfrac{x^{n/2} \cdot y^{n/3}}{z^{1/6}}\right)^6\right]^{1/n}$ **44.** $\left[\left(\dfrac{x^{2n}}{y^{3n}}\right)^{1/6}\right]^{2/n}$

In the foregoing problems, the values of the variable bases were restricted to positive real numbers.   In Problems 45–50, consider variable bases to be any element of the set of real numbers, and state all necessary restrictions.

Examples:

a. $[(-3)^2]^{1/2}$

$[(-3)^2]^{1/2} = |-3|$

Ans.   3

b. $[u^2(u+5)]^{1/2}$

$[u^2(u+5)]^{1/2} = |u|(u+5)^{1/2}$

Ans. $|u|(u+5)^{1/2}$

45. $[(-5)^2]^{1/2}$ **46.** $[(-3)^{12}]^{1/4}$ **47.** $(4x^2)^{1/2}$

48. $(9y^6)^{1/2}$ **49.** $\dfrac{2}{[x^2(x+5)]^{1/2}}$ **50.** $\left[\dfrac{9}{x^6(x^2+2)}\right]^{1/2}$

4.3   Zero and Negative Rational Exponents

In order for the first law of exponents to hold for zero exponents, that is, for

$$a^0 a^n = a^{0+n} = a^n,$$

it is clear that a^0 *must be defined as* 1. This also follows if the second law of exponents is to hold for the case where $m = n$, since

$$\frac{a^n}{a^n} = a^{n-n} = a^0 \quad (a \neq 0)$$

and

$$\frac{a^n}{a^n} = 1 \quad (a \neq 0),$$

where it is evident that in writing $a^0 = 1$, we must make the restriction $a \neq 0$. (Why?) Thus,

$$3^0 = 1; \quad (\tfrac{1}{2})^0 = 1; \quad (-4)^0 = 1; \quad (x)^0 = 1 \quad (x \neq 0).$$

Formally, then, for all real numbers a, we define

$$a^0 = 1 \quad (a \neq 0).$$

If the first law of exponents is to hold for negative exponents, we have

$$a^n \cdot a^{-n} = a^{n-n} = a^0 = 1.$$

Since

$$a^n \cdot \frac{1}{a^n} = 1 \quad (a \neq 0),$$

it is evident that for consistency a^{-n} *must be defined by*

$$a^{-n} = \frac{1}{a^n} \quad (a \neq 0).$$

It follows that

$$\frac{1}{a^{-n}} = \frac{1}{\frac{1}{a^n}} = a^n \quad (a \neq 0).$$

For example,

$$3^{-2} = \frac{1}{3^2} = \frac{1}{9},$$

$$\frac{1}{2^{-3}} = 2^3 = 8,$$

$$\frac{x^{-2}}{y^{-1}} = \frac{y}{x^2} \quad (x, y \neq 0).$$

Having defined a^{-n} $(a \neq 0)$ as $1/a^n$ and a^0 as 1, it follows that, for all rational exponents m and n,

$$\frac{1}{a^{n-m}} = \frac{1}{a^{-(m-n)}} = a^{m-n},$$

and the laws of exponents II and IIa can be generalized into one law and written

$$\text{II.} \quad \frac{a^m}{a^n} = a^{m-n} \quad (a \neq 0),$$

where m and n are any rational numbers.

Moreover, since zero and negative exponents have now been defined so that their properties are consistent with the basic properties of positive rational exponents, all of these properties can be applied in the case of *all rational exponents*.

Although the matter will not be discussed here, powers of positive numbers can be and are defined for all *real-number* exponents. You will learn more about this in Chapter 11 when we consider exponential functions.

EXERCISE 4.3

Assume that all variables in this exercise represent positive real numbers only.

Write as a basic numeral or basic fraction.

Examples:

a. $\dfrac{3^{-2}}{2^{-3}}$

$\dfrac{2^3}{3^2}$

Ans. $\dfrac{8}{9}$

b. $\dfrac{(16)^{1/2}}{8^{-2/3}}$

$(16)^{1/2}(8)^{2/3}$

Ans.   16

c. $4^{1/2} + 4^{-1/2}$

$4^{1/2} + \dfrac{1}{4^{1/2}}$

Ans. $\dfrac{5}{2}$

1. 2^{-1}

2. $\dfrac{1}{3^{-1}}$

3. $(\frac{3}{5})^{-1}$

4. $(-\frac{1}{3})^{-2}$

5. $\dfrac{2^0}{3^{-2}}$

6. $\dfrac{5^{-1}}{3^{-2}}$

7. $(-8)^{-1/3}$

8. $(16)^{-1/4}$

9. $3^{-2} + 3^2$

10. $5^{-1} + 25^0$

11. $16^{-1/2} - 16^{1/4}$

12. $8^{-1/3} - 2^0$

Write each of the following as a product or quotient of powers in which each variable occurs but once, and all exponents are positive.

Examples:

a. $x^{-3} \cdot x^5$

x^{-3+5}

Ans. x^2

b. $(x^2 y^{-3})^{-1}$

$x^{-2} y^3$

Ans. $\dfrac{y^3}{x^2}$

c. $\left(\dfrac{x^{-1} y^2 z^0}{x^3 y^{-4} z^2}\right)^{-1}$

$\dfrac{x y^{-2} z^0}{x^{-3} y^4 z^{-2}}$

Ans. $\dfrac{x^4 z^2}{y^6}$

13. $x^{-3} \cdot x^4$ **14.** $x^2 \cdot x^{-3}$ **15.** $\dfrac{x^5}{x^{-2}}$ **16.** $\dfrac{x^{-2}}{x^3}$

17. $(x^{-3})^2$ **18.** $(x^2)^{-4}$ **19.** $(x^{1/2})^{-3}$ **20.** $(x^3)^{-1/3}$

21. $(x^2 y^{-1})^{-1/2}$ **22.** $(x^3 y^{-2})^{-1/6}$ **23.** $(x^{-2} y^3)^0$ **24.** $(x^0 y^2)^0$

25. $\dfrac{x^{-1}}{y^{-1}}$ **26.** $\dfrac{x^{-2}}{y^{-3}}$ **27.** $\dfrac{a^2 x^{-3}}{b^2 y^{-2}}$ **28.** $\dfrac{a^{-2} b^{-2} c}{ab^{-3} c^0}$

29. $\dfrac{8^{-1} x^0 y^{-3}}{(2xy)^{-5}}$ **30.** $\dfrac{16^{-1/4} r^2 s^{-3}}{(2)^{-2} rs^{-2}}$ **31.** $\left(\dfrac{x^{-1} y^3}{2x^0 y^{-5}}\right)^{-2}$ **32.** $\left(\dfrac{a^{-1} b^{-2}}{3^0 ab}\right)^{-1}$

33. $\left[\left(\dfrac{a^{-1} b^{-1} c}{a^2 b^2 c^{-2}}\right)^{-3/2}\right]^2$ **34.** $\left[\left(\dfrac{ab^{-2} c^{-1}}{a^{-2} bc}\right)^4\right]^{-1/2}$

Write as a single fraction involving positive exponents only.

Examples:

a. $x^{-1} + y^{-2}$ b. $(x^{-1} + x^{-2})^{-1}$ c. $x^{-1} + \dfrac{1}{x^{-1}}$

$\dfrac{1}{x} + \dfrac{1}{y^2}$ $\left(\dfrac{1}{x} + \dfrac{1}{x^2}\right)^{-1}$ $\dfrac{1}{x} + x$

$\dfrac{(y^2)1}{(y^2)x} + \dfrac{1(x)}{y^2(x)}$ $\left(\dfrac{(x)1}{(x)x} + \dfrac{1}{x^2}\right)^{-1}$ $\dfrac{1}{x} + \dfrac{x(x)}{(x)}$

Ans. $\dfrac{y^2 + x}{xy^2}$ $\left(\dfrac{x+1}{x^2}\right)^{-1}$ $\dfrac{1}{x} + \dfrac{x^2}{x}$

                                   Ans. $\dfrac{x^2}{x+1}$ Ans. $\dfrac{1 + x^2}{x}$

35. $a^{-2} + b^{-2}$ **36.** $\dfrac{x^{-1}}{y^{-1}} + \dfrac{y}{x}$ **37.** $\dfrac{r}{s^{-1}} + \dfrac{r^{-1}}{s}$

38. $(x + y)^{-1}$ **39.** $(a - b)^{-2}$ **40.** $xy^{-1} + x^{-1} y$

41. $x^{-1} y - xy^{-1}$ **42.** $\dfrac{x^{-1} + y^{-1}}{(xy)^{-1}}$ **43.** $\dfrac{a}{b^{-1}} + \left(\dfrac{a}{b}\right)^{-1}$

44. $(x^{-1} - y^{-1})^{-1}$ **45.** $\dfrac{x^{-1} + y^{-1}}{x^{-1} - y^{-1}}$ **46.** $\dfrac{x^{-1} - y^{-1}}{x^{-1} + y^{-1}}$

Write as a product free of fractions in which each variable occurs but once.

Examples:

a. $x^{-2n} \cdot x^n$ b. $\left(\dfrac{x^{1-n}}{x^{2-n}}\right)^{-2}$ c. $\left(\dfrac{x^n y^{2n-1}}{y^n}\right)^2$

x^{-2n+n} $(x^{(1-n)-(2-n)})^{-2}$ $(x^n y^{2n-1-n})^2$

Ans. x^{-n} $(x^{-1})^{-2}$ Ans. $x^{2n} y^{2n-2}$

                              Ans. x^2

47. $a^{3-n}a^0$ **48.** $x^{-n}x^{n+1}$ **49.** $\left(\dfrac{a^{2n}}{a^{n+1}}\right)^{-2}$ **50.** $\dfrac{x^n y^{n+1}}{x^{2n-1} y^n}$

51. $\dfrac{b^n c^{2n-1}}{b^{n+1} c^{2n}}$ **52.** $\left(\dfrac{x^{n-1} y^n}{x^{-2} y^{-n}}\right)^2$ **53.** $\left(\dfrac{x^n}{x^{n-1}}\right)^{-1}$ **54.** $\left(\dfrac{a^{2n} b^{n-1}}{a^{n-1} b}\right)^2$

4.4 Scientific Notation

In certain scientific applications of mathematics, very small and very large quantities have to be considered. Such numbers can be represented very conveniently by means of an exponential form called **scientific notation.** For example,

$$3796 = 3.796 \times 10^3,$$
$$30.21 = 3.021 \times 10^1,$$
$$0.0214 = 2.14 \times 10^{-2},$$
$$0.000301 = 3.01 \times 10^{-4}.$$

In each case we have represented a number as the product of a number between 1 and 10, and a power of 10; that is, we have factored a power of 10 from each number. Furthermore, the exponent of the power of 10 is identical to the number of places we have moved the decimal point in going from the first digital form to the second.

A number written in scientific notation may be written in standard form by moving the decimal point in the numeral for the first factor the number of places indicated by the exponent on 10—to the left if the exponent is negative and to the right if it is positive. For example,

$$3.75 \times 10^4 = 37,500,$$
$$2.03 \times 10 = 20.3,$$
$$7.34 \times 10^{-4} = 0.000734,$$
$$2.98 \times 10^{-1} = 0.298.$$

Scientific notation can frequently be used to simplify numerical calculations. For example, if we write the quotient

$$\frac{248,000}{0.0124}$$

in the form

$$\frac{2.48 \times 10^5}{1.24 \times 10^{-2}},$$

we may perform the computation as follows:

$$\frac{2.48}{1.24} \times \frac{10^5}{10^{-2}} = 2 \times 10^7 = 20,000,000.$$

EXERCISE 4.4

Express in scientific notation.

Examples:

  a. 680,000   b. 0.000043   c. 0.002451

  Ans. 6.8×10^5 **Ans.** 4.3×10^{-5} **Ans.** 2.451×10^{-3}

1. 34,000   **2.** 253   **3.** 21   **4.** -3190

5. 8,372,000   **6.** 25,300,000,000   **7.** 0.0014   **8.** 0.3

9. 0.0000006   **10.** 0.0234   **11.** -0.0000230 **12.** -0.5020

Write in standard form.

Examples:

  a. 1.01×10^3 b. 6.3×10^{-4} c. 4.317×10^{-2}

  Ans. 1010   **Ans.** 0.00063   **Ans.** 0.04317

13. 1.6×10^3 **14.** -2.1×10^3 **15.** 6×10^5

16. 3.8×10^1 **17.** 1.95×10^4 **18.** 2.02×10^{-6}

19. 2.3×10^{-7} **20.** 4.8×10^{-1} **21.** 1.234×10^4

Compute.

Examples:

a. $\dfrac{4 \times 10^3 \times 6 \times 10^{-5}}{8 \times 10^{-3}}$ b. $\dfrac{0.006 \times 3 \times 0.0008}{0.009}$

$\dfrac{24 \times 10^{-2}}{8 \times 10^{-3}}$ $\dfrac{6 \times 10^{-3} \times 3 \times 8 \times 10^{-4}}{9 \times 10^{-3}}$

Ans. 3×10 or 30 $\dfrac{6 \times 3 \times 8}{9} \times 10^{-4}$

                              Ans. 1.6×10^{-3} or 0.0016

22. $\dfrac{10^3 \times 10^5}{10^2}$ **23.** $\dfrac{10^3 \times 10^{-6}}{10^2}$

24. $\dfrac{10^3 \times 10^{-7} \times 10^2}{10^{-2} \times 10^4}$ **25.** $\dfrac{10^2 \times 10^5 \times 10^{-3}}{10^2 \times 10^2}$

26. $\dfrac{(4 \times 10^3) \times (6 \times 10^{-2})}{3 \times 10^{-7}}$ **27.** $\dfrac{(2 \times 10^2)^2 \times (3 \times 10^{-3})}{2 \times 10^4}$

28. $\dfrac{0.6 \times 0.00084 \times 0.093}{0.00021 \times 0.00031}$ **29.** $\dfrac{0.065 \times 2.2 \times 50}{1.30 \times 0.011 \times 0.05}$

30. $\dfrac{28 \times 0.0006 \times 450}{1.5 \times 700 \times 0.018}$ **31.** $\dfrac{0.0054 \times 0.05 \times 300}{0.0015 \times 0.27 \times 80}$

4.5 Products and Factors of Expressions Containing Rational Exponents

In Chapter 2 we multiplied and factored expressions in which the exponents on factors were limited to positive integers. In this section we shall extend the applications of the distributive law and factoring techniques to include expressions containing rational exponents.

EXERCISE 4.5

Write each product without using parentheses and in a form in which each base of a power occurs only once in each term.

Examples:

a. $(y)(y^{3/4})$

Ans. $y^{7/4}$

b. $y^{1/3}(y + y^{2/3})$

Ans. $y^{4/3} + y$

1. $x^{1/3}x^{2/3}$

2. $x^{3/7}x^{2/7}$

3. $x^{1/3}x^{-2/3}$

4. $a^{3/4}a^{-1/4}$

5. $x^{1/3}x$

6. $y^{2/3}y^{5/3}$

7. $x^{1/2}(x + x^{1/2})$

8. $x^{1/5}(x^{2/5} + x^{4/5})$

9. $x^{1/3}(x^{2/3} - x^{1/3})$

10. $x^{3/8}(x^{1/4} - x^{1/2})$

11. $x^{-3/4}(x^{-1/4} + x^{3/4})$

12. $y^{-1/4}(y^{3/4} + y^{5/4})$

13. $x^{-1/2}(x^{3/2} - x + 4)$

14. $z^{-1/6}(z^{2/3} - z^{1/3} + 1)$

15. $(x + y)^{1/2}[(x + y)^{1/2} - (x + y)]$

16. $(a - b)^{2/3}[(a - b)^{-1/3} + (a - b)]$

Factor as indicated.

Examples:

a. $y^{3/4} = y^{1/4}(?)$

Ans. $y^{1/4}(y^{1/2})$

b. $y^{-1/2} + y^{1/2} = y^{-1/2}(\ ? \ )$

Ans. $y^{-1/2}(1 + y)$

17. $x^{3/5} = x^{1/5}(\ ? \ )$

18. $x^{7/8} = x^{3/8}(\ ? \ )$

19. $x^{-1/3} = x^{-2/3}(\ ? \ )$

20. $y^{-1/4} = y(\ ? \ )$

21. $x^{1/3} = x(\ ? \ )$

22. $y^{3/5} = y(\ ? \ )$

23. $x^{3/2} + x = x(\quad ? \quad)$

24. $y^{1/2} + y = y(\quad ? \quad)$

25. $x - x^{2/3} = x^{1/3}(\quad ? \quad)$

26. $a^{2/3} + a^{1/3} = a(\quad ? \quad)$

27. $x^{1/2} + x^{3/2} = x^{3/2}(\quad ? \quad)$

28. $b^{3/5} + b^{6/5} = b^{6/5}(\quad ? \quad)$

29. $x^{-3/2} + x^{-1/2} = x^{-1/2}(\quad ? \quad)$

30. $z^{1/2} + z^{-1/2} = z^{-1/2}(\quad ? \quad)$

31. $(x + 1)^{1/2} - (x + 1)^{-1/2} = (x + 1)^{-1/2}[\quad ? \quad]$

32. $(x + 1)^{1/5} - (x + 1)^{-4/5} = (x + 1)^{-4/5}[\quad ? \quad]$

33. $(y + 2)^{1/3} - (y + 2)^{-2/3} = (y + 2)^{-2/3}(\quad ? \quad)$

34. $(y - 3)^{1/4} + (y - 3)^{-3/4} = (y - 3)^{-3/4}($? $)$

35. $x^{2n} + x^{n/2} = x^{n/2}($? $)$

36. $y^{n+1} + y^2 = y($? $)$

37. $x - y = (x^{1/2} - y^{1/2})($? $)$

38. $(x + y) = (x^{1/3} + y^{1/3})($? $)$

4.6 Radicals

In Section 4.2 we referred to $a^{1/n}$ (with appropriate restrictions on a) as the nth root of a; that is, $a^{1/n}$ is one of n equal factors of a. An alternative form for the nth root of a, when $n \in N$ and $n \geq 2$, is defined by

$$a^{1/n} = \sqrt[n]{a},$$

and in many cases the latter form is more convenient to use. In such a representation, the symbol $\sqrt{\ }$ is called a **radical**, a is called the **radicand**, n is called the **index**, and the expression is said to be a **radical of order n**. We require that the index be a natural number greater than or equal to 2. If no index is written, the index is understood to be 2, and the expression is called the **square root** of the radicand.

Since, from Section 4.2,

$$a^{m/n} = (a^m)^{1/n} = (a^{1/n})^m,$$

we may write a power with a rational exponent $a^{m/n}$ as either

$$\sqrt[n]{a^m} \quad \text{or} \quad (\sqrt[n]{a})^m,$$

where the denominator of the exponent is the index of the radical, and the numerator of the exponent is either the exponent of the radicand or the exponent of the root. For example,

$$x^{2/3} = \sqrt[3]{x^2} \quad \text{or} \quad (\sqrt[3]{x})^2,$$

and

$$8^{2/3} = \sqrt[3]{8^2} \quad \text{or} \quad (\sqrt[3]{8})^2.$$

Since we have restricted the index of a radical to be a natural number, we must always express a fractional exponent in standard form (m/n or $-m/n$) before writing the power in radical form. Thus

$$x^{-(3/4)} = x^{(-3/4)} = \sqrt[4]{x^{-3}}.$$

In general, we have

$$\sqrt[n]{a^n} = |a| \quad (a^n \geq 0, \ n \text{ even}),$$

for we wish to use the symbol $\sqrt[n]{a^n}$ only for the positive nth root of a^n when n is even. In particular,

$$\sqrt{a^2} = |a|.$$

If we wish the negative root, we write $-\sqrt[n]{a^n}$. Considering odd indices, there is no ambiguous interpretation possible. That is,

$$\sqrt[n]{a^n} = a \quad (n \text{ odd})$$

for all values of a. For example,

$$\sqrt{2^2} = 2, \qquad -\sqrt{2^2} = -2,$$
$$\sqrt{(-2)^2} = 2, \qquad -\sqrt{(-2)^2} = -2,$$
$$\sqrt[3]{8} = 2, \qquad -\sqrt[3]{8} = -2,$$
$$\sqrt[3]{-8} = -2, \qquad -\sqrt[3]{-8} = 2.$$

Recall that any real number that can be expressed as the quotient of two integers is called a rational number and any real number that cannot be so expressed is called an irrational number. Any radical expression $\sqrt[n]{a}$ represents a rational number if and only if a is the nth power of a rational number. Thus $\sqrt{4}$, $-\sqrt[3]{27}$, $\sqrt[4]{81}$, and $\sqrt[5]{-32}$ are rational numbers equal to $2, -3, 3,$ and -2, while $\sqrt{5}$, $\sqrt[3]{9}$, $\sqrt[4]{15}$, and $\sqrt[5]{61}$, etc., are irrational numbers. Although an irrational number does not have an exact decimal representation we can obtain a decimal approximation correct to any desired degree of accuracy. Thus

$$\sqrt{2} \approx 1.4,$$
$$\sqrt{2} \approx 1.41,$$
$$\sqrt{2} \approx 1.414,$$

where the symbol $\approx$ is read "is approximately equal to."

A table of square roots appears in Table I of the Appendix.

EXERCISE 4.6

In this exercise assume that each radicand represents a positive real number unless otherwise specified. Write in radical form.

Examples:

a. $5^{1/2}$

b. $(xy)^{2/3}$

c. $(x - y^2)^{-1/2}$

Ans. $\sqrt{5}$

Ans. $\sqrt[3]{x^2y^2}$

Ans. $\dfrac{1}{\sqrt{x - y^2}}$

1. $3^{1/2}$ **2.** $5^{1/3}$ **3.** $x^{3/2}$ **4.** $a^{2/3}$

5. $3x^{1/3}$ **6.** $5x^{1/5}$ **7.** $-6xy^{1/2}$ **8.** $-2x^{1/2}$

9. $(xy)^{1/2}$ **10.** $(ab)^{1/7}$ **11.** $-2(ab^2)^{1/5}$ **12.** $-3(r^2s)^{1/3}$

13. $(x + 2y)^{1/2}$ **14.** $(a - b)^{1/3}$ **15.** $(x - y)^{2/3}$ **16.** $(2r - 3s)^{3/5}$

17. $x^{1/2} - y^{1/2}$ **18.** $a^{1/3} - b^{2/3}$ **19.** $4^{-1/3}$ **20.** $6^{-2/5}$

21. $x^{-2/3}$ **22.** $y^{-2/7}$ **23.** $(x^2 - y^2)^{-1/2}$ **24.** $(a^3 - b^3)^{-1/5}$

Represent with positive fractional exponents.

Examples:

a. $\sqrt{2^3}$

Ans. $2^{3/2}$

b. $\sqrt[3]{7a^2}$

$(7a^2)^{1/3}$

Ans. $7^{1/3}a^{2/3}$

c. $\dfrac{1}{\sqrt{x-1}}$

Ans. $\dfrac{1}{(x-1)^{1/2}}$

25. $\sqrt{3}$ **26.** $\sqrt[3]{7}$ **27.** $\sqrt[3]{x^2}$ **28.** $\sqrt[4]{x^3}$

29. $\sqrt[3]{xy}$ **30.** $\sqrt[5]{a^2b^3}$ **31.** $4\sqrt{x}$ **32.** $3\sqrt[3]{rs^2}$

33. $\sqrt[3]{2xy^2}$ **34.** $-5\sqrt[4]{a^3b}$ **35.** $a\sqrt[5]{x^2y^3}$ **36.** $-4\sqrt[6]{a^5b^5}$

37. $\sqrt{x-y}$ **38.** $\sqrt[4]{a+2b}$ **39.** $3\sqrt[3]{x^2-y}$ **40.** $-2\sqrt[5]{x^4-y^4}$

41. $\sqrt{x}-2\sqrt{y}$ **42.** $\sqrt[3]{a}+2\sqrt[3]{b}$ **43.** $\dfrac{1}{\sqrt{x}}$ **44.** $\dfrac{2}{\sqrt[3]{y}}$

45. $\dfrac{x}{\sqrt[3]{y}}$ **46.** $\dfrac{-2a}{\sqrt[5]{b^3c}}$ **47.** $\dfrac{2}{\sqrt{x+y}}$ **48.** $\dfrac{5}{\sqrt[3]{a^2+b^2}}$

Find the root indicated.

Examples:

a. $\sqrt{49}$

Ans. 7

b. $\sqrt[3]{-8}$

Ans. -2

c. $\sqrt[3]{x^6y^3}$

Ans. x^2y

d. $-\sqrt[4]{81x^4}$

Ans. $-3x$

49. $\sqrt{16}$ **50.** $\sqrt{144}$ **51.** $-\sqrt{25}$ **52.** $-\sqrt{169}$

53. $\sqrt[3]{27}$ **54.** $\sqrt[3]{125}$ **55.** $\sqrt[3]{-64}$ **56.** $\sqrt[5]{32}$

57. $-\sqrt[4]{16}$ **58.** $\sqrt[6]{64}$ **59.** $\sqrt{x^4}$ **60.** $-\sqrt{a^6}$

61. $\sqrt[3]{8y^6}$ **62.** $\sqrt[3]{27y^9}$ **63.** $-\sqrt{x^4y^6}$ **64.** $-\sqrt{a^8b^{10}}$

65. $\sqrt{\frac{4}{9}x^2y^8}$ **66.** $\sqrt{\frac{9}{16}a^2b^4}$ **67.** $\sqrt[3]{\frac{-8}{125}x^3}$ **68.** $\sqrt[3]{\frac{8}{27}a^3b^6}$

In the previous problems, radicands were restricted to represent positive numbers. In Problems 69–74, consider radicands to represent elements of the set of real numbers, and state all necessary restrictions.

Examples:

a. $\sqrt{16x^2}$

Ans. $4|x|$

b. $\sqrt{x^2-2xy+y^2}$

$\sqrt{(x-y)^2}$

Ans. $|x-y|$

69. $\sqrt{4x^2}$ **70.** $\sqrt{9x^2y^4}$ **71.** $\sqrt{x^2+2x+1}$

72. $\sqrt{4x^2-4x+1}$ **73.** $\dfrac{2}{\sqrt{x^2+2xy+y^2}}$ **74.** $\sqrt{x^4+2x^2y^2+y^4}$

Represent each of the following sets of real numbers on a separate line graph. (Use Table I in the Appendix to obtain rational number approximations for irrational numbers.)

Example: $\sqrt{4}, -\sqrt{3}, \sqrt{17}, -\sqrt{9}$

   Ans.

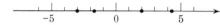

75. $-\sqrt{7}, -\sqrt{1}, \sqrt{5}, \sqrt{9}$ **76.** $-\frac{2}{3}, 0, \sqrt{3}, -\sqrt{1} - \sqrt{11}$

77. $-\sqrt{20}, -\sqrt{6}, \sqrt{1}, 6$ **78.** $\sqrt{41}, \sqrt{7}, -\sqrt{7}, \frac{3}{4}$

79. $\frac{27}{4}, 6, -\sqrt{6}, -1$ **80.** $\frac{7}{4}, \sqrt{12}, -\sqrt{12}, 12$

81. $-8, \sqrt{7}, -\frac{3}{4}, 8$ **82.** $\sqrt{16}, -4, 0, \frac{3}{4}$

83. $-10, \sqrt{5}, \sqrt{37}, -\sqrt{2}$ **84.** $-\sqrt{74}, \sqrt{32}, \sqrt{49}, -6$

85. $\sqrt{24}, -\sqrt{24}, 24, -24$ **86.** $13, -\sqrt{13}, \sqrt{13}, -13$

87. Show that $|x| = \sqrt{x^2}$ is equivalent to the definition of $|x|$ given in Section 1.4.

4.7   Changing Forms of Radicals

   From the definition of a radical and from the laws of exponents, we can derive three important relationships. (In all cases, a, $b > 0$ and n is a natural number.)   We have, first,

$$\sqrt[n]{ab} = \sqrt[n]{a}\,\sqrt[n]{b} \tag{1}$$

or

$$\sqrt[n]{a}\,\sqrt[n]{b} = \sqrt[n]{ab}. \tag{1a}$$

This relationship follows from

$$\sqrt[n]{ab} = (ab)^{1/n} = a^{1/n}b^{1/n} = \sqrt[n]{a}\,\sqrt[n]{b}.$$

Relationship (1) can be used to write a radical in a form in which the radicand contains no prime factor or polynomial factor raised to a power greater than or equal to the index of the radical.   Thus we can write

$$\sqrt{18} = \sqrt{3^2}\,\sqrt{2}$$

$$= 3\sqrt{2}$$

and

$$\sqrt[3]{16x^3y^5} = \sqrt[3]{2^3x^3y^3}\,\sqrt[3]{2y^2}$$

$$= 2xy\,\sqrt[3]{2y^2},$$

where in each case the radicand is factored into two factors, one of which consists of factors raised to the same power as the index of the radical. This factor is then "removed" from the radicand.

The second important relationship is

$$\sqrt[n]{\frac{a}{b}} = \frac{\sqrt[n]{a}}{\sqrt[n]{b}} \tag{2}$$

or

$$\frac{\sqrt[n]{a}}{\sqrt[n]{b}} = \sqrt[n]{\frac{a}{b}}. \tag{2a}$$

This relationship follows from

$$\sqrt[n]{\frac{a}{b}} = \left(\frac{a}{b}\right)^{1/n} = \frac{a^{1/n}}{b^{1/n}} = \frac{\sqrt[n]{a}}{\sqrt[n]{b}}.$$

We use relationship (2) to write a radical in a form in which the radicand contains no fraction. For example,

$$\sqrt{\frac{3}{4}} = \frac{\sqrt{3}}{\sqrt{4}}$$

$$= \frac{\sqrt{3}}{2}.$$

If the denominator of the radicand is not the square of a monomial, we can use the fundamental principle of fractions to obtain an equivalent form that has such a denominator. Thus, if $x > 0$,

$$\sqrt{\frac{2}{5x}} = \frac{\sqrt{2}}{\sqrt{5x}} \qquad \text{Relationship (2).}$$

$$= \frac{\sqrt{2}\ \sqrt{5x}}{\sqrt{5x}\ \sqrt{5x}} \qquad \text{Fundamental principle of fractions.}$$

$$= \frac{\sqrt{10x}}{5x}. \qquad \text{Relationship (1a) and the definition of square root.}$$

The foregoing process is called "rationalizing the denominator" of the fraction because the result is a fraction with a denominator free of radicals. In the event the radical is of order n, we must build to a denominator that is the nth power of a monomial. For example, if $x \neq 0$,

$$\sqrt[5]{\frac{6}{16x^3}} = \frac{\sqrt[5]{6}}{\sqrt[5]{16x^3}} \qquad \text{Relationship (2).}$$

$$= \frac{\sqrt[5]{6}\ \sqrt[5]{2x^2}}{\sqrt[5]{16x^3}\ \sqrt[5]{2x^2}} \qquad \text{Fundamental principle of fractions.}$$

$$= \frac{\sqrt[5]{12x^2}}{\sqrt[5]{32x^5}} \qquad \text{Relationship (1a).}$$

$$= \frac{\sqrt[5]{12x^2}}{2x}. \qquad \text{Definition of a radical.}$$

The third important relationship is

$$\sqrt[cn]{a^{cm}} = \sqrt[n]{a^m} \tag{3}$$

or

$$\sqrt[n]{a^m} = \sqrt[cn]{a^{cm}}, \tag{3a}$$

where $m \in J$, c, $n \in N$, and $n \geq 2$. This follows from

$$\sqrt[cn]{a^{cm}} = a^{cm/cn} = a^{m/n} = \sqrt[n]{a^m}.$$

If the right member in (3) is to have meaning in the sense in which we have defined radicals, c must be a natural number factor of the index.

Relationship (3) permits us to reduce the order of a radical by dividing the index of the radical and the exponent of the radicand by the same natural number. For example,

$$\sqrt[6]{8} = \sqrt[6]{2^3} = \sqrt{2},$$

$$\sqrt[4]{x^2} = \sqrt{x} \quad (x \geq 0).$$

We must be careful in reading equality into two radicals. For instance, in rewriting $\sqrt[4]{x^2}$ as $\sqrt{x}$, it is necessary that we restrict x to nonnegative values. If x is -3, for example,

$$\sqrt[4]{x^2} = \sqrt[4]{9} = \sqrt{3},$$

which is a real number, but

$$\sqrt{x} = \sqrt{-3},$$

which is not a real number.

Relationship (3a) permits us to change the order of a radical by multiplying the index of a radical and the exponent of the power in the radicand by the same natural number, providing the radicand is nonnegative. For example,

$$\sqrt[3]{2^2} = \sqrt[2(3)]{2^{2(2)}} = \sqrt[6]{2^4},$$

$$\sqrt{x} = \sqrt[3(2)]{x^3} = \sqrt[6]{x^3} \quad (x \geq 0).$$

Because $\sqrt[n]{a^m} = a^{m/n}$, radical expressions similar to those above can be rewritten by first writing the expression in exponential form. For example,

$$\sqrt[4]{x^2} = x^{2/4} = x^{1/2} = \sqrt{x}$$

and

$$\sqrt{x} = x^{1/2} = x^{\frac{1 \cdot 3}{2 \cdot 3}} = \sqrt[6]{x^3}.$$

Application of (1), (2), or (3) above can be used to rewrite radical expressions in various ways, and, in particular, to write them in what is called "simplest" form. A radical expression is said to be in **simplest form** if:

a. The radicand contains no polynomial factor raised to a power equal to or greater than the index of the radical,
b. The radicand contains no fractions,
c. No radical expressions are contained in denominators of fractions, and
d. The index of the radical and exponents on factors in the radicand have no common factors.

Although we generally change the form of radicals to one of the forms above, there are times when such forms are not preferred. For example, in certain situations, $\sqrt{1/2}$ or $1/\sqrt{2}$ may be more useful than the equivalent form $\sqrt{2}/2$.

EXERCISE 4.7

Assume that all variables in radicands in this exercise denote positive real numbers only.

Change to simplest form.

Examples:

a. $\sqrt{300}$

$\sqrt{100}\sqrt{3}$

Ans. $10\sqrt{3}$

b. $\sqrt[3]{2x^7y^3}$

$\sqrt[3]{x^6y^3}\sqrt[3]{2x}$

Ans. $x^2y\sqrt[3]{2x}$

c. $\sqrt{2xy}\sqrt{8x}$

$\sqrt{16x^2y}$

$\sqrt{16x^2}\sqrt{y}$

Ans. $4x\sqrt{y}$

1. $\sqrt{9}$

2. $\sqrt{36}$

3. $-\sqrt{200}$

4. $-\sqrt{160}$

5. $\sqrt{x^4}$

6. $\sqrt{y^6}$

7. $-\sqrt{x^3}$

8. $-\sqrt{y^{11}}$

9. $\sqrt{4x^5}$

10. $\sqrt{16y^3}$

11. $-\sqrt{8x^6}$

12. $-\sqrt{18z^8}$

13. $\sqrt[3]{64}$

14. $\sqrt[3]{125}$

15. $\sqrt[3]{-8x^6}$

16. $\sqrt[5]{32x^5}$

17. $\sqrt[3]{x^5}$

18. $\sqrt[4]{3x^5y^5}$

19. $\sqrt[6]{x^{11}y}$

20. $\sqrt[4]{32xy^7}$

21. $\sqrt{18}\sqrt{2}$

22. $\sqrt{3}\sqrt{27}$

23. $\sqrt{xy}\sqrt{x^5y}$

24. $\sqrt{a}\sqrt{ab^2}$

25. $\sqrt[3]{2}\sqrt[3]{4}$

26. $\sqrt[4]{3}\sqrt[4]{27}$

27. $\sqrt[4]{x^3}\sqrt[4]{x}$

28. $\sqrt[6]{a^3}\sqrt[6]{a^4}$

29. $\sqrt{3\times10^2}$

30. $\sqrt{5\times10^3}$

31. $\sqrt{60,000}$

32. $\sqrt{800,000}$

33. $\sqrt{3\times10^{-4}}$

34. $\sqrt{9\times10^{-5}}$

35. $\sqrt{0.000042}$

36. $\sqrt{0.0071}$

Rationalize denominators.

Examples:

a. $\sqrt{\dfrac{1}{3}}$ b. $\sqrt[3]{\dfrac{2}{y^2}}$ c. $\dfrac{\sqrt{6a}\,\sqrt{5a}}{\sqrt{15}}$

$\dfrac{\sqrt{1}\,\sqrt{3}}{\sqrt{3}\,\sqrt{3}}$ $\dfrac{\sqrt[3]{2}\,\sqrt[3]{y}}{\sqrt[3]{y^2}\,\sqrt[3]{y}}$ $\sqrt{\dfrac{15}{15}\cdot 2a^2}$

Ans. $\dfrac{\sqrt{3}}{3}$ Ans. $\dfrac{\sqrt[3]{2y}}{y}$ Ans. $a\sqrt{2}$

37. $\sqrt{\dfrac{1}{5}}$ 38. $\sqrt{\dfrac{2}{3}}$ 39. $\dfrac{-1}{\sqrt{2}}$ 40. $\dfrac{-\sqrt{3}}{\sqrt{7}}$

41. $\sqrt{\dfrac{x}{2}}$ 42. $-\sqrt{\dfrac{y}{3}}$ 43. $-\sqrt{\dfrac{y}{x}}$ 44. $\sqrt{\dfrac{2a}{b}}$

45. $\dfrac{x}{\sqrt{x}}$ 46. $\dfrac{-x}{\sqrt{2y}}$ 47. $\dfrac{-xy}{\sqrt{y}}$ 48. $\dfrac{x}{\sqrt{xy}}$

49. $-\sqrt[3]{\dfrac{y}{2x}}$ 50. $\sqrt[3]{\dfrac{1}{6x^2}}$ 51. $\dfrac{1}{\sqrt[4]{8}}$ 52. $\dfrac{3}{\sqrt[4]{9}}$

53. $\dfrac{\sqrt{a^5 b^3}}{\sqrt{ab}}$ 54. $\dfrac{\sqrt{x}\,\sqrt{xy^3}}{\sqrt{y}}$ 55. $\dfrac{\sqrt{ab}\,\sqrt{ab^4}}{\sqrt{b}}$ 56. $\dfrac{\sqrt[3]{ab}\,\sqrt[3]{b^2}}{\sqrt[3]{a}}$

Rationalize numerators.

57. $\dfrac{\sqrt{3}}{3}$ 58. $\dfrac{\sqrt{2}}{3}$ 59. $\dfrac{\sqrt{x}}{\sqrt{y}}$ 60. $\dfrac{\sqrt{xy}}{x}$

Reduce the order of each radical.

Examples:

a. $\sqrt[4]{5^2}$ b. $\sqrt[8]{9}$ c. $\sqrt[4]{x^2 y^2}$

Ans. $\sqrt{5}$ $\sqrt[8]{3^2}$ Ans. $\sqrt{xy}$

Ans. $\sqrt[4]{3}$

61. $\sqrt[4]{3^2}$ 62. $\sqrt[6]{2^2}$ 63. $\sqrt[6]{3^3}$ 64. $\sqrt[8]{5^2}$

65. $\sqrt[8]{81}$ 66. $\sqrt[10]{32}$ 67. $\sqrt[4]{16x^2}$ 68. $\sqrt[9]{8a^3}$

69. $\sqrt[6]{8x^3}$ 70. $\sqrt[4]{16a^2 b^2}$ 71. $\sqrt[6]{x^3 y^6}$ 72. $\sqrt[6]{125z^3}$

Express as radicals of the same order and multiply.

Examples:

a. $\sqrt{3}, \sqrt[3]{5}$

(Least common index is 6.)

$\sqrt[3\cdot2]{3^3}, \sqrt[2\cdot3]{5^2}$

$\sqrt[6]{27}, \sqrt[6]{25}$

Ans. $\sqrt[6]{675}$

b. $\sqrt[3]{xy}, \sqrt[4]{xy}$

(Least common index is 12.)

$\sqrt[4\cdot3]{x^4y^4}, \sqrt[3\cdot4]{x^3y^3}$

$\sqrt[12]{x^4y^4}, \sqrt[12]{x^3y^3}$

Ans. $\sqrt[12]{x^7y^7}$

73. $\sqrt[3]{3}, \sqrt{2}$

74. $\sqrt[3]{2}, \sqrt[4]{2}$

75. $\sqrt[4]{5}, \sqrt{2}$

76. $\sqrt[3]{x}, \sqrt{x}$

77. $\sqrt[6]{y}, \sqrt{y}$

78. $\sqrt{2x}, \sqrt[4]{3y^2}$

79. $\sqrt[3]{2x}, \sqrt{y}, \sqrt[4]{xy}$

80. $\sqrt[3]{x}, \sqrt[4]{y}, \sqrt{z}$

4.8 Expressions Containing Radicals

The distributive law,

$$a(b + c) = ab + ac, \tag{1}$$

is assumed to hold for all real numbers. By the symmetric law of equality and the commutative law of multiplication, (1) can be written as

$$ba + ca = (b + c)a.$$

Since at this time all radical expressions have been defined so that they represent real numbers, the distributive law holds for radical expressions. For example,

$$3\sqrt{3} + 4\sqrt{3} = (3 + 4)\sqrt{3} = 7\sqrt{3}$$

and

$$2\sqrt{x} + 7\sqrt{x} = (2 + 7)\sqrt{x} = 9\sqrt{x}.$$

Thus we may invoke the distributive law and write sums containing radicals of the same order as a single term. Of course, if no numeral coefficient is written before a radical, we understand that the coefficient 1 is intended. Thus $\sqrt{5}$ means $(1)\sqrt{5}$.

A direct application of (1) permits us to write certain products which contain parentheses as expressions without parentheses. For example,

$$x(\sqrt{2} + \sqrt{3}) = x\sqrt{2} + x\sqrt{3},$$

$$\sqrt{3x}(2 - \sqrt{2}) = 2\sqrt{3x} - \sqrt{6x},$$

$$\sqrt{3}(\sqrt{2x} + \sqrt{6}) = \sqrt{6x} + \sqrt{18}$$

$$= \sqrt{6x} + 3\sqrt{2}.$$

In Chapter 2 we agreed to factor from each term of an expression only those common factors that were integers or positive integral powers of variables. However, we can (if we wish) consider other real numbers for factors. Thus, invoking the distributive law in the form

$$ab + ac = a(b + c),$$

radicals common to each term in an expression may be factored from the expression. For example,

$$\sqrt{a} + \sqrt{ab} = \sqrt{a} + \sqrt{a}\,\sqrt{b}$$
$$= \sqrt{a}(1 + \sqrt{b}).$$

The distributive law also provides us with a means of rationalizing denominators of fractions in which radicals occur in one or both of two terms. To accomplish this, we first recall that

$$(a - b)(a + b) = a^2 - b^2,$$

where the product contains no linear term. Each of the two factors of a product exhibiting this property is said to be the **conjugate** of the other. Now consider a fraction of the form

$$\frac{a}{b + \sqrt{c}} \quad (b + \sqrt{c} \neq 0).$$

If we multiply the numerator and denominator of this fraction by the conjugate of the denominator, the denominator of the resulting fraction will contain no term linear in $\sqrt{c}$, and hence will be free of radicals. That is,

$$\frac{a(b - \sqrt{c})}{(b + \sqrt{c})(b - \sqrt{c})} = \frac{ab - a\sqrt{c}}{b^2 - c} \quad (b^2 - c \neq 0),$$

where the denominator has been rationalized. This process is equally applicable to fractions of the form

$$\frac{a}{\sqrt{b} + \sqrt{c}},$$

since

$$\frac{a(\sqrt{b} - \sqrt{c})}{(\sqrt{b} + \sqrt{c})(\sqrt{b} - \sqrt{c})} = \frac{a\sqrt{b} - a\sqrt{c}}{b - c} \quad (b - c \neq 0).$$

EXERCISE 4.8

Assume that all radicands in this exercise are positive real numbers.

Write each sum as a single term.

Examples:

a. $\sqrt{20} + \sqrt{45}$

$2\sqrt{5} + 3\sqrt{5}$

Ans. $5\sqrt{5}$

b. $\sqrt{32x} + \sqrt{2x} - \sqrt{18x}$

$4\sqrt{2x} + \sqrt{2x} - 3\sqrt{2x}$

Ans. $2\sqrt{2x}$

c. $\dfrac{3}{4} - \dfrac{\sqrt{2}}{2}$

$\dfrac{3}{4} - \dfrac{\sqrt{2}\,(2)}{2(2)}$

Ans. $\dfrac{3 - 2\sqrt{2}}{4}$

1. $\sqrt{3} + 2\sqrt{3}$

2. $3\sqrt{5} - 6\sqrt{5}$

3. $2\sqrt{3} + \sqrt{27}$

4. $\sqrt{75} - 2\sqrt{27}$

5. $\sqrt{50x} + 2\sqrt{32x} - \sqrt{2x}$

6. $\sqrt{4a} - \sqrt{25a} + \sqrt{a}$

7. $\sqrt{4xy} + 3\sqrt{9xy} - \sqrt{xy}$

8. $\sqrt{8r^3} - \sqrt{18r^3} + \sqrt{2r^3}$

9. $3\sqrt[3]{16} - \sqrt[3]{2}$

10. $\sqrt[3]{54} + 2\sqrt[3]{128}$

11. $5\sqrt[3]{2x} + 2\sqrt[3]{16x}$

12. $\sqrt[3]{250x} + 2\sqrt[3]{16x}$

13. $\dfrac{2}{3} + \dfrac{\sqrt{2}}{3}$

14. $\dfrac{5}{7} - \dfrac{\sqrt{3}}{7}$

15. $\dfrac{1}{2} + \dfrac{\sqrt{3}}{6}$

16. $\dfrac{1}{6} - \dfrac{\sqrt{2}}{3}$

17. $\dfrac{2\sqrt{3}}{3} - \dfrac{\sqrt{2}}{2}$

18. $\dfrac{2}{5} - \dfrac{\sqrt{2}}{3}$

Write each expression without parentheses and then write all radicals in simple form.

Examples:

a. $4(\sqrt{3} + 1)$

Ans. $4\sqrt{3} + 4$

b. $\sqrt{x}(\sqrt{2x} - \sqrt{x})$

Ans. $x\sqrt{2} - x$

c. $(\sqrt{x} - \sqrt{y})(\sqrt{x} + \sqrt{y})$

Ans. $x - y$

19. $2(3 - \sqrt{5})$

20. $5(2 - \sqrt{7})$

21. $\sqrt{2}\,(3 + \sqrt{3})$

22. $\sqrt{3}\,(5 - \sqrt{2})$

23. $(3 + \sqrt{5})(2 - \sqrt{5})$

24. $(1 - \sqrt{2})(2 + \sqrt{2})$

25. $(\sqrt{x} - 3)(\sqrt{x} + 3)$

26. $(2 + \sqrt{x})(2 - \sqrt{x})$

27. $(\sqrt{x} - 3)^2$

28. $(\sqrt{a} + b)^2$

29. $(\sqrt{2} - \sqrt{3})(\sqrt{2} + 2\sqrt{3})$

30. $(\sqrt{3} - \sqrt{5})(2\sqrt{3} + \sqrt{5})$

31. $(\sqrt{5} - \sqrt{2})^2$

32. $(\sqrt{2} - 2\sqrt{3})^2$

33. $(\sqrt{a} + \sqrt{a - b})(\sqrt{a} - \sqrt{a - b})$

34. $(\sqrt{b} + \sqrt{a + b})(\sqrt{b} - \sqrt{a + b})$

35. $(2 - \sqrt[3]{4})(2 + \sqrt[3]{4})$

36. $(\sqrt[3]{a^2} + \sqrt[3]{b^2})(\sqrt[3]{a} - \sqrt[3]{b})$

Change each expression to the form indicated.

Examples:

a. $3 + \sqrt{18} = 3($? $)$

    $3 + 3\sqrt{2}$

Ans. $3(1 + \sqrt{2})$

b. $\sqrt{x} + \sqrt{xy} = \sqrt{x}($? $)$

    $\sqrt{x} + \sqrt{x}\sqrt{y}$

Ans. $\sqrt{x}(1 + \sqrt{y})$

37. $2 + 2\sqrt{3} = 2($? $)$ 38. $5 + 10\sqrt{2} = 5($? $)$

39. $2\sqrt{27} + 6 = 6($? $)$ 40. $5\sqrt{5} - \sqrt{25} = 5($? $)$

41. $4 + \sqrt{16y} = 4($? $)$ 42. $3 + \sqrt{18x} = 3($? $)$

43. $y\sqrt{3} - x\sqrt{3} = \sqrt{3}($? $)$ 44. $x\sqrt{2} - \sqrt{8} = \sqrt{2}($? $)$

45. $\sqrt{2} - \sqrt{6} = \sqrt{2}($? $)$ 46. $\sqrt{12} - 2\sqrt{6} = 2\sqrt{3}($? $)$

47. $\sqrt{x} + \sqrt{3x} = \sqrt{x}($? $)$ 48. $\sqrt{2x} - \sqrt{x} = \sqrt{x}($? $)$

Reduce fractions to lowest terms.

Examples:

a. $\dfrac{4 + 6\sqrt{3}}{2}$ b. $\dfrac{2x - \sqrt{8x^2}}{4x}$ c. $\dfrac{\sqrt{6} - \sqrt{8}}{\sqrt{2}}$

   $\dfrac{2(2 + 3\sqrt{3})}{2}$ $\dfrac{2x - 2x\sqrt{2}}{4x}$ $\dfrac{\sqrt{2}\sqrt{3} - 2\sqrt{2}}{\sqrt{2}}$

   Ans. $2 + 3\sqrt{3}$ $\dfrac{2x(1 - \sqrt{2})}{4x}$ $\dfrac{\sqrt{2}(\sqrt{3} - 2)}{\sqrt{2}}$

      Ans. $\dfrac{1 - \sqrt{2}}{2}$ Ans. $\sqrt{3} - 2$

49. $\dfrac{2 + 2\sqrt{3}}{2}$ 50. $\dfrac{6 + 2\sqrt{5}}{2}$ 51. $\dfrac{6 + 2\sqrt{18}}{6}$ 52. $\dfrac{8 - 2\sqrt{12}}{4}$

53. $\dfrac{x - \sqrt{x^3}}{x}$ 54. $\dfrac{xy - x\sqrt{xy^2}}{xy}$ 55. $\dfrac{x\sqrt{y} - \sqrt{y^3}}{\sqrt{y}}$ 56. $\dfrac{\sqrt{x} - y\sqrt{x^3}}{\sqrt{x}}$

Rationalize denominators.

Examples:

a. $\dfrac{3}{\sqrt{2} - 1}$

   $\dfrac{3(\sqrt{2} + 1)}{(\sqrt{2} - 1)(\sqrt{2} + 1)}$

   $\dfrac{3\sqrt{2} + 3}{2 - 1}$

   Ans. $3\sqrt{2} + 3$

b. $\dfrac{1}{\sqrt{x} - \sqrt{y}}$ $(x \neq y)$

   $\dfrac{1(\sqrt{x} + \sqrt{y})}{(\sqrt{x} - \sqrt{y})(\sqrt{x} + \sqrt{y})}$

   Ans. $\dfrac{\sqrt{x} + \sqrt{y}}{x - y}$ $(x \neq y)$

57. $\dfrac{-4}{1 + \sqrt{3}}$ **58.** $\dfrac{1}{2 - \sqrt{2}}$ **59.** $\dfrac{2}{\sqrt{7} - 2}$ **60.** $\dfrac{2}{4 - \sqrt{5}}$

61. $\dfrac{4}{1 + \sqrt{x}}$ **62.** $\dfrac{1}{2 - \sqrt{y}}$ **63.** $\dfrac{x}{\sqrt{x} - 3}$ **64.** $\dfrac{y}{\sqrt{3} - y}$

65. $\dfrac{\sqrt{x}}{\sqrt{x} - \sqrt{y}}$ **66.** $\dfrac{\sqrt{6} - 3}{2 - \sqrt{6}}$ **67.** $\dfrac{\sqrt{x} + \sqrt{y}}{\sqrt{x} - \sqrt{y}}$ **68.** $\dfrac{\sqrt{x + a}}{1 - \sqrt{x + a}}$

Write each of the following as a single fraction in which the denominator is rationalized.

69. $\sqrt{x + 1} - \dfrac{x}{\sqrt{x + 1}}$ **70.** $\sqrt{x^2 - 2} - \dfrac{x^2 + 1}{\sqrt{x^2 - 2}}$

71. $\dfrac{x}{\sqrt{x^2 + 1}} - \dfrac{\sqrt{x^2 + 1}}{x}$ **72.** $\dfrac{x}{\sqrt{x^2 - 1}} + \dfrac{\sqrt{x^2 - 1}}{x}$

Rationalize numerators.

73. $\dfrac{1 - \sqrt{2}}{2}$ **74.** $\dfrac{\sqrt{3} + \sqrt{2}}{\sqrt{3}}$ **75.** $\dfrac{\sqrt{x} - 1}{3}$

76. $\dfrac{4 - \sqrt{2y}}{2}$ **77.** $\dfrac{\sqrt{x} - \sqrt{y}}{x}$ **78.** $\dfrac{2\sqrt{x} + \sqrt{y}}{\sqrt{xy}}$

4.9 Complex Numbers

Until now, our discussion has been concerned entirely with the set of real numbers. In this section we shall introduce and briefly discuss a different kind of number, which we shall encounter again in later chapters.

We have observed that the set of real numbers is closed with respect to the four fundamental operations of addition, subtraction, multiplication, and division. However, the set of real numbers is not closed with respect to the operation of taking square roots of the elements in this set. For example, $\sqrt{-a}$ ($a > 0$) does not represent a real number. We can, however, introduce a new set of numbers among whose elements can be found square roots for negative numbers. We define $\sqrt{-a}$ ($a > 0$) to be a number such that

$$\sqrt{-a} \, \sqrt{-a} = -a,$$

and as a special case $\sqrt{-1} \, \sqrt{-1} = -1$. Sometimes $\sqrt{-1}$ is designated by the symbol i; then

$$i^2 = -1.$$

Since for $a > 0$, $\sqrt{-a} \, \sqrt{-a} = -a$, and assuming that

$$i\sqrt{a} \cdot i\sqrt{a} = i^2 \cdot a = -a,$$

it follows that

$$\sqrt{-a} = i\sqrt{a} \quad (a > 0),$$

so that the square root of any negative number can now be represented as the product of a real number and the number $\sqrt{-1}$ or i.

Sums of the form

$$a + bi, \tag{1}$$

where a and b are real numbers, for example, $3 + 2i$, $5 - i$, and $3 + (2/5)i$, are called **imaginary numbers.** If $a = 0$, then (1) is written bi and such numbers are called **pure imaginary numbers.** The set of all real numbers and all imaginary numbers is called the set of **complex numbers** and is usually designated by the letter C. In Chapter 6 complex numbers will appear as solutions to certain types of equations.

The complex numbers $a + bi$ and $c + di$ are equal if and only if $a = c$ and $b = d$, and the complex number $a + bi$ is equal to 0 if and only if $a = 0$ and $b = 0$.

The sum or difference of two complex numbers is defined by:

$$(a + bi) + (c + di) = (a + c) + (b + d)i,$$

$$(a + bi) - (c + di) = (a - c) + (b - d)i.$$

It can be shown that the addition of complex numbers is commutative and associative. For instance, to establish the commutative law of addition, we have

$$(a + bi) + (c + di) = (a + c) + (b + d)i$$

$$= (c + a) + (d + b)i$$

$$= (c + di) + (a + bi).$$

An associative law of addition for complex numbers can be verified in a similar way.

The product of two complex numbers is defined so that it can be obtained by multiplying them in the same way we multiply two binomial expressions and then replacing i^2 with -1. That is,

$$(a + bi)(c + di) = ac + adi + bci + bdi^2$$

$$= ac + (ad + bc)i - bd,$$

$$(a + bi)(c + di) = (ac - bd) + (ad + bc)i.$$

It can be shown that the multiplication of complex numbers is commutative and associative, and that multiplication distributes over addition.

Certain relationships valid for real numbers are not valid for complex numbers. For instance, if $\sqrt{a}$ and $\sqrt{b}$ are both real,

$$\sqrt{a}\,\sqrt{b} = \sqrt{ab},$$

but if $\sqrt{a}$ and $\sqrt{b}$ are both imaginary,

$$\sqrt{a}\,\sqrt{b} = -\sqrt{ab}$$

Specifically,

$$\sqrt{2}\,\sqrt{3} = \sqrt{6}$$

but

$$\sqrt{-2}\,\sqrt{-3} = (i\sqrt{2})(i\sqrt{3}) = i^2\sqrt{6} = -\sqrt{6}.$$

To avoid difficulty with this point, all factors of the form $\sqrt{-a}$ $(a > 0)$ should be changed to the form $i\sqrt{a}$ before multiplying or dividing.

We can find the quotient of two complex numbers by the rationalizing process developed in the preceding section. Thus

$$\frac{a + bi}{c + di} = \frac{(a + bi)(c - di)}{(c + di)(c - di)} \quad (c \text{ and } d \text{ not both } 0)$$

$$= \frac{(ac + bd) + (bc - ad)i}{c^2 + d^2}$$

$$= \left(\frac{ac + bd}{c^2 + d^2}\right) + \left(\frac{bc - ad}{c^2 + d^2}\right)i.$$

The results of operations with complex numbers are again complex numbers; that is, the complex numbers are closed with respect to the fundamental operations.

The powers of i exhibit an interesting periodic property:

$$i = \sqrt{-1},$$

$$i^2 = (\sqrt{-1})^2 = -1,$$

$$i^3 = i^2 \cdot i = -i,$$

$$i^4 = (i^2)^2 = 1,$$

$$i^5 = i^4 \cdot i = i, \text{ etc.}$$

Thus any integral power of i is equivalent to one of the four numbers, i, -1, $-i$, 1.

EXERCISE 4.9

Write in the form $a + bi$ or $a + ib$.

Examples:

a. $\sqrt{-16}$

$\sqrt{-1 \cdot 16}$

$\sqrt{-1}\,\sqrt{16}$

Ans. $0 + 4i$ or $4i$

b. $2 - 3\sqrt{-16}$

$2 - 3\sqrt{-1 \cdot 16}$

$2 - 3\sqrt{-1}\,\sqrt{16}$

Ans. $2 - 12i$

c. $\dfrac{2 + \sqrt{-8}}{2}$

$\dfrac{2 + 2i\sqrt{2}}{2}$

Ans. $1 + i\sqrt{2}$

1. $\sqrt{-9}$ 2. $\sqrt{-25}$ 3. $3\sqrt{-4}$

4. $2\sqrt{-16}$ 5. $4\sqrt{-32}$ 6. $3 - \sqrt{-48}$

7. $\dfrac{\sqrt{-16}}{2}$ 8. $\dfrac{4\sqrt{-9}}{6}$ 9. $\dfrac{2 - \sqrt{-4}}{2}$

10. $\dfrac{4 - \sqrt{-32}}{2}$ 11. $\dfrac{-2 - \sqrt{-8}}{2}$ 12. $\dfrac{-3 + \sqrt{-18}}{-3}$

Examples:

  a. $(3 - i) - (6 + 2i)$ b. $(4 - 3\sqrt{-1}) + (2 + \sqrt{-1})$
   $(3 - 6) + (-1 - 2)i$ $(4 - 3i) + (2 + i)$
   Ans. $-3 - 3i$ **Ans.** $6 - 2i$

13. $(2 + i) + (3 - 2i)$ 14. $(1 - 5i) + (3 + i)$

15. $(1 - 3i) - (6 + 2i)$ 16. $(5 - 2i) - (6 + 3i)$

17. $(5 - 2\sqrt{-9}) - (3 + 2\sqrt{-9})$ 18. $(3 - \sqrt{-1}) - (3 + \sqrt{-1})$

19. $(\sqrt{-4} - 3) - (\sqrt{-4} + 3)$ 20. $\sqrt{-9} + (2 - \sqrt{-16})$

Examples:

  a. $i(3 + 2i)$ b. $(2 - i)(3 + 2i)$ c. $\sqrt{-3}(3 - \sqrt{-3})$
   $3i + 2i^2$ $6 + 4i - 3i - 2i^2$ $i\sqrt{3}(3 - i\sqrt{3})$
   Ans. $-2 + 3i$ $6 + i + 2$ $3i\sqrt{3} - 3i^2$
     Ans. $8 + i$ **Ans.** $3 + 3i\sqrt{3}$

21. $3(2 + i)$ 22. $i(2 - i)$

23. $-2i(3 + 6i)$ 24. $(6 + i)(2 - i)$

25. $(3 - 2i)(3 + 2i)$ 26. $(7 - i\sqrt{2})(3 + i\sqrt{2})$

27. $(3 + i)^2$ 28. $(2 - \sqrt{-2})^2$

29. $2(3 - i) - 4(2 + i)$ 30. $5(3 - 2i) + 2(1 - i)$

31. $2i(3 - i) + 2(4 - 2i)$ 32. $i(2 - i) + 2i(3 - 2i)$

33. $(1 + i^2) - (1 - i)^2$ 34. $(3 + 2i)^2 + (3 - 2i)^2$

35. $\sqrt{-2}(1 + \sqrt{-2})$ 36. $\sqrt{-5}(3 - \sqrt{-5})$

37. $(4 + 2\sqrt{-3})(4 - \sqrt{-3})$ 38. $(2 - \sqrt{-2})(3 - \sqrt{-2})$

39. $(3 - \sqrt{-5})(3 + \sqrt{-5})$ 40. $(1 + 2\sqrt{-3})(1 - 2\sqrt{-3})$

Examples:

a. $\dfrac{-2}{i}$

$\dfrac{-2(i)}{i(i)}$

$\dfrac{-2i}{i^2}$

$\dfrac{-2i}{-1}$

Ans. $2i$

b. $\dfrac{i}{1 + 2i}$

$\dfrac{i(1 - 2i)}{(1 + 2i)(1 - 2i)}$

$\dfrac{i - 2i^2}{1 - 4i^2}$

$\dfrac{i + 2}{5}$

Ans. $\dfrac{2}{5} + \dfrac{1}{5}i$

c. $\dfrac{1}{2 - \sqrt{-9}}$

$\dfrac{1(2 + 3i)}{(2 - 3i)(2 + 3i)}$

$\dfrac{2 + 3i}{4 - 9i^2}$

$\dfrac{2 + 3i}{13}$

Ans. $\dfrac{2}{13} + \dfrac{3}{13}i$

41. $\dfrac{1}{i}$

42. $\dfrac{-3}{i}$

43. $\dfrac{-3}{\sqrt{-4}}$

44. $\dfrac{7}{\sqrt{-9}}$

45. $\dfrac{-2}{1 - i}$

46. $\dfrac{3}{2 + i}$

47. $\dfrac{3}{3 + 2i}$

48. $\dfrac{-5}{2 - i}$

49. $\dfrac{i}{2 + 3i}$

50. $\dfrac{3i}{1 - i}$

51. $\dfrac{\sqrt{-1} - 1}{\sqrt{-1} + 1}$

52. $\dfrac{1 + \sqrt{-4}}{1 - \sqrt{-4}}$

53. For what values of x is $\sqrt{x - 3}$ real?

54. What relationship must exist between a, b, and c for $\sqrt{b^2 - 4ac}$ to be imaginary?

55. Simplify. a. i^6 b. i^{12} c. i^{15}

56. Solve for x and y: $2 + 3x + 2yi = 11 + yi$. *Hint:* See the definition for equality on page 100.

57. Express each of the following with positive exponents and simplify:
a. i^{-1} b. i^{-2} c. i^{-3} d. i^{-4} e. i^{-5}

58. How would you define i^0 to be consistent with the laws of exponents?

59. Show that the addition of complex numbers is associative.

60. Show that the distributive law holds for complex numbers.

61. Show that the multiplication of complex numbers is commutative.

62. Show that the multiplication of complex numbers is associative.

CHAPTER REVIEW

Simplify. Assume that all variables denote positive numbers.

1. a. $(-27)^{2/3}$

b. $\left(\dfrac{a^{-1}b^2}{c^0 d^{-3}}\right)^{-1}$

2. a. $\dfrac{x^{2n+1}}{x^{2n-1}}$

b. $\dfrac{x^{2n+4}x^{n-1}}{x^{2n+1}}$

3. a. $\dfrac{(2 \times 10^{-3})(3 \times 10^4)(5 \times 10^2)}{(6 \times 10^2)}$ b. $\dfrac{(0.003)(4000)}{(0.0000012)}$

4. a. $(x^{-2} + y^{-3})^{-1}$ b. $\dfrac{2^{-2} + 3^{-1}}{2^{-2}}$

5. a. $\sqrt[3]{-27x^4y^3}$ b. $\sqrt[5]{\dfrac{1}{5}}$

6. a. $\sqrt[6]{8x^3y^6}$ b. $\dfrac{a}{\sqrt{ab}}$

7. a. $\sqrt{75a^3} - a\sqrt{3a}$ b. $\dfrac{a - b}{\sqrt{a} + \sqrt{b}}$

8. a. $(2 + 3i^5) - (3 + 2i^7)$ b. $(2 - i)(3 + 4i)$

9. a. $(3 - \sqrt{-4})(1 + \sqrt{-1})$ b. $\dfrac{1}{1 - \sqrt{-2}}$

10. Rationalize the numerator.

a. $\dfrac{\sqrt{3}}{3}$ b. $\dfrac{\sqrt{x + 1} - \sqrt{x}}{2}$

11. Simplify $(\sqrt[3]{4} + \sqrt[3]{2})^2 - (\sqrt[3]{4} - \sqrt[3]{2})^2$.

12. State the restriction on x so that $\sqrt{(x - 4)^2} = x - 4$.

13. If $\sqrt{(x - 3)^2} < 4$, between what two real numbers must x lie?

14. Assume x is an element of the set of real numbers. Rewrite $\sqrt{2x^2}$ using absolute value notation.

15. Justify each assertion by one or more of the laws of exponents (pages 73 and 74).

a. $\left(\dfrac{y^2}{x}\right)^2 = \dfrac{(y^2)^2}{x^2}$ $(x \neq 0)$ b. $\dfrac{(y^2)^2}{x^2} = \dfrac{y^4}{x^2}$ $(x \neq 0)$

c. $\left(\dfrac{x^{1/2}y^4}{x^{3/2}y^2}\right)^2 = \dfrac{y^4}{x^2}$ $(x, y \neq 0)$

5

FIRST-DEGREE EQUATIONS
AND INEQUALITIES—
ONE VARIABLE

5.1 Equations

Word sentences, such as "The sum of five and two is seven" or "The sum of five and two is nine," can be labeled true or false. Such sentences are called **statements**. Other word sentences, such as "He is six feet tall" or "It is less than three feet in length," cannot be labeled true or false, because the words "he" and "it" do not specify any particular person or object. Such sentences are called **open sentences**.

We can draw a useful analogy between word sentences and the symbolic sentences of mathematics. The symbolic sentences

$$5 + 2 = 7 \tag{1}$$

and

$$5 + 2 = 9 \tag{2}$$

are statements, and we can determine by inspection that (1) is true and (2) is false. The symbolic sentence

$$x + 3 = 5 \tag{3}$$

is an open sentence, because we cannot make a judgment about the truth or falsity thereof until the variable x has been replaced with an element from its replacement set. Symbolic sentences involving only equality relationships, whether statements or open sentences, are called **equations**.

Equations have certain advantages over word sentences when we are discussing numbers. Since symbols are used in place of whole groups of words, equations are much more concise; also, mechanical transformations of equations from one form to another are possible—transformations that enable us to generate a logical sequence of equivalent equations. Such transformations, and the logical assumptions upon which they rest, will be discussed in Section 5.2.

If we replace the variable in an equation with a numeral, and the resulting statement is true, the number represented by the numeral is called a **solution** or **root** of the equation, and is said to *satisfy* the equation. For example, if we substitute 2 for x in (3), we obtain the true statement

$$2 + 3 = 5$$

and 2 is a solution of the equation. The set of all numbers that satisfy the equation is called the **solution set**.

In discussing equations, a variable is frequently referred to as an **unknown**, although, again, its function is simply to represent an unspecified element of some set of numbers. The replacement set of any such variable will be the set of real numbers unless otherwise specified. In practical situations, however, it is always well to have a meaningful replacement set in mind. If we were investigating a situation involving the height of a man, we certainly would not consider negative numbers in the replacement set for any variable representing his height.

One major type of equation with which we shall be concerned in this book is the polynomial equation in one variable, $P(x) = 0$. This is an equation in which one member is zero and the other member is a polynomial in simplest form. The equations

$$x^2 + 2x + 1 = 0, \tag{4}$$

$$2y - 3 = 0, \tag{5}$$

$$-z^4 + z^3 + 1 = 0, \tag{6}$$

are polynomial equations in x, y, and z, respectively; (4) is of second degree, (5) is of first degree, and (6) is of fourth degree. In this chapter we shall study first-degree polynomial equations in one variable.

A **conditional equation** is an equation that is not true for every element in the replacement set of the variable. Thus, if x represents a real number,

$$x + 2 = 5 \tag{7}$$

places a condition on the variable x that is not met by all real numbers, and hence is a conditional equation. Now consider the equation

$$2(x + 1) = 2x + 2. \tag{8}$$

This differs from equation (7) in that the replacement of x by a numeral representing a real number always results in a true statement. Because the two members of an equation such as (8) are identical for every value of the variable, we refer to such an equation as an **identity**.

EXERCISE 5.1

Determine whether the equation is satisfied by the given number.

Example: $3y + 6 = 4y - 4$, by 10

Substitute 10 for y and simplify each member.

Does $3(10) + 6 = 4(10) - 4$?

Does $30 + 6 = 40 - 4$?

Does $36 = 36$?

Ans. Yes.

1-25

1. $x - 3 = 7$, by 4

2. $2x - 6 = 3$, by 4

3. $2x + 6 = 3x - 5$, by 3

4. $5x - 1 = 2x + 2$, by 1

5. $3a + 2 = 8 + a$, by 3

6. $3x - 5 = 2x + 7$, by -1

7. $3 = 6x + 3(x - 2)$, by $\frac{4}{7}$

8. $6 = 2x + 6(2x + 1)$, by 0

9. $0 = 6r - 24$, by 4

10. $0 = 7x + 5$, by $-\frac{7}{5}$

11. $\frac{1}{4}x - 3 = x + 2$, by 8

12. $\frac{1}{3}x - 2x = -12 + \frac{1}{2}x$, by 6

13. $\frac{2x + 7}{5} + 3 = 0$, by 4

14. $\frac{3(2x + 5)}{9} - x = 0$, by 5

15. $\frac{3}{x + 1} = 1 - \frac{2}{x + 1}$, by $\frac{1}{2}$

16. $\frac{x - 3}{2} + \frac{5}{4} = 1$, by $\frac{3}{2}$

In each of the following sentences, select from the sets of numbers (a) to (d) the most appropriate replacement set for the variable.

(a) natural numbers
(b) integers

(c) positive real numbers
(d) real numbers

17. There are n students enrolled at the college.

18. x per cent of the students in this college are mathematics majors (to the nearest one per cent).

19. The length of the diagonal of a rectangle is l inches.

20. The altitude of a triangle is a feet.

21. The temperature (to the nearest degree) at Great Falls, Montana is T degrees.

22. The altitude of Death Valley, California is f feet (to the nearest foot).

23. N is a number less than seven.

24. y is a number greater than -3.

25. An airmail stamp costs c cents.

26. A car costs d dollars (to the nearest dollar).

5.2 Conditional Equations

In this section, we are concerned with procedures for finding solution sets of first-degree conditional equations. We shall sometimes refer to this process as "solving the equation."

We define **equivalent equations** to be equations that have identical solution sets. Thus

$$2x + 1 = x + 4,$$
$$2x = x + 3,$$

and

$$x = 3$$

are equivalent equations, because {3} is the solution set of each.

Since equations whose solution sets contain at least one member assert that, for some or all values of the variable, the left and right members are names for the same number, and since for each value of the variable a polynomial represents a number, the equality axioms for the real numbers imply the following:

1. *The addition of the same expression representing a real number to each member of an equation produces an equivalent equation.*
2. *The multiplication of each member of an equation by the same expression representing a nonzero real number produces an equivalent equation.*

Stated in symbols, these assertions are:

If $P(x)$, $Q(x)$, and $R(x)$ are expressions, then for all values of x for which these expressions represent real numbers, the equation

$$P(x) = Q(x)$$

is equivalent to:

1. $P(x) + R(x) = Q(x) + R(x)$,
2. $P(x) \cdot R(x) = Q(x) \cdot R(x)$,

where replacements for x in 2 are such that $R(x) \neq 0$.

Let us prove assertion (1). If r is a real number satisfying $P(x) = Q(x)$, that is, if $P(r) = Q(r)$, then the addition property of equality assures us that, for any real number $R(r)$,

$$P(r) + R(r) = Q(r) + R(r).$$

But this is a statement that r satisfies $P(x) + R(x) = Q(x) + R(x)$. Conversely, if r is any real number such that

$$P(r) + R(r) = Q(r) + R(r),$$

then, by the addition property of equality,

$$P(r) + R(r) + (-R(r)) = Q(r) + R(r) + (-R(r)),$$

from which

$$P(r) = Q(r).$$

Thus every real number r that satisfies $P(x) = Q(x)$ also satisfies $P(x) + R(x) = Q(x) + R(x)$, and conversely, so that these are equivalent equations as asserted.   A similar argument will establish (2).

The application of these properties permits us to transform an equation whose solution set may not be obvious through a series of equivalent equations until we reach an equation that has an obvious solution.   For example, consider the equation

$$2x + 1 = x + 4.$$

We can add $-x - 1$ to each member to obtain the equivalent equation

$$x = 3,$$

where the solution 3 is obvious.   Any application of Properties 1 or 2 above is called an **elementary transformation.**   An elementary transformation *always* results in an equivalent equation.   Care must be exercised in the application of the second property, for we have specifically excluded multiplication by zero.   For example, to solve the equation

$$\frac{x}{x-3} = \frac{3}{x-3} + 2, \tag{1}$$

we might first multiply each member by $(x - 3)$ to attempt to produce an equivalent equation that is free of fractions.   We have

$$(x - 3)\frac{x}{x-3} = (x-3)\frac{3}{x-3} + (x-3)2$$

or

$$x = 3 + 2x - 6, \tag{2}$$

from which

$$x = 3$$

and 3 *appears* to be a solution of (1).   But, upon substituting 3 for x in (1), we have

$$\frac{3}{0} = \frac{3}{0} + 2$$

and neither member is defined.   In obtaining equation (2), each member of equation (1) was multiplied by $(x - 3)$, but if x is 3, then $(x - 3)$ is zero, and our second property is not applicable.   Equation (2) is not equivalent to equation (1) for $x = 3$, and equation (1) has no solution.

We can always ascertain whether what we think is a solution of an equation is such in reality by substituting the suggested solution in the original equation and verifying that the resulting statement is true.   If each of the equations in a sequence is obtained by means of an elementary transformation, the sole purpose for such checking is to detect arithmetic errors.   We shall dispense with checking solution sets in the examples that follow except in cases where we apply what may be a nonelementary transformation—that is, where we multiply or divide by an expression containing a variable.

Throughout this section, "equation" has been used in its general sense—that of an open sentence. We are primarily concerned at this time with first-degree equations. Any equation of the form

$$ax + b = 0 \quad (a \neq 0) \tag{3}$$

is called a first-degree equation in one variable. We can show that such an equation always has one and only one solution, namely $-b/a$. For (3) is equivalent to

$$x + \frac{b}{a} = 0,$$

and the additive inverse of each real number b/a is unique. Since a first-degree equation in one variable has one and only one solution, this solution constitutes the solution set.

Equations in which the variable appears within absolute value notation require additional comment. Because the variable does appear within such a symbol, any equation of the form $|x - a| = b$ is not a polynomial equation, and hence cannot be assigned a degree. For example, although the equation

$$|x - 3| = 5$$

contains the first-degree polynomial $x - 3$, it has *two* solutions, 8 and -2, as may be verified by direct substitution. The equation is not a first-degree equation, however, and the presence of two solutions in no way contradicts our earlier discussion concerning the number of roots of a first-degree equation.

We have defined the absolute value of a real number by

$$|x| = \begin{cases} x, & \text{if } x \geq 0 \\ -x, & \text{if } x < 0, \end{cases}$$

and interpreted it in terms of distance on a number line. For example, $|-5| = 5$ by definition, but 5 also denotes the distance the graph of -5 is located from the origin. More generally, we have

$$|x - a| = \begin{cases} x - a, & \text{if } (x - a) \geq 0, \text{ or equivalently, if } x \geq a \\ -(x - a), & \text{if } (x - a) < 0, \text{ or equivalently, if } x < a, \end{cases}$$

and $|x - a|$ can be interpreted on a line graph as denoting the distance the graph of x is located from the graph of a (Figure 5.1).

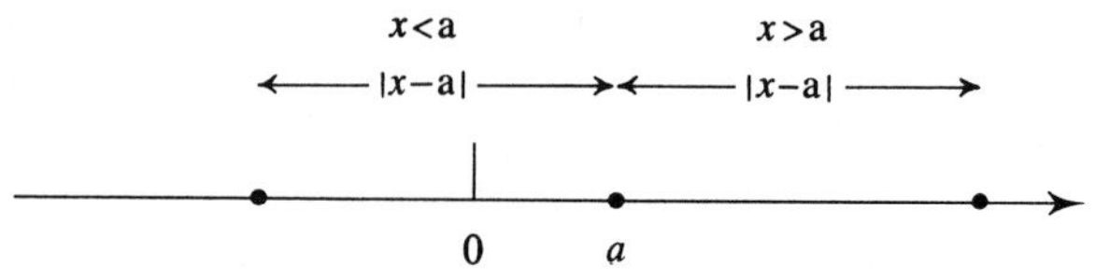

Fig. 5.1

We can solve equations of the form

$$|x - a| = b$$

by appealing to the definition of absolute value.   For example, the equation

$$|x - 3| = 5$$

implies that

$$(x - 3) = 5, \quad \text{if } x - 3 \geq 0, \, (x \geq 3),$$

or

$$-(x - 3) = 5, \quad \text{if } x - 3 < 0, \, (x < 3).$$

In terms of sets, then, the solution set of $|x - 3| = 5$ is

$$(\{x \mid x - 3 = 5\} \cap \{x \mid x \geq 3\}) \cup (\{x \mid -(x - 3) = 5\} \cap \{x \mid x < 3\}).$$

Since

$$\{x \mid x - 3 = 5\} \cap \{x \mid x \geq 3\} = \{8\},$$

$$\{x \mid -(x - 3) = 5\} \cap \{x \mid x < 3\} = \{-2\},$$

the solution set we seek is

$$\{8\} \cup \{-2\} = \{-2, 8\}.$$

Notice that the intersection symbol, $\cap$, can be interpreted in terms of the everyday word "and," while the union symbol, $\cup$, can be interpreted in terms of the nonexclusive use of the everyday word "or," that is, as "either one or the other, or both."

EXERCISE 5.2

Solve.

Examples:

a. $4 - (x - 1)(x + 2) = 8 - x^2$

Apply distributive law.

$4 - (x^2 + x - 2) = 8 - x^2$

$4 - x^2 - x + 2 = 8 - x^2$

Add $x^2 - 6$ to each member.

$-x = 2$

Multiply each member by -1.

$x = -2$

Ans. $\{-2\}$

b. $\dfrac{x}{3} + 4 = x - 2$

Multiply each member by 3.

$3\left(\dfrac{x}{3} + 4\right) = 3(x - 2)$

$x + 12 = 3x - 6$

Add $-x + 6$ to each member.

$18 = 2x$

Multiply each member by $\frac{1}{2}$.

$9 = x$

Ans. $\{9\}$

Note: Of course the solution set can be specified at any time the solution becomes evident by inspection.

1. $x + 2 = 5$ **2.** $3 = x - 4$ **3.** $2x = 3 + x$

4. $3x + 2 = 4x - 6 + x$ **5.** $6x - 2 = 3x + 10$ **6.** $3x - 1 = 2x - 1$

7. $0 = 6x + 4$ **8.** $3x - 2 = x - 5$ **9.** $2(x + 5) = 16$

10. $3(x + 1) = 3$ **11.** $x - (8 - x) = 2$ **12.** $2x - (3 - x) = 0$

13. $-3[x - (2x + 3) - 2x] = -9$ **14.** $5[2 + 3(x - 2)] + 20 = 0$

15. $-2[x - (x - 1)] = -3(x + 1)$ **16.** $3[2x - (x + 2)] = -3(3 - 2x)$

17. $(x - 1)(x - 1) = x^2 - 11$ **18.** $(2x + 1)(x - 3) = (x - 2)(x + 1) + x^2$

19. $(x - 2)^2 = x^2 - 8$ **20.** $(x - 1)^2 = x^2 - 15$

21. $6 + 3x - x^2 = 4 - (x + 2)(x + 3)$ **22.** $0 = x^2 + (2 - x)(5 + x)$

23. $\dfrac{x}{3} = 2$ **24.** $\dfrac{2x}{3} = -4$ **25.** $\dfrac{3x + x}{5} = -2$

26. $7 - \dfrac{x}{3} = x - 1$ **27.** $6 - \dfrac{x}{2} = x$ **28.** $\dfrac{x + 3}{2} = x$

29. $1 + \dfrac{x}{9} = \dfrac{4}{3}$ **30.** $\dfrac{x}{5} - \dfrac{x}{2} = 9$

31. $\dfrac{2x - 1}{5} = \dfrac{x + 1}{2}$ **32.** $\dfrac{2x}{3} - \dfrac{2x + 5}{6} = \dfrac{1}{2}$

Example: $\dfrac{2}{3} = 6 - \dfrac{x + 10}{x - 3}$

Multiply each member by the L.C.D. $[(3)(x - 3)]$.

$$(3)(x - 3)\frac{2}{3} = (3)(x - 3)6 - (3)(x - 3)\frac{(x + 10)}{x - 3}$$

$$2(x - 3) = 18(x - 3) - 3(x + 10)$$

Apply the distributive law.

$$2x - 6 = 18x - 54 - 3x - 30$$

Combine like terms and add $-15x + 6$ to each member.

$$-13x = -78$$

Multiply each member by $-\frac{1}{13}$.

$$x = 6$$

Ans.   {6}

Check: $\dfrac{2}{3} = 6 - \dfrac{(6) + 10}{(6) - 3}$ A check is required since we multiplied each

$\dfrac{2}{3} = 6 - \dfrac{16}{3}$ member of the equation by an expression containing the variable.

$\dfrac{2}{3} = \dfrac{2}{3}$

33. $\dfrac{x}{x-2} = \dfrac{2}{x-2} + 7$

34. $\dfrac{2}{x-9} = \dfrac{9}{x+12}$

35. $\dfrac{2}{y+1} + \dfrac{1}{3y+3} = \dfrac{1}{6}$

36. $\dfrac{5}{x-3} = \dfrac{x+2}{x-3} + 3$

37. $\dfrac{4}{2x-3} + \dfrac{4x}{4x^2-9} = \dfrac{1}{2x+3}$

38. $\dfrac{y}{y+2} - \dfrac{3}{y-2} = \dfrac{y^2+8}{y^2-4}$

Example: $|x + 5| = 8$

Use the definition of $|x|$ and write as two first-degree equations.

$x + 5 = 8 \qquad -(x + 5) = 8$

Solve each equation.

$\qquad x = 3 \qquad\quad -x - 5 = 8$

$\qquad\qquad\qquad\qquad -x = 13$

$\qquad\qquad\qquad\qquad\; x = -13$

Ans. $\{3, -13\}$

39. $|x| = 3$

40. $|x| = 6$

41. $|x - 6| = 3$

42. $|x - 1| = 4$

43. $|x - \tfrac{3}{4}| = \tfrac{1}{2}$

44. $|x - \tfrac{2}{3}| = \tfrac{1}{4}$

45. $|3x + 7| = 1$

46. $|2x + 5| = 2$

47. $|1 + \tfrac{3}{2}x| = \tfrac{1}{2}$

48. $|1 - \tfrac{1}{2}x| = \tfrac{3}{4}$

49. $|\tfrac{1}{3} - 4x| = \tfrac{2}{3}$

50. $|2x + \tfrac{1}{2}| = \tfrac{1}{4}$

51. Show that for any $a, k \in R$, and $k \neq 1$, the equation $\dfrac{x}{(x-a)} = \dfrac{a}{(x-a)} + k$ has no solution.

52. Why can we tell by inspection that $\dfrac{(x+2)}{(x+1)} = 1$ has no solution?

53. Why can we tell by inspection that $|2x - 5| = -3$ has no solution?

54. For what value of k will the equation $2x - 3 = \dfrac{(4+x)}{k}$ have as its solution set $\{-1\}$?

55. Find a value for k in $3x - 1 = k$ so that the equation is equivalent to $2x + 5 = 1$.

56. Prove Assertion 2 on page 108.

57. An equation of the form

$$\frac{a}{b} = \frac{c}{d} \quad (a, b, c, d \neq 0)$$

is called a **proportion** (see Section 8.4). The terms b and c are called *means* and the terms a and d are called *extremes*. Show that, in any proportion, the product of the means is equal to the product of the extremes.

58. If $\dfrac{a}{b} = \dfrac{c}{d}$, show that $\dfrac{b}{a} = \dfrac{d}{c}$.

59. If $\dfrac{a}{b} = \dfrac{c}{d}$, show that $\dfrac{a}{c} = \dfrac{b}{d}$.

60. If $\dfrac{a}{b} = \dfrac{c}{d}$, show that $\dfrac{d}{b} = \dfrac{c}{a}$.

61. If $\dfrac{a}{b} = \dfrac{c}{d}$, show that $\dfrac{a + b}{b} = \dfrac{c + d}{d}$.   *Hint:* Consider $\dfrac{a}{b} + 1 = \dfrac{c}{d} + 1$.

62. If $\dfrac{a}{b} = \dfrac{c}{d}$, show that $\dfrac{a - b}{b} = \dfrac{c - d}{d}$.

5.3 Solving Equations for Specified Symbols

An equation containing more than one variable, or containing symbols such as a, b, and c, representing constants, can be solved for one of the symbols in terms of the remaining symbols by using the methods developed in the preceding section.   In general, we apply elementary transformations until we obtain the desired symbol by itself as one member of an equation.

EXERCISE 5.3

Solve for x, y, or z.   (Leave the results in the form of an equation equivalent to the given equation.)

Example: $5by - 2a = 2ay$

Add $2a - 2ay$ to each member.

$5by - 2ay = 2a$

Factor the left-hand member.

$y(5b - 2a) = 2a$

Multiply each member by $\dfrac{1}{5b - 2a}$.

Ans. $y = \dfrac{2a}{5b - 2a}$ $(5b - 2a \neq 0)$

1. $3y - 3b = y - b$

2. $b = x - c + a$

3. $2abx + 6a = abx$

4. $a^2x = a - 1$

5. $cz + b^2 = 0$

6. $ax = a^2b - ax$

7. $\dfrac{a}{b} y + c = 0$

8. $\dfrac{ax}{b} - c = a$

9. $cx = c - x$

10. $a^2x + b = ax$

11. $a(a - x) = b(b - x)$

12. $4z - 3(z - b) = 8b$

13. $(x - 2)(a + 3) = a$

14. $(y - 4)(b + 3) = 2b$

15. $\dfrac{1}{x} + \dfrac{1}{a} = 6$

16. $\dfrac{b}{2y} - \dfrac{1}{3} = \dfrac{b}{3y}$

17. $\dfrac{1}{a} + \dfrac{1}{b} = \dfrac{1}{x}$

18. $\dfrac{x}{a} - \dfrac{a}{b} = \dfrac{b}{c}$

19. $\dfrac{a-2}{b} + \dfrac{3}{2b} = \dfrac{2}{x}$
    20. $\dfrac{2x+4a}{3a} - \dfrac{3x+4a}{2a} = a$

Solve.

Example: $v = k + gt$, for g

Add $-k$ to each member.

$v - k = gt$

Multiply each member by $\dfrac{1}{t}$.

$\dfrac{v-k}{t} = g$

$2\,1\text{-}39$

Ans. $g = \dfrac{v-k}{t}$ $(t \neq 0)$

21. $v = k + gt$, for k **22.** $E = mc^2$, for m **23.** $f = ma$, for m

24. $I = prt$, for p **25.** $pv = K$, for v **26.** $E = IR$, for R

27. $s = \frac{1}{2}at^2$, for a **28.** $p = 2l + 2w$, for l **29.** $v = k + gt$, for t

30. $y = \dfrac{k}{z}$, for z **31.** $V = lwh$, for h **32.** $W = I^2R$, for R

33. $180 = A + B + C$, for B **34.** $S = \dfrac{a}{1-r}$, for r

35. $A = \dfrac{h}{2}(b + c)$, for c **36.** $S = 2r(r + h)$, for h

37. $S = 3\pi d + 5\pi D$, for d **38.** $A = 2\pi rh + 2\pi r^2$, for h

39. $l = a + (n - 1)d$, for n **40.** $\dfrac{1}{r} = \dfrac{1}{r_1} + \dfrac{1}{r_2}$, for r

41. $x_1x_2 - 2x_1x_3 = x_4$ for x_1 **42.** $3x_1x_2 + x_1x_2 = x_4$, for x_1

43. $x^2y' - 3x - 2y^3y' = 1$, for y' **44.** $2xy' - 3y' + x^2 = 0$, for y'

5.4 Identities

We have observed that an equation such as

$$x + 2 = x + 2,$$

which is satisfied by every element in the replacement set of the variable (for which both members are defined), is called an identity.

We can determine whether a given equation is or is not an identity by changing one or both members of the equation to obtain a sequence of equivalent equations until we arrive at either an obvious identity—that is, an equation where both members are the same—or an equation that is obviously conditional. For example,

$$x^2 = (x - 1)(x + 1) + 1$$

may be written

$$x^2 = (x^2 - 1) + 1,$$

from which

$$x^2 = x^2,$$

and the identity is established. If we attempt to write all of the variables in one member by adding $-x^2$ to each member, we obtain

$$0 = 0,$$

which is true for any value of x.

As another example, consider the equation

$$(x - 2)^2 = x^2 - 3x + 2.$$

Upon performing the multiplication indicated in the left-hand member, we have

$$x^2 - 4x + 4 = x^2 - 3x + 2,$$

from which

$$x = 2.$$

Since this is clearly a conditional equation, the original equation is not an identity.

We can also show that a given equation is not an identity by citing a single counterexample, that is, a single number that does not satisfy the equation. Thus we can be sure that

$$\frac{x - 2}{3} = x^2 - 1$$

is not an identity, since it is not true for $x = 0$; that is,

$$\frac{0 - 2}{3} \neq 0 - 1.$$

Some identities are called "laws." The equations

$$a + b = b + a,$$
$$ab = ba,$$
$$(a + b) + c = a + (b + c),$$
$$(ab)c = a(bc),$$

expressing the commutative and associative laws of addition and multiplication, are identities. The same is true with respect to the distributive law, the fundamental principle of fractions, etc.

EXERCISE 5.4

Verify that the equations are identities.

Example: $\dfrac{3x - x}{2} + 3 = x + 3$

Simplify left-hand member.

$\dfrac{2x}{2} + 3 = x + 3$

$x + 3 = x + 3$ Left-hand member is identical to right-hand member.

1. $\dfrac{x - 4x}{3} + 3x = 2x$

2. $\dfrac{y}{3} - \dfrac{2}{5} = \dfrac{5y - 6}{15}$

3. $(x + 2)(x - 2) - x^2 = -4$

4. $\dfrac{x(x - 1)}{3} + x = \dfrac{x^2 + 2x}{3}$

5. $\dfrac{4x - 6x}{2} + 1 = 1 - x$

6. $(x + 2)(x + 3) - 6 = x(x + 5)$

7. $x(3 + x) - (x^2 + x) = 2x$

8. $x(x + 3) = (x + 1)^2 + x - 1$

9. $4x - \dfrac{5}{2}x - x = \dfrac{x}{2}$

10. $\dfrac{x^2}{4} + x + 1 = \dfrac{(x + 2)^2}{4}$

11. $\dfrac{y - 3}{3} = 2y - \dfrac{5y + 3}{3}$

12. $x(x + 1) = \dfrac{(2x + 1)^2 - 1}{4}$

13. $(x - 2)^2 - 3 = x^2 - 4x + 1$

14. $\dfrac{5y}{4} = \dfrac{2 + 3y}{4} - \dfrac{1 - y}{2}$

15. $14 = 3(x + 4) + \dfrac{4 - 6x}{2}$

16. $\dfrac{2z - 3}{2} + 1 = z - \dfrac{1}{2}$

Example: $\dfrac{x^2 - 2x - 3}{x + 1} = x - 3$

Factor left-hand member and reduce fraction.

$\dfrac{(x - 3)(x + 1)}{(x + 1)} = x - 3$

$x - 3 = x - 3.$

Original equation is an identity for every real value of x except $x = -1$. The left-hand member in the original equation is not defined for $x = -1$.

17. $y + 2 = \dfrac{(y + 3)(y - 1) + 3}{y}$

18. $z + 3 = \dfrac{(z + 1)(z + 2) - 2}{z}$

19. $\dfrac{x + 3}{x} + \dfrac{2}{x} = \dfrac{5}{x} + 1$

20. $\dfrac{(x + 2)^2 - 4(x + 1)}{x} = x$

21. $\dfrac{x^2 - 5x + 4}{x - 4} = x - 1$

22. $\dfrac{x^3 + 6x^2 + 5x}{x^2 + x} = x + 5$

Determine which of the following equations are identities and which are conditional equations. Find the solution set for each conditional equation.

23. $(x + 2)^2 + (x - 1)^2 = (x + 1)^2 + x^2 + 4$

24. $x(x - 2) - (x - 2)(x + 2) = (x + 2)^2 - x(x + 6)$

25. $\dfrac{x}{x - 2} - 7 = \dfrac{2}{x - 2}$

26. $\dfrac{6}{x + 1} - \dfrac{1}{2} = \dfrac{-1}{x + 1}$

27. $\dfrac{1}{x - 2} = \dfrac{2}{x - 2} + 3$

28. $\dfrac{x^2 - x - 6}{x + 2} = \dfrac{x^2 - 8x + 15}{x - 5}$

29. $\dfrac{2}{3}(y - 4) + \dfrac{2}{5}(y + 3) = y - 1$

30. $\dfrac{1}{2x - 3} + \dfrac{x}{4x^2 - 9} = \dfrac{1}{8x + 12}$

5.5   Inequalities

Open sentences of the form

$$x + 3 \geq 10, \tag{1}$$

$$\frac{-2y - 3}{3} < 5, \tag{2}$$

etc., are called **inequalities**. For appropriate values of the variable, one member of an inequality represents a real number that is less than ($<$), less than or equal to ($\leq$), greater than or equal to ($\geq$), or greater than ($>$) the real number represented by the other member.

Any element of the replacement set of the variable for which an inequality is true is called a **solution**, and the set of all solutions of an inequality is called the **solution set** of the inequality. Inequalities that are true for every element in the replacement set of the variable—such as $x^2 + 1 > 0$, $x \in R$—are called **absolute inequalities**. Inequalities that are not true for every element of the replacement set are called **conditional inequalities**—for example, (1) and (2) above.

As in the case with equations, we shall solve a given inequality by generating a series of equivalent inequalities (inequalities having the same solution set) until we arrive at one whose solution set is obvious. To do this we shall need some fundamental properties of inequalities.

Notice that

$$2 < 3,$$

and that

$$2 + 5 < 3 + 5,$$

and

$$2 - 5 < 3 - 5.$$

Line graphs (I) and (II) in Figure 5.2 demonstrate that the addition of 5 or −5 to each member of 2 < 3 simply shifts the members the same number of units to the right or left on the number line, with the order of the members

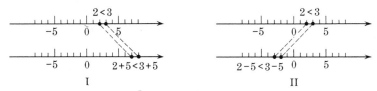

Fig. 5.2

left unchanged. This will be the case for the addition of any real number to each member of an inequality. Since for any real value of the variable for which an expression is defined the expression represents a real number, we generalize this idea and assert that:

1. *The addition of the same expression representing a real number to each member of an inequality produces an equivalent inequality in the same sense.*

Next, if we multiply each member of

$$2 < 3$$

by 2, we have

$$4 < 6,$$

where the products form an inequality in the same sense. If, however, we multiply each member of

$$2 < 3$$

by −2, we have

$$-4 > -6,$$

where the inequality is in the opposite sense. The line graphs in Figure 5.3 show why this is so.

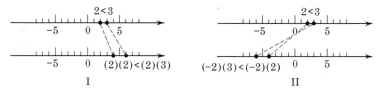

Fig. 5.3

Multiplying each member of 2 < 3 by 2 simply moves each member out twice as far in a positive direction (I). Multiplying by −2, however, doubles the absolute value of each member, but the products will be negative and hence reflected through 0, and the sense of the inequality is reversed (II). In general, we have:

2. *If each member of an inequality is multiplied by the same expression representing a positive number, the result is an equivalent inequality in the same sense.*
3. *If each member of an inequality is multiplied by the same expression representing a negative number, the result is an equivalent inequality in the opposite sense.*

Statements 1, 2, and 3 above can be expressed in symbols as follows:

If $P(x)$, $Q(x)$, and $R(x)$ are expressions, then, for all values of x for which these expressions represent real numbers

$$P(x) < Q(x)$$

is equivalent to:

1. $P(x) + R(x) < Q(x) + R(x)$,
2. $P(x) \cdot R(x) < Q(x) \cdot R(x)$,   if $R(x) > 0$,
3. $P(x) \cdot R(x) > Q(x) \cdot R(x)$,   if $R(x) < 0$.

These relationships are true with $<$ replaced by $\leq$ and $>$ replaced by $\geq$. Also similar relationships are true with $<$ replaced by $>$ or $\geq$ and $>$ replaced by $<$ or $\leq$, respectively. The proofs of these properties are omitted.

Note that none of these assertions permit multiplying by zero, and that variables in expressions used as multipliers are restricted from values for which the expression vanishes or is not defined. The result of applying any of these three properties is called an **elementary transformation.**

These properties can be applied to solve first-degree inequalities in the same way the equality properties are applied to solve first-degree equations. As an example, let us find the solution set of

$$\frac{x - 3}{4} < \frac{2}{3}.$$

By Assertion 2, we can multiply each member by 12 to obtain

$$3(x - 3) < 8,$$

or

$$3x - 9 < 8.$$

By Assertion 1, we can add 9 to each member, giving us

$$3x < 17,$$

and finally, by Assertion 2, we can multiply each member by 1/3 and obtain

$$x < \frac{17}{3},$$

where the solution set is $S = \{x \mid x < 17/3\}$.   Recall that this symbolism is read, "S is the set of all x such that x is less than 17/3."

This solution set can be graphed on a line graph as shown in Figure 5.4, where the heavy line shows points whose coordinates are in the solution set.

Fig. 5.4

Inequalities sometimes appear in the form

$$-6 < 3x \leq 15, \tag{3}$$

where an expression is bracketed between two inequality symbols.   The solution set of such an inequality is obtained in the same manner as the solution set of any other inequality.   In (3) above, each expression may be multiplied by 1/3 to obtain

$$-2 < x \leq 5.$$

The solution set,

$$S = \{x \mid -2 < x \leq 5\},$$

is illustrated on a line graph in Figure 5.5.

Inequalities involving absolute value notation are encountered quite frequently, and require some additional discussion.   For example, consider the inequality

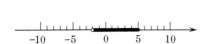

$$|x + 1| < 3. \tag{4}$$

Fig. 5.5

From the definition of absolute value, this inequality is equivalent to

$$x + 1 < 3, \quad \text{for } x + 1 \geq 0 \text{ or } x \geq -1$$

or

$$-(x + 1) < 3, \quad \text{for } x + 1 < 0 \text{ or } x < -1.$$

But, by Property 3,

$$-(x + 1) < 3$$

is equivalent to

$$x + 1 > -3,$$

and (4) can be written in the compact form

$$-3 < x + 1 < 3. \tag{5}$$

Any expression of the form (4) should be written in the form (5) before undertaking elementary transformations to find the solution set. Adding -1 to each expression in (5), we have

$$-4 < x < 2,$$

from which the solution set is

$$S = \{x \mid -4 < x < 2\}$$

Fig. 5.6

or, alternatively,

$$S = \{x \mid x > -4\} \cap \{x \mid x < 2\}.$$

The graph of this set is shown in Figure 5.6. Now consider

$$|x + 1| > 3.$$

From the definition of absolute value, this inequality is equivalent to

$$x + 1 > 3, \quad \text{for } x + 1 \geq 0 \text{ or } x \geq -1$$

and

$$-(x + 1) > 3, \quad \text{for } x + 1 < 0 \text{ or } x < -1,$$

and the solution set is given by

$$S = \{x \mid x > 2 \text{ or } x < -4\}.$$

The graph of S is shown in Figure 5.7.

Fig. 5.7

Observe that S can also be given by

$$S = \{x \mid x > 2\} \cup \{x \mid x < -4\}$$

where $\cup$ is associated with the word "or."

EXERCISE 5.5

Solve and represent the solution set on a line graph.

Example: $\dfrac{x + 4}{3} \leq 6 + x$

    Multiply each member by 3.

$x + 4 \leq 18 + 3x$

    Add $-4 - 3x$ to each member.

$-2x \leq 14$

Multiply each member by $-\frac{1}{2}$ and reverse the sense of the inequality.

$x \geq -7$

Ans. $\{x \mid x \geq -7\}$

1-17

1. $3x < 6$ 2. $x + 7 > 8$ 3. $x - 5 \leq 7$

4. $2x - 3 < 4$ 5. $3x - 2 > 1 + 2x$ 6. $2x + 3 \leq x - 1$

7. $\dfrac{2x - 6}{3} > 0$ 8. $\dfrac{2x - 3}{2} \leq 5$ 9. $\dfrac{5x - 7x}{3} > 4$

10. $\dfrac{x - 3x}{5} \leq 6$ 11. $\dfrac{2x - 5x}{2} \leq 7$ 12. $\dfrac{x - 6x}{2} < -20$

13. $\dfrac{x}{2} + 1 < \dfrac{x}{3} - x$ 14. $\dfrac{1}{2}(x + 2) \geq \dfrac{2x}{3}$

15. $2(x + 2) \leq \dfrac{3}{4}x - 1$ 16. $\dfrac{2}{3}(x - 1) + \dfrac{3}{4}(x + 1) < 0$

17. $\dfrac{3}{4}(2x - 1) - \dfrac{1}{2}(4x + 3) \geq 0$ 18. $\dfrac{3}{5}(3x + 2) - \dfrac{2}{3}(2x - 1) \leq 2$

Example: $|2x - 1| \leq 7$

Rewrite without the absolute value symbol.

$-7 \leq 2x - 1 \leq 7$

Add $+1$ to each expression.

$-6 \leq 2x \leq 8$

Multiply each expression by $\frac{1}{2}$.

19-29

$-3 \leq x \leq 4$

Ans.

$\{x \mid -3 \leq x \leq 4\}$
or $\{x \mid -3 \leq x \text{ and } x \leq 4\}$
or $\{x \mid -3 \leq x\} \cap \{x \mid x \leq 4\}$

19. $1 < 2x + 3 \leq 3$ 20. $3 \leq 2x + 1 \leq 7$ 21. $-6 \leq 2x + 1 \leq 6$

22. $-3 \leq 2x + 5 < 9$ 23. $|x| < 2$ 24. $|x| \leq 5$

25. $|x + 3| < 4$ 26. $2|x + 1| \leq 8$ 27. $|2x - 5| < 3$

28. $3|2x + 4| < 6$ 29. $|4 - x| \leq 8$ 30. $|5 - 2x| \leq 6$

Example: $|3x - 6| > 9$

Rewrite without the absolute value symbol and solve.

$3x - 6 > 9$ or $-(3x - 6) > 9$

$\qquad 3x > 15 \qquad\qquad 3x - 6 < -9$

$\qquad\quad x > 5 \qquad\qquad\quad 3x < -3$

$\qquad\qquad\qquad\qquad\qquad x < -1$

Ans. $\{x \mid x < -1 \text{ or } x > 5\}$
$\quad$ or $\{x \mid x < -1\} \cup \{x \mid x > 5\}$

31. $|x| > 3$ **32.** $|x| \geq 5$ **33.** $|x - 2| > 5$

34. $|x + 5| > 2$ **35.** $|2x + 3| \geq 7$ **36.** $|4 - 3x| > 10$

37. $\dfrac{1}{(x - 1)} > 1$ *Hint:* Is $(x - 1) > 0$ or < 0?   Consider each possibility.

38. $\dfrac{4}{(x + 3)} < 3$ *Hint:* Is $(x + 3) > 0$ or < 0?   Consider each possibility.

39. Explain why we can assert that it is obvious that $|x + 2| < -1$ has an empty solution set.

40. Show that $\{x \mid x < 0\}$ is the solution set of $\dfrac{x + 1}{x} < 1$.

5.6 Word Problems

Word problems state relationships between numbers. The problem may be explicitly concerned with numbers or it may be concerned with numerical measures of physical quantities. In either event, we seek a number or numbers for which the stated relationship holds. To express the quantitative ideas symbolically in the form of an equation is the most difficult part of solving word problems. Although, unfortunately, there is no single means available to do this, the following suggestions are frequently helpful:

1. Determine the quantities asked for and represent them by symbols. Since at this time we are using one variable only, all relevant quantities should be represented in terms of this variable.
2. Where applicable, draw a sketch and label all known quantities thereon; label the unknown quantities in terms of symbols.
3. Find in the problem a quantity that can be represented in two different ways and write this representation as an equation. The equation may derive from:
   a. the problem itself, which may state a relationship explicitly; for example, "What number added to 4 gives 7?" produces the equation $x + 4 = 7$;
   b. formulas or relationships that are part of your general mathematical background; for example, $A = \pi r^2$, $d = rt$, etc.
4. Solve the resulting equation.
5. Check the results against the original problem. It is not sufficient to check the result in the equation because the equation itself may be in error.

The key to working word problems is an ability to understand what you read. If you do not understand the problem, you cannot set up the requisite equation. You should always read a problem through carefully, because a hasty glance often leads to an erroneous interpretation of what is being said.

At this stage of your mathematical development, as much or more attention should be given to the setting up of equations as is given to their solution. Although some of the problems in this book can be solved without recourse to algebra, the practice obtained in setting up the equations involved will help when more difficult problems are encountered.

EXERCISE 5.6

(a) Set up an equation for each problem.

(b) Solve.

Example: If $\frac{1}{3}$ of a certain integer is added to $\frac{1}{2}$ of the next consecutive integer, the result is 33. Find the integers.

   (a) Represent the unknown quantities symbolically.

Let x represent an integer;
then $x + 1$ represents the next consecutive integer.

   Write an equation representing the word sentence.

Ans. (a) $\frac{1}{3}x + \frac{1}{2}(x + 1) = 33$

   (b) Solve the equation.

1 - 12 odd

$$(6)\tfrac{1}{3}x + (6)\tfrac{1}{2}(x + 1) = (6)33$$
$$2x + 3x + 3 = 198$$
$$5x = 195$$
$$x = 39; \text{ therefore } x + 1 = 40$$

Ans. (b) The integers are 39 and 40. **Check:** Does $\frac{1}{3}(39) + \frac{1}{2}(40) = 33$? Yes.

1. Find three consecutive even integers whose sum is 78.

2. If $\frac{2}{3}$ of a certain number is subtracted from twice the number, the result is 32. Find the number.

3. The denominator of a certain fraction is 6 more than the numerator and the fraction is equal to $\frac{2}{3}$. Find the numerator.

4. In a recent election the winning candidate received 150 votes more than his opponent. How many votes did each candidate receive if there were 4376 votes cast?

5. The length of a rectangle is 10 feet greater than its width. Find the dimensions if its perimeter is 168 feet.

6. A 48-foot rope is cut into two pieces so that one piece is 10 feet longer than the other. How long is each piece?

7. When each side of a square is increased by 5 inches, the area is increased by 85 square inches. Find the side of the original square.

8. Find the length of the diameter of a circle whose circumference is 154 inches. (Use $\frac{22}{7}$ for π.)

Example: A collection of coins consisting of dimes and quarters has a value of $11.60. How many dimes and quarters are in the collection if there are 32 more dimes than quarters?

(a) Represent the unknown quantities symbolically.

Let x represent a number of quarters;
then $x + 32$ represents the number of dimes.

Write an equation relating the value of the quarters and value of the dimes to the value of the entire collection.

$$\begin{bmatrix} \text{value of} \\ \text{quarters} \\ \text{in cents} \end{bmatrix} + \begin{bmatrix} \text{value of} \\ \text{dimes} \\ \text{in cents} \end{bmatrix} = \begin{bmatrix} \text{value of} \\ \text{collection} \\ \text{in cents} \end{bmatrix}$$

Ans. (a) $25x + 10(x + 32) = 1160$

(b) Solve for x.

$$25x + 10x + 320 = 1160$$
$$35x = 840$$
$$x = 24; \text{ therefore } x + 32 = 56$$

Ans. (b) There are 24 quarters and 56 dimes in the collection.

Check: Do 24 quarters and 56 dimes have a value of $11.60? Yes.

9. A man has $1.80 in change consisting of three more dimes than nickels. How many dimes and nickels does he have?

10. A vendor bought a supply of ice cream bars at three for 20 cents. He ate one and sold the remainder at 10 cents each. If he made $2.00, how many bars did he buy?

11. The admission at a baseball game was $1.50 for adults and $.85 for children. The receipts were $93.10 for 82 paid admissions. How many adults and children attended the game?

12. A man has $446 in ten-dollar, five-dollar, and one-dollar bills. There are 94 bills in all and 10 more five-dollar bills than ten-dollar bills. How many of each kind does he have?

Example: How many gallons of a 10% solution of acid should be added to 20 gallons of a 60% solution of acid to obtain a 50% solution?

(a) Represent the unknown quantity symbolically.

Let n represent a number of gallons of 10% solution.

Write an equation relating the amount of pure acid before and after combining the acids.

$$\begin{bmatrix} \text{pure acid in} \\ \text{10\% solution} \end{bmatrix} + \begin{bmatrix} \text{pure acid in} \\ \text{60\% solution} \end{bmatrix} = \begin{bmatrix} \text{pure acid in} \\ \text{50\% solution} \end{bmatrix}$$

Ans. (a) $0.10(n) + 0.60(20) = 0.50(n + 20)$

  (b) Solve for n.

$$10n + 1200 = 50n + 1000$$
$$-40n = -200$$
$$n = 5$$

Ans.   (b) 5 gallons of the 10% solution.

Check: Does 5 gallons of a 10% solution when added to 20 gallons of a 60% solution form a 50% solution?   Does $0.10(5) + 0.60(20) = 0.50(25)$?   Yes.

13. How many gallons of a 30% salt solution must be added to 40 gallons of a 12% salt solution to obtain a 20% solution?

14. How many pounds of an alloy containing 45% silver must be melted with an alloy containing 60% silver to obtain 40 pounds of an alloy containing 48% silver?

15. How much pure alcohol should be added to 12 ounces of a 45% solution to obtain a 60% solution?

16. How much water should be added to one gallon of pure acid to obtain a 15% solution?

Example: A man has an annual income of $6000 from two investments.   He has $10,000 more invested at 4% than he has invested at 3%.   How much does he have invested at each rate?

  (a) Represent the amount invested at each rate symbolically.

Let A represent an amount in dollars invested at 3%;
then $A + 10,000$ represents an amount invested at 4%.

  Write an equation relating the interest from each investment and the total interest received.

$$\begin{bmatrix}\text{interest} & \text{from} \\ 3\% & \text{investment}\end{bmatrix} + \begin{bmatrix}\text{interest} & \text{from} \\ 4\% & \text{investment}\end{bmatrix} = [\text{total interest}]$$

Ans.   (a) $0.03A + 0.04(A + 10,000) = 6000$

  (b) Solve for A.

$$3A + 4A + 40,000 = 600,000$$
$$7A = 560,000$$
$$A = 80,000; \text{ therefore } A + 10,000 = 90,000$$

Ans.   (b) $80,000 invested at 3% and $90,000 invested at 4%.

Check: Does $0.03(80,000) + 0.04(90,000) = 6000$?   Yes.

17. A sum of $2000 is invested, part at 3% and the remainder at 4%.   Find the amount invested at each rate if the yearly income from the two investments is $66.

18. A sum of $2700 is invested, part at 4% and the remainder at 5%.   Find the yearly interest on both investments if the interest on each investment is the same.

19. A man has three times as much money invested in 3% bonds as he has in stocks paying 5%. How much does he have invested in each if his yearly income from the investments is $1680?

20. A man has $1000 more invested at 5% than he has invested at 4%. If his annual income from the two investments is $698, how much does he have invested at each rate?

Example: An express train travels 150 miles in the same time that a freight train travels 100 miles. If the express goes 20 miles per hour faster than the freight, find the rate of each. $\left(Given: \text{time} = \dfrac{\text{distance}}{\text{rate}}\right)$

(a) Represent the unknown quantities symbolically.

Let r represent a rate for the freight train;
then $r + 20$ represents the rate of the express train.

The fact that the times are equal is the significant equality in the problem.

[t of freight] = [t of express]

Express the time of each train in terms of r.

Ans. (a) $\dfrac{100}{r} = \dfrac{150}{r + 20}$

(b) Solve for r.

$(r + 20)100 = (r)150$
$100r + 2000 = 150r$
$-50r = -2000$
$r = 40; \text{ therefore } r + 20 = 60$

Ans. (b) Freight train's rate is 40 mph; express train's rate is 60 mph.

Check: Does the time of the freight train (100/40) equal the time of the express train (150/60)? Yes.

21. An airplane travels 1260 miles in the same time that an automobile travels 420 miles. If the rate of the airplane is 120 miles per hour greater than the rate of the automobile, find the rate of each.

22. Two cars start together and travel in the same direction, one going twice as fast as the other. At the end of 3 hours they are 96 miles apart. How fast is each traveling?

23. A freight train leaves town A for town B, traveling at an average rate of 40 miles per hour. Three hours later a passenger train also leaves town A for town B, on a parallel track traveling at an average rate of 80 miles per hour. How far from town A does the passenger train pass the freight train?

24. A boy walked to his friend's house at the rate of 4 miles per hour and he ran back home at the rate of 6 miles per hour. How far apart are the two houses if the round trip took 20 minutes?

(a) Set up an inequality for each problem.

(b) Solve.

Example: A student must have an average of 80% to 90% inclusive on five tests in a course to receive a *B*. His grades on the first four tests were 98%, 76%, 86%, and 92%. What grade on the fifth test would qualify him for a *B* in the course?

(a) Represent the unknown quantity symbolically.

Let *x* represent a grade (in percent) on the last test.
Write an inequality expressing the word sentence.

Ans. (a) $80 \le \dfrac{98 + 76 + 86 + 92 + x}{5} \le 90$

(b) Solve for *x*.

$400 \le 352 + x \le 450$
$48 \le x \le 98$

Ans. (b) Any grade equal to or greater than 48 and less than or equal to 98.

25. In the preceding example, what grade on the fifth test would qualify the student for a *B* if his grades on the first four tests were 78%, 64%, 88%, and 76%?

26. The Fahrenheit and Centigrade temperatures are related by $C = \frac{5}{9}(F - 32)$. Within what range must the temperature be in Fahrenheit degrees for the temperature in Centigrade degrees to lie between $-10°$ and $20°$?

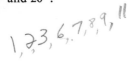

CHAPTER REVIEW

Solve.

1. $2[x - (2x + 1)] = 6$

2. $1 - \dfrac{x - 2}{x - 3} = \dfrac{3}{x - 1}$

3. $\dfrac{x - y}{3} = \dfrac{x + y}{2}$, for *y* in terms of *x*.

4. Verify that $[(a - b)^2 + 2ab] = a^2 + b^2$ is an identity.

5. a. Show by counterexample that

$$\sqrt{x^2 - 2x + 1} = x - 1$$

is not an identity.

b. State a condition on *x* for which the equation is true.

6. Solve $\dfrac{x - 3}{4} \le 6$, and graph the solution set on a line.

7. Solve $|2x + 1| = 7$.

8. Solve $|x - 2| < 5$, and graph the solution set on a line.

9. Solve $|x + \frac{1}{4}| \ge \frac{5}{2}$, and graph the solution set on a line.

10. Graph $\{x \mid 2x + 3 < 7\} \cap \{x \mid 3x + 2 > 2\}$ on a line.

11. What is the solution set of $x^2 - 2x + 2 = (x - 1)^2$?

12. Find the altitude of a triangle whose area is 24 square inches and whose base is 12 inches.

13. A man wishes to fence a rectangular lot which measures 80 feet by 140 feet. The fence along the front (80 feet) of the lot costs one and one-half times as much per foot as that along the other three sides. If the total cost of the fence is $960, find the cost per foot of each type of fence.

14. One freight train travels 6 miles an hour faster than a second freight train. The first freight travels 280 miles in the same time the second freight travels 210 miles. Find the rate of each.

15. A baseball team wins 40 of its first 50 games. How many games may it lose of the remaining 40 it must play in order that it have an average of at least 60% wins in its entire schedule?

6

SECOND-DEGREE EQUATIONS AND INEQUALITIES— ONE VARIABLE

An open sentence in one variable that, in simplest form, contains the second but no higher power of the variable is commonly called a second-degree **or quadratic equation** in that variable. We shall designate as standard form for such equations

$$ax^2 + bx + c = 0,$$

where a, b, and c are constants representing real numbers and $a \neq 0$.

In Chapter 5 we solved linear equations by performing certain elementary transformations. The transformations were based on the argument that we always obtain an equivalent equation when we add the same expression to each member of an equation or when we multiply each member by the same expression (not representing zero). These transformations are equally applicable to equations of higher degree and, in particular, to quadratic equations. For example,

$$2x = 6 - 8x^2$$

is equivalent to

$$8x^2 + 2x - 6 = 0,$$

which is equivalent to

$$4x^2 + x - 3 = 0.$$

6.1 Solution of Quadratic Equations by Factoring

If the left-hand member of a quadratic equation in standard form is factorable, we may solve the equation by making use of the principle:

The product of two factors equals zero if and only if one or both of the factors equals zero.

That is,

$ab = 0$ if and only if $a = 0$ or $b = 0$.

(The word "or" is used here in an inclusive sense to mean either one or the other or both.) The truth of this assertion is a consequence of the zero-factor law. The "if" part stems directly from the law. That is, if either a or b is 0, then ab must be zero because $0 \cdot b = 0$ for every real number b. The "only if" part can be established quickly. Note that we can assume that either $a = 0$ or $a \neq 0$. If $a = 0$, the conclusion of the theorem is true, and if $a \neq 0$, then we can multiply each member of $ab = 0$ by $1/a$ to obtain $(1/a)ab = (1/a)0$ or $b = 0$, and the conclusion is also true. Since these are the only possibilities, the assertion is established.

For an application of the theorem, consider the equation

$$x^2 + 2x - 15 = 0, \tag{1}$$

from which

$$(x + 5)(x - 3) = 0, \tag{2}$$

which will be true if and only if

$$(x + 5) = 0 \quad \text{or} \quad (x - 3) = 0.$$

We observe that if $x = -5$, $x + 5$ equals zero, and if $x = 3$, $x - 3$ equals zero, and either -5 or 3, when substituted for x in (2) or (1), will make the left-hand member zero. The solution set of (1) is $\{-5, 3\}$.

In general, the solution set of a quadratic equation can be expected to contain two members. However, if the left-hand member of a quadratic equation in standard form is the square of a binomial, we find that the solution set contains but one member. Consider the equation

$$x^2 - 2x + 1 = 0.$$

Factoring the left-hand member, we have

$$(x - 1)(x - 1) = 0,$$

and the solution set is $\{1\}$, which contains but one member. Because, for reasons of convenience and consistency in more advanced work, we wish to consider each quadratic equation to have two roots, a solution of this sort is said to be of multiplicity two; that is, it is considered twice as a solution.

Notice that the solution set of the quadratic equation

$$(x - r_1)(x - r_2) = 0 \qquad (3)$$

is $\{r_1, r_2\}$.   Therefore, if r_1 and r_2 are given as solutions of a quadratic equation, the equation can be written directly as (3).   By completing the indicated multiplication, the equation can be transformed to standard form.   For example, if 2 and -3 are the roots of a quadratic equation, then

$$[x - (2)][x - (-3)] = 0$$

or

$$(x - 2)(x + 3) = 0,$$

from which

$$x^2 + x - 6 = 0.$$

To find a quadratic equation whose solutions are 1/4 and 3/2, we write

$$\left(x - \frac{1}{4}\right)\left(x - \frac{3}{2}\right) = 0,$$

from which

$$x^2 - \frac{7}{4}x + \frac{3}{8} = 0.$$

This equation can be transformed to one with integral coefficients by multiplying each member by 8 to obtain the equivalent equation

$$8x^2 - 14x + 3 = 0.$$

EXERCISE 6.1

What is the set of values of x for which each of the following products yields zero?   Determine your answer by inspection or follow the procedure in the example.

Example: $(x - 3)(2x + 1)$

    Set each factor equal to zero.

$x - 3 = 0; \quad 2x + 1 = 0$

    Solve each linear equation.

    $x = 3 \qquad\qquad x = -\frac{1}{2}$

Ans. $\{3, -\frac{1}{2}\}$

1. $(x - 2)(x - 3)$ **2.** $2x(x + 1)$

3. $x(2x - 3)(x + 2)$ **4.** $3x(3x - 4)(2x - 1)$

5. $4(x - 1)(2x + 5)$ **6.** $3x(x - 3)(2x - 5)$

7. $2(x - a)$ **8.** $(x - a)(x + a)$

9. $(2x - a)(x - 2a)$ **10.** $(3x - 2a)(2x + a)$

Solve for x. Determine your answer by inspection or follow the procedure in the example.

Example: $x(x + 3) = 0$

    Set each factor equal to zero.

$x = 0; \quad x + 3 = 0$

    Solve each linear equation.

$$x = -3$$

Ans. $\{0, -3\}$

11. $(x - 3)(x + 2) = 0$ 12. $x(x - 5) = 0$

13. $(2x - 3)(x + 1) = 0$ 14. $(3x - 1)(2x - 1) = 0$

15. $4(2x + 1)(x - 3) = 0$ 16. $2x(x + 1) = 0$

17. $(x - a)(x + 2a) = 0$ 18. $ax(bx + c) = 0$

Example: $x^2 + x = 30$

    Write in standard form.

$x^2 + x - 30 = 0$

    Factor the left-hand member.

$(x + 6)(x - 5) = 0$

    Set each factor equal to zero.

$x + 6 = 0; \quad x - 5 = 0$

    Solve each linear equation.

$x = -6 \quad\quad x = 5$

Ans. $\{-6, 5\}$

19. $x^2 + 2x = 0$ 20. $2x^2 = 5x$ 21. $x^2 - x = 5x$

22. $x^2 - 4 = 0$ 23. $2x^2 - 18 = 0$ 24. $3x^2 - 3 = 0$

25. $x^2 - \frac{4}{9} = 0$ 26. $x^2 - \frac{1}{4} = 0$ 27. $3x^2 = \frac{75}{4}$

28. $\frac{1}{9}x^2 - 1 = 0$ 29. $x^2 = bx$ 30. $4x^2 - c^2 = 0$

31. $x^2 - 3x - 4 = 0$ 32. $x^2 + 3x + 2 = 0$ 33. $x^2 + 5x - 14 = 0$

34. $x^2 + x - 42 = 0$ 35. $3x^2 - 6x = -3$ 36. $12x^2 = 8x + 15$

Example: $3x(x + 1) = 2x + 2$

    Write in standard form.

$3x^2 + x - 2 = 0$

    Factor the left-hand member.

$(3x - 2)(x + 1) = 0$

Set each factor equal to zero.

$3x - 2 = 0; \quad x + 1 = 0$

Solve each linear equation.

$x = \frac{2}{3} \qquad x = -1$

Ans. $\{\frac{2}{3}, -1\}$

37. $x(2x - 3) = -1$ **38.** $2x(x - 2) = x + 3$ **39.** $(x - 2)(x + 1) = 4$

40. $x(3x + 2) = (x + 2)^2$ **41.** $x^2 - 4ax + 4a^2 = 0$ **42.** $x^2 = 2ax + 8a^2$

43. $\dfrac{2x^2}{3} + \dfrac{x}{3} - 2 = 0$ **44.** $x - 1 = \dfrac{x^2}{4}$ **45.** $\dfrac{x^2}{6} + \dfrac{x}{3} = \dfrac{1}{2}$

46. $\dfrac{x}{4} - \dfrac{3}{4} = \dfrac{1}{x}$ **47.** $3 = \dfrac{10}{x^2} - \dfrac{7}{x}$ **48.** $\dfrac{4}{3x} + \dfrac{3}{3x + 1} + 2 = 0$

49. $\dfrac{2}{x - 3} - \dfrac{6}{x - 8} = -1$ **50.** $\dfrac{x}{x - 1} - \dfrac{x}{x + 1} = \dfrac{4}{3}$

Given the solutions of a quadratic equation, r_1 and r_2, write the equation in standard form with integral coefficients.

Example: $\frac{3}{4}$ and -2

Write in the form $(x - r_1)(x - r_2) = 0$.

$(x - \frac{3}{4})[x - (-2)] = 0$

Write in standard form.

$(x - \frac{3}{4})(x + 2) = 0$
$x^2 + \frac{5}{4}x - \frac{3}{2} = 0$

Ans. $4x^2 + 5x - 6 = 0$

51. 3 and 2   **52.** 5 and 1   **53.** $-\frac{1}{2}$ and 3

54. $\frac{2}{3}$ and 2   **55.** $\frac{1}{2}$ and $\frac{3}{4}$ **56.** $-\frac{2}{3}$ and $\frac{1}{2}$

57. a and $-a$ **58.** a and $\frac{1}{2}a$ **59.** i and $-i$

60. $3i$ and $-3i$ **61.** $2 + i$ and $2 - i$ **62.** $a + i$ and $a - i$

Although the following equations are not quadratic, their solution sets can also be obtained directly from the factored form.

Solve.

63. $x^3 - 5x^2 + 6x = 0$ **64.** $x^3 - 2x^2 + x = 0$

65. $x^3 + 2x^2 - x - 2 = 0$, where one solution is 1. *Hint:* If 1 is a solution, $x - 1$ is a factor. Use long division or synthetic division to determine the other factor.

66. $x^3 - 6x^2 - x + 30 = 0$, where one solution is 3.

67. $x^3 - 3x^2 - 6x + 8 = 0$, where one solution is -2.

68. $x^3 + 8x^2 + 19x + 12 = 0$, where one solution is -1.

69. $x^4 - 3x^3 - 10x^2 + 24x = 0$, where one solution is -3.

70. $x^4 + 5x^3 - x^2 - 5x = 0$, where one solution is -5.

6.2   Solution of Equations of the Form $x^2 = a$; Completing the Square

Quadratic equations of the form

$$x^2 = a,$$

where a is any real number, may be solved by a method often termed the *extraction of roots*. If the equation has a solution, then from the definition of a square root, x must be a square root of a. Since each nonzero real number a has two square roots (either real or imaginary), we have two solutions. These are given by

$$x = \sqrt{a}, \quad x = -\sqrt{a},$$

and the solution set is clearly $\{\sqrt{a}, -\sqrt{a}\}$, whose elements are real if $a \geq 0$ and imaginary if $a < 0$. If $a = 0$, we have one number, 0, satisfying the equation, and the solution set of $x^2 = 0$ is $\{0\}$.

The same conclusion can be reached by noting that, if we factor

$$x^2 - a = 0$$

over the complex numbers, we have

$$(x - \sqrt{a})(x + \sqrt{a}) = 0,$$

which, when solved by the methods of the preceding section, also leads to the solution set $\{\sqrt{a}, -\sqrt{a}\}$.

Equations of the form

$$(x - a)^2 = b$$

can be solved by the same method. For example,

$$(x - 2)^2 = 16$$

implies that

$$x - 2 = 4 \quad \text{or} \quad x - 2 = -4,$$

from which we have

$$x = 6 \quad \text{or} \quad x = -2,$$

and the solution set is $\{6, -2\}$.

This technique can be used to find the solution set of any quadratic equation. Let us first consider a specific example,

$$x^2 - 4x - 12 = 0,$$

which can be written

$$x^2 - 4x \qquad = 12.$$

If the square of one half of the coefficient of the first-degree term,

$$[\tfrac{1}{2}(4)]^2,$$

is added to each member, we obtain

$$x^2 - 4x + 4 = 12 + 4,$$

in which the left-hand member is the square of $(x - 2)$. Therefore, the equation can be written

$$(x - 2)^2 = 16$$

and the solution set obtained as above.

Now consider the general quadratic equation in standard form

$$ax^2 + bx + c = 0,$$

for the special case where $a = 1$; that is,

$$x^2 + bx + c = 0. \tag{1}$$

If we can factor the left-hand member of (1), we can solve the equation by factoring; if not, we can write it in the form

$$(x - p)^2 = q,$$

which we can solve by the extraction of roots. We begin the latter process by adding $-c$ to each member of (1), which yields

$$x^2 + bx \quad = -c. \tag{2}$$

If we then add $(b/2)^2$ to each member of (2),

$$x^2 + bx + \left(\frac{b}{2}\right)^2 = -c + \left(\frac{b}{2}\right)^2, \tag{3}$$

the left-hand member is equivalent to $\left(x + \frac{b}{2}\right)^2$ and we have

$$\left(x + \frac{b}{2}\right)^2 = -c + \frac{b^2}{4}. \tag{4}$$

Since we have performed only elementary transformations, (4) is equivalent to (2) and we can solve (4) by the method of the preceding section.

The technique used to obtain equations (3) and (4) is called *completing the square*. We can determine the term necessary to complete the square in (2) by dividing the coefficient b of the linear term by the number 2 and squaring the result. The expression obtained, $x^2 + bx + \left(\frac{b}{2}\right)^2$, can always be written in the form $\left(x + \frac{b}{2}\right)^2$.

We began with the special case

$$x^2 + bx + c = 0 \tag{1}$$

rather than the general form

$$ax^2 + bx + c = 0,$$

because the term necessary to complete the square is more obvious when $a = 1$. However, a quadratic equation in standard form can always be written in the form (1) by multiplying each member of

$$ax^2 + bx + c = 0$$

by $\dfrac{1}{a}$ $(a \neq 0)$ and obtaining

$$x^2 + \frac{b}{a} x + \frac{c}{a} = 0.$$

EXERCISE 6.2

Solve for x by the extraction of roots.

Example: $7x^2 - 63 = 0$

Obtain an equivalent equation with x^2 as the only term in the left-hand member.

$$x^2 = 9$$

Set x equal to each square root of 9.

$$x = +3; \quad x = -3$$

Ans. $\{3, -3\}$

1. $x^2 = 4$ **2.** $x^2 = 16$ **3.** $3x^2 = 12$

4. $5x^2 = 125$ **5.** $9x^2 - 100 = 0$ **6.** $9x^2 - 4 = 0$

7. $x^2 = 5$ **8.** $3x^2 = 21$ **9.** $\dfrac{x^2}{4} = 3$

10. $\dfrac{2x^2}{7} = 8$ **11.** $x^2 - c = 0$ **12.** $ax^2 - b = 0$

13. $\dfrac{x^2}{b} = a$ **14.** $\dfrac{ax^2}{b} = c$

Example: $(x + 3)^2 = 7$

Set $x + 3$ equal to each square root of 7.

$$x + 3 = \sqrt{7}; \quad x + 3 = -\sqrt{7}$$

$$x = -3 + \sqrt{7}; \quad x = -3 - \sqrt{7}$$

Ans. $\{-3 + \sqrt{7}, -3 - \sqrt{7}\}$

15. $(x - 1)^2 = 4$ **16.** $(x - 3)^2 = 16$ **17.** $(2x + 5)^2 = 9$

18. $(2x + 1)^2 = 25$ **19.** $(x - 6)^2 = 5$ **20.** $(x + 2)^2 = 7$

21. $(x - 2)^2 = 3$ **22.** $(x - 3)^2 = 18$ **23.** $(x - a)^2 = 4$

24. $(x + a)^2 = 5$ **25.** $(ax + b)^2 = 16$ **26.** $(ax - b)^2 = 9$

27. $(x - c)^2 = b^2$ **28.** $(x + c)^2 = a^4$

(a) What term must be added to each expression to make a perfect square?
(b) Write the expression as the square of a binomial.

Example: $x^2 - 9x$

Square one half of the coefficient of the first-degree term (-9).

Ans.   (a) $\frac{81}{4}$

Rewrite $x^2 - 9x + \frac{81}{4}$ as the square of an expression.

Ans.   (b) $(x - \frac{9}{2})^2$

29. $x^2 + 2x$ **30.** $x^2 - 4x$ **31.** $x^2 - 6x$ **32.** $x^2 + 10x$

33. $x^2 + 3x$ **34.** $x^2 - 5x$ **35.** $x^2 - 7x$ **36.** $x^2 + 11x$

37. $x^2 - x$ **38.** $x^2 + 15x$ **39.** $x^2 + \frac{1}{2}x$ **40.** $x^2 - \frac{3}{4}x$

Solve by completing the square.

Example: $2x^2 + x - 1 = 0$

Rewrite equation with the constant term as the right-hand member and the coefficient of x^2 equal to 1.

$$x^2 + \tfrac{1}{2}x = \tfrac{1}{2}$$

Add the square of one half of the coefficient of the first-degree term to each member.

$$x^2 + \tfrac{1}{2}x + \tfrac{1}{16} = \tfrac{1}{2} + \tfrac{1}{16}$$

Rewrite left-hand member as the square of an expression.

$$(x + \tfrac{1}{4})^2 = \tfrac{9}{16}$$

Set $x + \frac{1}{4}$ equal to each square root of $\frac{9}{16}$.

$$x + \tfrac{1}{4} = \tfrac{3}{4}; \quad x + \tfrac{1}{4} = -\tfrac{3}{4}$$
$$x = \tfrac{1}{2} \qquad x = -1$$

Ans. $\{\frac{1}{2}, -1\}$

41. $x^2 + 4x - 12 = 0$ **42.** $x^2 - x - 6 = 0$ **43.** $x^2 - 2x + 1 = 0$

44. $x^2 + 4x + 4 = 0$ **45.** $x^2 + 9x + 20 = 0$ **46.** $x^2 - x - 20 = 0$

47. $x^2 - 2x - 1 = 0$ **48.** $x^2 + 3x - 1 = 0$ **49.** $2x^2 = 4 - 3x$

50. $2x^2 = 6 - 5x$ **51.** $2x^2 + 4x = -3$ **52.** $3x^2 + x = -4$

Reduce each of the following equations to the form $y = (x - a)^2 + b$, where a and b are constants, by completing the square in x.

Example: $y = x^2 + 6x + 4$

Write the equation in the indicated form.

$y = [x^2 + 6x + (\quad)] + 4$

Complete the square in x.

$y = [x^2 + 6x + (9)] + 4 + (-9)$

$y = (x + 3)^2 - 5$

53. $y = x^2 + 2x + 3$ **54.** $y = x^2 - 6x + 7$

55. $y = x^2 - 8x + 2$ **56.** $y = x^2 + 10x - 4$

57. $y = x^2 - 3x - 1$ **58.** $y = x^2 - 7x - 1$

Reduce each of the following equations to the form $(x - h)^2 + (y - k)^2 = r^2$, where h, k, and r are constants, by completing the squares in x and y.

Example:

$x^2 + y^2 - 4x + 6y = 5$

Write the equation in the indicated form.

$[x^2 - 4x + (\quad)] + [y^2 + 6y + (\quad)] = 5$

Complete the squares in x and y.

$[x^2 - 4x + 4] + [y^2 + 6y + 9] = 5 + 4 + 9$

Ans. $(x - 2)^2 + (y + 3)^2 = 18$ or $(x - 2)^2 + (y + 3)^2 = (\sqrt{18})^2$

59. $x^2 + y^2 - 4x - 4y - 17 = 0$ **60.** $x^2 + y^2 + 6x - 6y + 18 = 0$

61. $x^2 + y^2 + 6x - 2y + 6 = 0$ **62.** $x^2 + y^2 - 2x + 4y + 2 = 0$

63. $x^2 + y^2 - 2x + 8y + 15 = 0$ **64.** $x^2 + y^2 + 2x - 2y + 1 = 0$

65. Solve $ax^2 + bx + c = 0$ for x in terms of a, b, and c by using the method of completing the square.

6.3 The Quadratic Formula

We can complete the square on the general quadratic equation

$$ax^2 + bx + c = 0 \quad (a \neq 0)$$

as follows:

$$x^2 + \frac{b}{a}x + \frac{c}{a} = 0,$$

$$x^2 + \frac{b}{a}x + \left(\frac{b}{2a}\right)^2 = -\frac{c}{a} + \left(\frac{b}{2a}\right)^2,$$

$$\left(x + \frac{b}{2a}\right)^2 = \frac{b^2}{4a^2} - \frac{c}{a},$$

$$\left(x + \frac{b}{2a}\right)^2 = \frac{b^2 - 4ac}{4a^2},$$

$$x + \frac{b}{2a} = \pm\sqrt{\frac{b^2 - 4ac}{4a^2}},$$

$$x = -\frac{b}{2a} \pm \frac{\sqrt{b^2 - 4ac}}{2a},$$

$$x = \frac{-b \pm \sqrt{b^2 - 4ac}}{2a}.$$

The result is a formula for the roots of a quadratic equation expressed in terms of the coefficients. The symbol "$\pm$" is used to condense the writing of the two equations

$$x = \frac{-b + \sqrt{b^2 - 4ac}}{2a} \quad \text{and} \quad x = \frac{-b - \sqrt{b^2 - 4ac}}{2a}$$

into a single equation. We need only substitute the coefficients a, b, and c of a given quadratic equation in the formula to find the solution set for the equation.

In the quadratic formula, the number represented by $b^2 - 4ac$ is called the **discriminant** of the equation. If a, b, and c are real numbers, the discriminant affects the solution set in the following ways:

1. If $b^2 - 4ac = 0$, there is one real solution.
2. If $b^2 - 4ac < 0$, there are two imaginary solutions.
3. If $b^2 - 4ac > 0$, there are two unequal real solutions. In addition, if a, b, and c are *rational*, then
   (a) if $b^2 - 4ac$ is the square of a rational number, the solutions are rational;
   (b) if $b^2 - 4ac$ is not the square of a rational number, the solutions are irrational.

We note from the form

$$x = \frac{-b}{2a} \pm \frac{\sqrt{b^2 - 4ac}}{2a}$$

that, if the solutions of a quadratic equation are irrational or complex, they are conjugates.

Also, if we denote by r_1 and r_2 the solutions of

$$ax^2 + bx + c = 0 \quad (a \neq 0),$$

then

$$r_1 + r_2 = \left(\frac{-b}{2a} + \frac{\sqrt{b^2 - 4ac}}{2a}\right) + \left(\frac{-b}{2a} - \frac{\sqrt{b^2 - 4ac}}{2a}\right) = \frac{-2b}{2a} = -\frac{b}{a}$$

and

$$r_1 r_2 = \left(\frac{-b}{2a} + \frac{\sqrt{b^2 - 4ac}}{2a}\right)\left(\frac{-b}{2a} - \frac{\sqrt{b^2 - 4ac}}{2a}\right) = \frac{b^2 - b^2 + 4ac}{4a^2} = \frac{c}{a}.$$

That is, the sum of the solutions of $ax^2 + bx + c = 0$ is always $-b/a$, and the product of the solutions is always c/a.

EXERCISE 6.3

In Problems 1–14, solve for x, y, or z using the quadratic formula and state whether the solutions are:

    (a) rational and equal (one solution—multiplicity two);
    (b) rational and unequal;
    (c) irrational and unequal;
    (d) imaginary.

$$x = \frac{-b \pm \sqrt{b^2 - 4ac}}{2a}$$

Example: $\dfrac{x^2}{4} + \dfrac{x}{4} = 3$

    Write in standard form.

$$x^2 + x = 12$$
$$x^2 + x - 12 = 0$$

    Substitute 1 for a, 1 for b, and -12 for c in the quadratic formula and simplify.

$$x = \frac{-1 \pm \sqrt{1 + 48}}{2}$$

$$x = \frac{-1 \pm 7}{2}$$

    Ans. $\{3, -4\}$; rational and unequal.

1. $x^2 - 3x + 2 = 0$ **2.** $x^2 + 4x + 4 = 0$ **3.** $x^2 - 2x = -1$

4. $z^2 - 5z = 6$ **5.** $y^2 + y = 1$ **6.** $x^2 - 3x = -1$

7. $2x^2 = 7x - 6$ **8.** $3y^2 = 5y - 1$ **9.** $2x^2 - x + 1 = 0$

10. $6z^2 = 5z + 6$ **11.** $x^2 = \dfrac{15}{4} - x$ **12.** $\dfrac{y^2 - y}{2} + 1 = 0$

13. $\dfrac{x^2}{3} = \dfrac{1}{2}x + \dfrac{3}{2}$ **14.** $\dfrac{x^2 - 3}{2} + \dfrac{x}{4} = 1$

Solve for x in terms of the other variables or constants.

Example: $x^2 - xy + y = 2$

    Write the equation in standard form.

$$x^2 - xy + y - 2 = 0$$

Substitute 1 for a, $-y$ for b, and $y - 2$ for c in the quadratic formula and simplify.

$$x = \frac{y \pm \sqrt{(-y)^2 - 4(1)(y - 2)}}{2}$$

Ans. $x = \dfrac{y \pm \sqrt{y^2 - 4y + 8}}{2}$

15. $x^2 - kx - 2k^2 = 0$

16. $2x^2 - kx + 3 = 0$

17. $ax^2 - x + c = 0$

18. $x^2 + 2x + c + 3 = 0$

19. $x^2 + 2x - y = 0$

20. $2x^2 - 3x + 2y = 0$

21. $2x^2 - x + y = 2$

22. $3x^2 + 2x - 3y = 4$

23. $x^2 - 2xy - 3y = 2$

24. $3x^2 + xy + 5y = 1$

25. $3x^2 + xy + y^2 = 2$

26. $x^2 - 3xy + y^2 = 3$

27. In Problem 25, solve for y in terms of x.

28. In Problem 26, solve for y in terms of x.

In Problems 29–40, find only the discriminant and determine whether the two solutions are:

  (a) rational and equal (one solution—multiplicity two);
  (b) rational and unequal;
  (c) irrational and unequal;
  (d) imaginary.

Example: $x^2 - x - 3 = 0$

  Substitute 1 for a, -1 for b, and -3 for c in the discriminant.

$b^2 - 4ac = 1 + 12$
$\qquad\quad\ = 13$

Ans. Solutions are irrational and unequal.

29. $x^2 - 7x + 12 = 0$ **30.** $y^2 - 2y - 3 = 0$ **31.** $5x^2 + 2x - 1 = 0$

32. $2y^2 + 3y + 7 = 0$ **33.** $x^2 - 2x + 1 = 0$ **34.** $2z^2 - z = 12$

35. $8x^2 + 17 = x$ **36.** $y^2 + 4y = -4$ **37.** $3x^2 + 2x = -1$

38. $3y^2 = 2 - y$ **39.** $\frac{2}{3}x^2 + \frac{1}{2}x = 4$ **40.** $\frac{1}{4}x^2 - 3x = \frac{1}{3}$

Using the observation on page 141 that, in the equation $ax^2 + bx + c = 0\ (a \neq 0)$, $r_1 + r_2 = -\dfrac{b}{a}$ and $r_1 \cdot r_2 = \dfrac{c}{a}$, find the sum and product of the roots in each of the following equations.

41. $x^2 + 5x - 2 = 0$ **42.** $x^2 - 3x + 1 = 0$ **43.** $2x^2 - 3x + 1 = 0$

44. $3x^2 + 4x - 2 = 0$ **45.** $x^2 = 6x - 1$ **46.** $3x^2 = 4 - x$

47. Determine k so that $kx^2 + 4x + 1 = 0$ has one root.

48. Determine k so that $x^2 - kx + 9 = 0$ has one root.

49. Determine k so that the roots of $x^2 + 2x + k + 3 = 0$ will be real.

50. Determine k so that the roots of $x^2 - x + k = 2$ will be real.

51. Determine k so that the roots of $x^2 - 2x + 1 = k$ will be imaginary.

52. Show that an alternate form for the quadratic formula is

$$x = \frac{-2c}{b \pm \sqrt{b^2 - 4ac}}$$

provided $c \neq 0$.

6.4 Equations Involving Radicals

In order to solve equations containing radicals, we shall assume that:

If each member of an equation is raised to the same power, the solution set of the resulting equation will contain all of the solutions of the original equation.

For example, if $x = 3$, then the solution set of $x^2 = 9$ contains 3 as a member. In general, if

$$x = \sqrt[n]{a}, \tag{1}$$

then the equation resulting from raising each member to the nth power will be

$$x^n = a, \tag{2}$$

whose solution set will contain $\sqrt[n]{a}$ as a member.

The application of the foregoing assumption does not, however, result in an equivalent equation, and is not an elementary transformation. Equation (2) actually has $(n - 1)$ other solutions that are not solutions of (1). With respect to equation (1), these are called **extraneous solutions.** This situation derives from our restricting $\sqrt[n]{a}$ to a unique number. Thus the solution set of the equation $x^2 = 9$, obtained from $x = 3$ by squaring each member, contains -3 as an extraneous solution, since -3 does not satisfy the original equation. Because the result of applying the foregoing assumption is not an equivalent equation, each solution obtained through its use *must* be checked in the original equation to verify its validity.

EXERCISE 6.4

Solve and check. If there is no solution, so state.

Example: $\sqrt{x + 2} + 4 = x$

Obtain $\sqrt{x + 2}$ as the only term in one member.

$$\sqrt{x + 2} = x - 4$$

Square each member.

$$x + 2 = x^2 - 8x + 16$$

Solve the quadratic equation.

$$x^2 - 9x + 14 = 0$$
$$(x - 7)(x - 2) = 0$$
$$x = 7; \ x = 2$$

Check.

Does $\sqrt{7 + 2} + 4 = 7$?   Does $\sqrt{2 + 2} + 4 = 2$?
Does $7 = 7$?   Yes.   Does $6 = 2$?   No.   2 is not a solution.

Ans. $\{7\}$

1. $\sqrt{x} = 8$ **2.** $\sqrt{y} - 4 = 1$ **3.** $\sqrt{y + 8} = 1$

4. $\sqrt{x - 3} = 5$ **5.** $2x - 3 = \sqrt{7x - 3}$ **6.** $\sqrt{3x + 10} = x + 4$

7. $\sqrt{x + 3} \sqrt{x - 9} = 8$ **8.** $\sqrt{x - 4} \sqrt{x + 4} = 3$

Example: $\sqrt{y - 5} - \sqrt{y} = 1$

Write with $\sqrt{y - 5}$ as left-hand member.

$$\sqrt{y - 5} = 1 + \sqrt{y}$$

Square each member.

$$y - 5 = 1 + 2\sqrt{y} + y$$

Write with $\sqrt{y}$ as right-hand member.

$$-3 = \sqrt{y}$$

(*Note:* At this point it is obvious that the equation has no solution, since $\sqrt{y}$ cannot be negative. We continue the solution process, however, for illustrative purposes.)

Square each member.

$$9 = y$$

Check.   Does $\sqrt{4} - \sqrt{9} = 1$?   Does $2 - 3 = 1$?   No.

9 is not a solution of the original equation.

Ans. $\emptyset$

9. $\sqrt{y + 4} = \sqrt{y + 20} - 2$ **10.** $4\sqrt{y} + \sqrt{1 + 16y} = 5$

11. $\sqrt{x} + \sqrt{2} = \sqrt{x + 2}$ **12.** $\sqrt{4x + 17} = 4 - \sqrt{x + 1}$

13. $(5 + x)^{1/2} + x^{1/2} = 5$ **14.** $(y + 7)^{1/2} + (y + 4)^{1/2} = 3$

15. $(y^2 - 3y + 5)^{1/2} - (y + 2)^{1/2} = 0$ **16.** $(z - 3)^{1/2} + (z + 5)^{1/2} = 4$

Solve. Leave the results in the form of an equation.

17. $r = \sqrt{\dfrac{A}{\pi}}$, for A **18.** $t = \sqrt{\dfrac{2v}{g}}$, for g

19. $x\sqrt{xy} = 1$, for y **20.** $P = \pi\sqrt{\dfrac{e}{g}}$, for g

21. $x = \sqrt{a^2 - y^2}$, for y **22.** $y = \dfrac{1}{\sqrt{1 - x}}$, for x

23. In the first example in this exercise set, the second equation in our sequence is $\sqrt{x + 2} = x - 4$. How can we tell by inspection that this equation will not be satisfied by any real number less than 4?

6.5 Equations Quadratic in Form

Some equations that are not quadratic equations are nevertheless quadratic in form, that is, of the form

$$au^2 + bu + c = 0, \tag{1}$$

where u represents some expression in terms of another variable. For example,

$$x^4 - 10x^2 + 9 = 0 \text{ is quadratic in } x^2, \tag{2}$$

$$(x^2 - 1)^2 + 3(x^2 - 1) + 2 = 0 \text{ is quadratic in } (x^2 - 1),$$

$$y + 2\sqrt{y} - 8 = 0 \text{ is quadratic in } \sqrt{y}, \text{ and}$$

$$\left(\frac{z + 1}{z}\right)^2 - 5\left(\frac{z + 1}{z}\right) + 6 = 0 \text{ is quadratic in } \left(\frac{z + 1}{z}\right).$$

We can solve an equation of the form (1) by first finding the solutions

$$u = r_1 \quad \text{and} \quad u = r_2$$

and solving these equations for the desired roots. For example, if we let $x^2 = u$, then (2) above reduces to

$$u^2 - 10u + 9 = 0.$$

When we solve this equation, we obtain

$$(u - 9)(u - 1) = 0,$$

and

$$u = 9, \quad u = 1.$$

Since $u = x^2$, we have

$$x^2 = 9, \quad x^2 = 1,$$

from which we obtain the solution set

$$\{3, -3, \ 1, -1\}.$$

As an alternative method, we could have factored the left-hand member of (2) directly as

$$(x^2 - 9)(x^2 - 1) = 0,$$

and then set each factor equal to zero.   Thus

$$x^2 - 9 = 0; \quad x^2 - 1 = 0$$
$$x = \pm 3; \qquad x = \pm 1$$

and the solution set is

$$\{3, -3, \quad 1, -1\}.$$

EXERCISE 6.5

Solve for x, y, or z.

Example: $y - 2\sqrt{y} - 8 = 0$

Let $\sqrt{y} = u$; therefore, $y = u^2$.

$u^2 - 2u - 8 = 0$

Solve for u.

$(u - 4)(u + 2) = 0$

$u = 4; \quad u = -2$

Replace u with $\sqrt{y}$ and solve for y.   Since $\sqrt{y}$ cannot be negative, only 4 need be considered.

$\sqrt{y} = 4$

$y = 16$

Check.   Does $16 - 2\sqrt{16} - 8 = 0$?   Does $0 = 0$?   Yes.

16 is a solution of $y - 2\sqrt{y} - 8 = 0$.

Ans. $\{16\}$

1. $x - 2\sqrt{x} - 15 = 0$
2. $x^4 - 5x^2 + 4 = 0$
3. $2x^4 + 17x^2 - 9 = 0$
4. $z^4 - 2z^2 - 24 = 0$
5. $(y^2 + 5y)^2 - 8y(y + 5) - 84 = 0$
6. $y^2 - 5 - 5\sqrt{y^2 - 5} + 6 = 0$
7. $y^{2/3} - 2y^{1/3} - 8 = 0$
8. $z^{2/3} - 2z^{1/3} = 35$
9. $y^{-2} - y^{-1} - 12 = 0$
10. $z^{-2} + 9z^{-1} - 10 = 0$
11. $(x - 1)^{1/2} - 2(x - 1)^{1/4} - 15 = 0$
12. $8x^{-2} + 7x^{-1} - 1 = 0$

6.6   Quadratic Inequalities

As in the case with first-degree inequalities, we can generate equivalent second-degree inequalities by applying Properties 1–3 in Section 5.5.   Additional procedures are necessary, however, to obtain the solution sets of such inequalities.   For example, consider the inequality

$$x^2 + 4x < 5.$$

To determine values of x for which this condition holds, we might first rewrite the sentence equivalently as

$$x^2 + 4x - 5 < 0,$$

and then as

$$(x + 5)(x - 1) < 0.$$

It is clear here that only those values of x for which the factors $x + 5$ and $x - 1$ are opposite in sign will be in the solution set. These can be determined analytically by noting that $(x + 5)(x - 1) < 0$ implies either

$$x + 5 < 0 \quad \text{and} \quad x - 1 > 0$$

or else

$$x + 5 > 0 \quad \text{and} \quad x - 1 < 0.$$

Each of these two cases can be considered separately.

First, $x + 5 < 0$ and $x - 1 > 0$ imply $x < -5$ and $x > 1$, a condition which is not satisfied by any values of x. But $x + 5 > 0$ and $x - 1 < 0$ imply $x > -5$ and $x < 1$, which lead to the solution set

$$S = \{x \mid -5 < x < 1\}.$$

An alternative set notation for this solution set is

$$S = \{x \mid x > -5\} \cap \{x \mid x < 1\}.$$

One relatively easy way to visualize the solution set of a quadratic inequality is to indicate on a number line the signs associated with each factor for number replacements for the variable. Figure 6.1 shows such an arrangement, or **sign graph**, for the example above. This picture is constructed by first showing on a number line the places where $x + 5$ is positive $(x > -5)$ and the places where it is negative $(x < -5)$, and then showing on a second

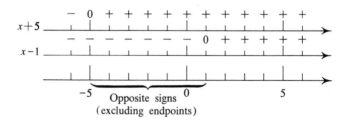

Fig. 6.1

line those places where $x - 1$ is positive $(x > 1)$ and those where it is negative $(x < 1)$. The third line can then be marked by observing those parts of the first two lines where the signs are alike and those parts where the signs are opposite. Since it is desired that the product $(x + 5)(x - 1)$ be negative, the third line shows clearly that this occurs where $-5 < x < 1$, so that the solution set of the inequality is $\{x \mid -5 < x < 1\}$. This solution set can be graphed as in Figure 6.2.

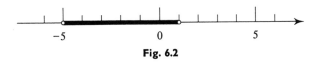

Fig. 6.2

Inequalities involving fractions have to be approached with care if any fraction contains a variable in the denominator. If each member of such an inequality is multiplied by an expression containing the variable, we have to be careful either to distinguish between those values of the variable for which the expression denotes a positive and negative number, respectively, or to make sure that the expression by which we multiply is always positive. Let us illustrate this latter approach. Consider the inequality

$$\frac{x}{x - 2} \geq 5.$$

The necessity of considering separate cases for $x - 2 > 0$ and $x - 2 < 0$ can be avoided if the given equation is "cleared" of fractions by multiplying each member by $(x - 2)^2$, which is positive for $x \neq 2$. Doing this we have

$$(x - 2)^2 \frac{x}{(x - 2)} \geq (x - 2)^2 \cdot 5,$$

$$x^2 - 2x \geq 5x^2 - 20x + 20,$$

$$0 \geq 4x^2 - 18x + 20,$$

$$0 \geq 2x^2 - 9x + 10,$$

$$0 \geq (2x - 5)(x - 2).$$

This latter inequality can then be solved either by sign graph or by noting that for $(2x - 5)(x - 2)$ to be nonpositive, either

$$(2x - 5) \geq 0 \quad \text{and} \quad (x - 2) < 0$$

or

$$(2x - 5) \leq 0 \quad \text{and} \quad (x - 2) > 0$$

must hold. The first of these implies that

$$x \geq \frac{5}{2} \quad \text{and} \quad x < 2,$$

which have no common elements in their solution sets, while the second implies that

$$x \leq \frac{5}{2} \quad \text{and} \quad x > 2,$$

which leads to the solution set $\{x \mid 2 < x \le \frac{5}{2}\}$. What we have accomplished here is to determine that the solution set is given by

$$\left[\left\{x \mid x \le \frac{5}{2}\right\} \cap \{x \mid x > 2\}\right] \cup \left[\left\{x \mid x \ge \frac{5}{2}\right\} \cap \{x \mid x < 2\}\right],$$

which we express equivalently as

$$\left\{x \mid 2 < x \le \frac{5}{2}\right\} \cup \emptyset, \quad \text{or} \quad \left\{x \mid 2 < x \le \frac{5}{2}\right\}.$$

EXERCISE 6.6

Solve and represent the solution set on a line graph.

1. $(x + 1)(x - 2) > 0$
2. $(x + 2)(x + 5) < 0$
3. $x(x - 2) \le 0$
4. $x(x + 3) \ge 0$
5. $x^2 - 3x - 4 > 0$
6. $x^2 - 5x - 6 \ge 0$
7. $x^2 < 5$
8. $4x^2 + 1 < 0$
9. $x^2 > -5$
10. $x^2 + 1 > 0$
11. $\dfrac{2}{x} \le 4$
12. $\dfrac{3}{x - 6} > 8$
13. $\dfrac{x}{x + 2} > 4$
14. $\dfrac{x + 2}{x - 2} \ge 6$
15. $\dfrac{2}{x - 2} \ge \dfrac{4}{x}$
16. $\dfrac{3}{4x + 1} > \dfrac{2}{x - 5}$
17. $x(x - 2)(x + 3) > 0$
18. $x^3 - 4x \le 0$

6.7 Word Problems

Some suggested procedures for writing equations for word problems were examined in Chapter 5, and should be reviewed at this time. In some cases, the mathematical model we obtain for a physical situation is a quadratic equation and consequently has two solutions. It may be that one but not both of the solutions of the equation fits the physical situation. For example, if we were asked to find two consecutive *natural numbers* whose product is 72, we would write the equation

$$x(x + 1) = 72$$

as our model. Solving this equation, we have

$$x^2 + x - 72 = 0,$$
$$(x + 9)(x - 8) = 0,$$

where the solution set is $\{8, -9\}$.   Since -9 is not a natural number, we must reject it as a possible answer to our original question; however, the solution 8 leads to the consecutive natural numbers 8 and 9.   As additional examples, we observe that we would not accept -6 feet as the height of a man or $27/4$ for the number of people in a room.

A quadratic equation used as a model for a physical situation may have two, one, or no meaningful solutions—meaningful, that is, in a physical sense.   Answers to word problems should always be checked against the original problem.

EXERCISE 6.7

Solve.   (For formulas, see Table III in the Appendix.)

1. Find two numbers whose sum is 13 and whose product is 36.

2. Find two numbers whose sum is -16 and whose product is 48.

3. Find two consecutive integers whose product is 56.

4. Find two consecutive odd integers whose product is 63.

5. Find two consecutive positive integers the sum of whose squares is 85.

6. Find two consecutive positive integers the difference of whose squares is 15.

7. The sum of a number and its reciprocal is $\frac{17}{4}$.   What is the number?

8. The difference of a number and twice its reciprocal is $\frac{31}{4}$.   What is the number?

9. What is the length of the diagonal of a rectangle whose length is 13 inches and whose width is 4 inches?

10. Two airplanes flying at right angles to each other pass each other at noon. One is flying at 140 miles per hour and one at 180 miles per hour.   How far apart are they at 12:30 PM?

11. If the perimeter of a rectangle is 240 inches and its area is 3200 square inches, what are the dimensions of the rectangle?

12. If increasing the length of the side of a square by 12 feet results in a square with nine times the area of the original square, what was the length of a side of the original square?

13. A box without a top is to be made from a square piece of tin by cutting a 2-inch square from each corner and folding up the sides.   If the box will hold 128 cubic inches, what should be the length of the side of the square?

14. A ball thrown vertically upward reaches a height h in feet given by the equation $h = 32t - 8t^2$, where t is the time in seconds after the throw.   How long will it take the ball to reach a height of 24 feet on its way up?   How long after the throw will the ball return to the ground?

15. The distance s a body falls in a vacuum is given by $s = v_0 t + \frac{1}{2}gt^2$, where s is in feet, t is in seconds, v_0 is the initial velocity in feet per second, and g is

the constant of acceleration due to gravity (approximately 32 ft/sec/sec). How long will it take a body to fall 150 feet if v_0 is 20 feet per second? If the body starts from rest?

16. A man sailed a boat across a lake and back in $2\frac{1}{2}$ hours. If his rate returning was 2 miles per hour less than his rate going, and if the distance each way was 6 miles, find his rate each way.

17. A man rode a bicycle for 6 miles and then walked an additional 4 miles. The total time for his trip was 6 hours. If his rate walking was 2 miles per hour less than his rate on the bicycle, what was each rate?

18. A man and his son working together can paint their house in 4 days. The man can do the job alone in 6 days less than the son can do it. How long would it take each of them to paint the house alone? *Hint:* What part of the job could each of them do in 1 day?

19. A theatre that is rectangular in shape seats 720 people. The number of rows needed to seat the people would be 4 less if each row held 6 more people. How many people would then be in each row?

20. Two tanks, each cylindrical in shape and 10 feet in length, are to be replaced by a single tank of the same length. If the two original tanks have radii that measure 6 feet and 8 feet, respectively, what must be the length of the radius of the single tank replacing them if it is to hold the same volume of liquid?

CHAPTER REVIEW

Solve for x.

1. a. $2x^2 = 3x$ **b.** $(x - 6)(x + 4) = -9$

2. a. $x - 1 = \dfrac{1}{5} x^2$ **b.** $x + \dfrac{3}{x} = 0$

3. a. $ax^2 = abx$ **b.** $cx^2 + bx + a = 0$

4. a. $x - 3\sqrt{x} + 2 = 0$ **b.** $\sqrt{x + 1} + \sqrt{x + 8} = 7$

5. a. $x^4 - 3x^2 - 4 = 0$ **b.** $\dfrac{1}{x^2} - \dfrac{5}{x} + 4 = 0$

6. Write an equation in standard form whose solutions are 3, -3, $2i$, $-2i$.

7. Solve $x^2 + 3xy + y^2 = 0$ for y in terms of x.

8. What is the (a) sum and (b) product of the roots of $3x^2 - 2x + 1 = 0$?

9. Solve for y:

$$a\left(\frac{-b + \sqrt{b^2 - 4ac}}{2a}\right)^2 + b\left(\frac{-b + \sqrt{b^2 - 4ac}}{2a}\right) + y = 0.$$

10. Solve $x^2 + 6x + 8 \le x + 2$ and graph the solution set on a line.

11. The base of a triangle is 1 inch longer than twice its altitude and its area is 18 square inches. Find the base and altitude.

12. A man drives his car for 20 miles at a certain speed. He then increases his speed by 20 miles per hour and continues for an additional 30 miles. If the total trip takes 1 hour, how fast was the man traveling originally?

13. Complex roots of equations solved in this chapter always occurred in conjugate pairs. What type of quadratic equation would give rise to two complex numbers that were not conjugate to each other, say $1 + 2i$ and $1 - 3i$? *Hint:* Write the equation with these roots.

14. Under what conditions if any will $x - 2 = k$ and $x^2 - 4x + 4 = k^2$ be equivalent over R?

15. Under what conditions if any will $|x - 2| = k$ and $x^2 - 4x + 4 = k^2$ be equivalent over R?

7

FUNCTIONS AND GRAPHS I

7.1 Ordered Pairs and Cartesian Products

An equation or inequality in two variables, such as

$$y = 2x + 3 \quad \text{or} \quad y < 2x + 3,$$

is said to be satisfied if the variables are replaced with a pair of numbers, one from the replacement set of x and one from the replacement set of y, which make the resulting statement true.   The pair of numbers, usually written in the form (x, y), is called a solution of the equation or inequality. The pair (x, y) is called an **ordered pair**, since it is understood that the numbers will be considered in a particular order, x first and y second.   These numbers are then called the first and second **components** of the ordered pair, respectively.   Although any letters may be used, in this book we shall usually use x and y for these variables.

We can generate sets of ordered pairs by forming what is called the **Cartesian product** of two sets.

If A and B are sets, the Cartesian product of A and B is denoted by $A \times B$ (read " A cross B") and is the set of all possible ordered pairs such that the first component is a member of A and the second is a member of B.

In symbols, $A \times B = \{(x, y) \mid x \in A \text{ and } y \in B\}$. For example, if $A = \{5, 6, 7\}$ and $B = \{3, 8\}$, then

$$A \times B = \{(5, 3), (5, 8), (6, 3), (6, 8), (7, 3), (7, 8)\}.$$

A convenient way to visualize the formation of a Cartesian product is to construct a tree graph as shown in Figure 7.1.

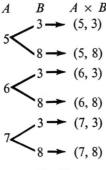

Fig. 7.1

A graphical depiction of $A \times B$ can be made in the form of a point lattice. Figure 7.2 shows a point lattice representing $\{2, 3, 4\} \times \{2, 3, 4\}$. Associated with each point shown is one of the ordered pairs in the Cartesian product.

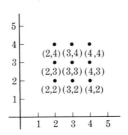

Fig. 7.2

To find ordered pairs that are solutions of a given equation, we can assign a value to one of the variables and then determine the related value of the other. Thus, for

$$y - x = 1,$$

we can obtain solutions by assigning to x any of the values in its replacement set and then determining the appropriate value of y. For example, using $\{2, 3, 4\}$ as the replacement set for x, we find upon assigning these numbers successively to x:

$$y - 2 = 1, \quad y = 3;$$
$$y - 3 = 1, \quad y = 4;$$
$$y - 4 = 1, \quad y = 5.$$

Thus, (2, 3), (3, 4), and (4, 5) are solutions of $y - x = 1$ providing the replacement set of y contains 3, 4, and 5.

In finding ordered pairs that satisfy a given equation or inequality, it is generally helpful if one variable is first expressed in terms of the other. For example, before assigning values to x in

$$y - 3x < 4, \tag{1}$$

it is useful if the inequality is first transformed to the equivalent inequality

$$y < 3x + 4. \tag{2}$$

In (1) the variables x and y are said to be **implicitly** related, while in (2) y is said to be expressed **explicitly** in terms of x.

In discussing solutions of a given equation or inequality in two variables, if the replacement set of x is the set A, and that of y the set B, then the solution set of the equation in $A \times B$ is the set of all members of $A \times B$ whose components satisfy the given equation or inequality. Thus, if $x \in \{2, 3, 4\}$ and $y \in \{4, 5, 6\}$, the solution set of $y - x = 1$ in $\{2, 3, 4\} \times \{4, 5, 6\}$ is $\{(3, 4),$ $(4, 5)\}$. The graph of this set on the lattice $\{2, 3, 4\} \times \{4, 5, 6\}$ is shown in Figure 7.3, where the ordered pairs associated with the circled points are members of the solution set. No other ordered pair in $A \times B$ will satisfy the equation.

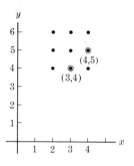

Fig. 7.3

We speak of this graph (circled points) as the **graph of the solution set** of $y - x = 1$ or simply as the **graph** of $y - x = 1$ in $A \times B$.

EXERCISE 7.1

List the members of $A \times B$ if A and B are as given. In each case, show $A \times B$ as a point lattice.

1. $A = \{1, 2, 3\}$, $B = \{1, 2\}$ 2. $A = \{2, 4, 6\}$, $B = \{1, 3\}$
3. $A = \{1, 2, 3\}$, $B = \{8, 9, 10\}$ 4. $A = \{6, 8, 10\}$, $B = \{1, 3, 5\}$
5. $A = \{1, 2, 3, 4\}$, $B = \{1, 2, 3, 4\}$ 6. $A = \{2, 4, 6, 8\}$, $B = \{1, 3, 5, 9\}$

Find the missing component so that the ordered pair will satisfy the equation.

Example: $y - 2x = 4$

a. $(0, \quad)$

$$y - 2x = 4$$
$$y - 2(0) = 4$$
$$y = 4$$

Ans. $(0, 4)$

b. $(\quad, 0)$

$$y - 2x = 4$$
$$0 - 2x = 4$$
$$x = -2$$

Ans. $(-2, 0)$

c. $(3, \quad)$

$$y - 2x = 4$$
$$y - 2(3) = 4$$
$$y = 10$$

Ans. $(3, 10)$

7. $y = x + 7$

a. $(0, \quad)$ b. $(2, \quad)$ c. $(-2, \quad)$

8. $x + 2y = 5$

a. $(0, \quad)$ b. $(5, \quad)$ c. $(-3, \quad)$

9. $3x - 4y = 6$

a. $(0, \quad)$ b. $(\quad, 0)$ c. $(-5, \quad)$

10. $y = 6 - 2x$

a. $(0, \quad)$ b. $(\quad, 0)$ c. $(-1, \quad)$

Transform the given equation or inequality into one in which y is expressed explicitly in terms of x.

Example: $x^2 + 4y^2 = 5$

$$4y^2 = 5 - x^2$$
$$y^2 = \tfrac{1}{4}(5 - x^2)$$

Ans. $y = \pm\tfrac{1}{2}\sqrt{5 - x^2}$

11. $xy - x = 2$

12. $3x - xy = 6$

13. $xy - y = 4$

14. $x^2y - xy + 5 = 0$

15. $x^2 - 4y < 7$

16. $x^2y - xy + 3 \geq 5y$

17. $x = \dfrac{1}{y^2 - 2}$ $\quad(y \neq -\sqrt{2}, \sqrt{2})$

18. $x^3 = \dfrac{2}{1 - y^2}$ $\quad(y \neq -1, 1)$

19. $3x^2 - 4y \geq 4$

20. $x^2y - 3x^2 + 2y < 0$

If $x \in A = \{-2, -1, 0, 1, 2\}$ and $y \in B = \{-2, -1, 0, 1, 2\}$, list the solution set of the given equation or inequality over $A \times B$. Graph the solution set on the lattice corresponding to $A \times B$.

21. $x + 2y = 0$

22. $x^2 = y$

23. $x - y < 0$

24. $x + y \geq 0$

25. $y = x^2$

26. $x^2 - y^2 = 0$

27. $x^2 \leq y + 1$

28. $x^2 > y - 1$

29. If A contains m members and B contains n members, how many members has $A \times B$?

7.2 Relations and Functions

Any set of ordered pairs is called a **relation.** The set of all first components of the ordered pairs in a relation is the **domain** of the relation, and the set of all second components of the ordered pairs is called the **range** of the relation. For example,

$$\{(1, 3), (2, 4), (3, 5)\}$$

is a relation with domain $\{1, 2, 3\}$ and range $\{3, 4, 5\}$. The term "relation" stems directly from the fact that a set of ordered pairs displays a precise relationship between the elements of two sets, the domain and the range. A variable representing an element in the domain of a relation is often referred to as an **independent variable,** while the variable representing an element in the range is called a **dependent variable.**

Because the solution set of an equation or inequality is a set of ordered pairs, and hence a relation, an equation or an inequality is said to **define** or **specify** a relation. If the replacement sets for the variables x and y are A and B, respectively, then the relation defined by a given equation or inequality in x and y is said to be **in** or **over** $A \times B$, because every ordered pair that is in the solution set of the equation or inequality will be a member of $A \times B$. For example, if $x \in A = \{-1, 0, 1\}$ and $y \in B = \{0, 1, 2\}$, then $y \leq x$ defines a relation R in $A \times B$; namely $R = \{(0, 0), (1, 0), (1, 1)\}$. Figure 7.4 shows the point lattice corresponding to $A \times B$, and the points

Fig. 7.4

in R are circled. Because every relation R is a subset of the Cartesian product $A \times B$ of its domain and range, an alternative definition of a relation can be formulated in terms of Cartesian products. Thus, we can say that:

Any subset of a Cartesian product $A \times B$ is a relation in $A \times B$.

If no two ordered pairs in a relation have the same first component and different second components, then the relation is called a **function.** For example, the equation

$$y = 2x - 1$$

defines a function over the Cartesian product of any two sets of numbers.

If x and y denote members of the set $A = \{1, 2, 3, 4, 5\}$, then the function over $A \times A$ defined by the given equation is

$$\{(1, 1), (2, 3), (3, 5)\},$$

with graph as shown in Figure 7.5. Notice that no two points in this graph lie on the same vertical line, while the graph of the relation shown in Figure 7.4 does have points that lie on the same vertical line. The definition of a function implies that if two or more points in the graph of a relation lie on the same vertical line, the relation is not a function.

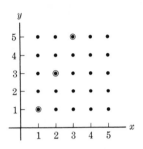

Fig. 7.5

Relations and functions are usually designated by means of a single symbol, R, f, g, or some other capital or lower-case letter. The symbol for the relation or function can be used in conjunction with the variable representing an element in the domain to represent the associated element in the range. Thus, $f(x)$ (read "f of x" or "the value of f at x") is *the element in the range of f associated with the element x in the domain*. This is precisely the same use we made of $P(x)$ in earlier chapters when discussing expressions, and, in particular, polynomial expressions. Suppose P is the function defined by the equation

$$y = x + 3;$$

then we can just as well write

$$P(x) = x + 3,$$

where $P(x)$ plays the same role as y. We sometimes refer to an element in the range, y, $P(x)$, or $x + 3$, as a **value of the function**, or a **function value**.

EXERCISE 7.2

Let $x \in A = \{-2, -1, 0, 1, 2\}$ and $y \in B = \{0, 1, 2, 3, 4\}$:

   a. draw a lattice for the Cartesian product $A \times B$;

   b. graph the relation defined by the given equation or inequality on the lattice;

   c. state whether the relation is a function in this Cartesian product.

Example: $y = 3x$

   Ans.

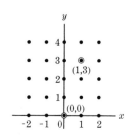

The relation is a function.

1. $y = x$ **2.** $y = 2x$

3. $y < x$ **4.** $y > x$

5. $y = x^2$ **6.** $y = x^2$

7. $y < x + 1$ **8.** $y < x - 1$

9. $y = |x|$ **10.** $y > |x|$

11–20. For each of Problems 1–10, state the domain and range of the specified
relation in $A \times B$.

In each of Problems 21–26, find:

   a. $f(x + h)$ b. $f(x + h) - f(x)$ c. $\dfrac{f(x + h) - f(x)}{h}$

Example: $f(x) = x^2 + 1$

   Ans.   a. $f(x + h) = (x + h)^2 + 1 = x^2 + 2xh + h^2 + 1$

           b. $f(x + h) - f(x) = (x^2 + 2xh + h^2 + 1) - (x^2 + 1) = 2xh + h^2$

           c. $\dfrac{f(x + h) - f(x)}{h} = \dfrac{2xh + h^2}{h} = 2x + h$

21. $f(x) = 3x - 4$ **22.** $f(x) = 3x^2 + 4$

23. $f(x) = x^2 - 3x + 5$ **24.** $f(x) = x^3$

25. $f(x) = \dfrac{1}{x}$ **26.** $f(x) = |x|$

27. If $g(x) = \dfrac{1}{\sqrt{x}}$, find $\dfrac{g(x + h) - g(x)}{h}$.

28. If $g(x) = \dfrac{\sqrt{x}}{a}$, find $\dfrac{g(x + h) - g(x)}{h}$ after first rationalizing the numerator of
$g(x)$.

7.3 Graphs in R × R; Linear Functions

Thus far, the relations and functions we have studied have had small, finite domains and ranges. Hereafter, we shall mainly be interested in relations and functions in $R \times R$, where R is the set of real numbers. Therefore such a relation or function will have as domain the subset of R containing all those real numbers for which real numbers exist in the range.

The graph of $R \times R$ is the entire plane rather than a point lattice, as illustrated in the figures in Sections 7.1 and 7.2. Such systems (called **Cartesian** or **rectangular coordinate** systems) are formed by establishing a pair of perpendicular line graphs (called **axes**) at some point in the geometric plane. An arbitrary scaling of the line graphs from their point of intersection (the **origin**) permits the establishment of a one-to-one correspondence between the geometric points in the plane and ordered pairs of real numbers (x, y).

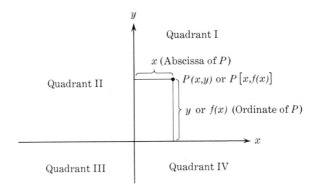

Fig. 7.6

That is, for each point in the plane, there corresponds a unique ordered pair and vice versa. This correspondence is established by using the first component x of the ordered pair to denote the directed (perpendicular) distance of the point from the vertical axis (the **abscissa** of the point), to the right if positive, to the left if negative. The second component y of the ordered pair is used to denote the directed (perpendicular) distance of the point from the horizontal axis (the **ordinate** of the point), above if positive and below if negative. Each axis is labeled with the variable it represents. Most commonly, the horizontal axis is called the **x-axis** and the vertical axis is called the **y-axis**. The components of the ordered pair that corresponds to a given point are called the **coordinates** of the point. Each of the four regions into which the axes divide the plane is called a **quadrant,** and they are referred to by number as illustrated in Figure 7.6.

In Section 7.2 we defined a relation or function to be a set of ordered pairs which we displayed as sets of points in the plane. We considered these over finite domains. Now let us consider a relation defined by an equation containing a polynomial of degree one in two variables in $R \times R$. One such function is defined by

$$f(x) = x - 3. \tag{1}$$

Solutions of this equation can be obtained by assigning values to x and computing corresponding values for $f(x)$. For instance, six solutions of (1) are

$$(-1, -4), (0, -3), (1, -2), (2, -1), (3, 0), (4, 1).$$

Locating these points on a coordinate system, we have Figure 7.7. The points appear to lie on a straight line as shown in Figure 7.8. It can be

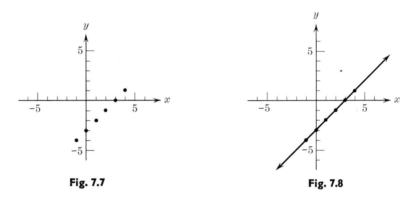

Fig. 7.7   **Fig. 7.8**

shown that the coordinates of each point on this line constitute a solution of (1), and conversely, every solution of (1) corresponds to a point on the line. The line is referred to as the **graph of the function** defined by (1), or, alternatively, as the **graph of the solution set of the equation** or as the **graph of the equation** in $R \times R$.

Function notation can be used to denote the ordinate associated with a given abscissa on a graph. For example, the graph of

$$f(x) = x - 3$$

is shown in Figure 7.9, and specific ordinates are shown as line segments labeled with their lengths in function notation. We mention this here because it is often useful to think of the ordinate of a point in terms of the length of the perpendicular line segment from the point to the x-axis.

The ordinate concept also provides a means of mentally checking to see whether a particular graph does or does not represent a function. If we imagine a line parallel to the y-axis to pass across the graph from left to right, we can examine whether or not it cuts the graph at more than one point at each position on the x-axis, that is, whether or not there are two or more different ordinates for any given abscissa. If there are, the graph is not that of a function.

More generally, any first-degree equation in two variables—that is, any equation of the form

$$Ax + By + C = 0 \quad (B \neq 0), \tag{2}$$

where A, B, and C are real numbers and B is not zero—defines a function and, although we do not prove it here, its graph is a straight line. For this reason, such equations are often called **linear equations**, and functions defined by such equations are called **linear functions**. Since any two distinct points determine a straight line, it is evident that we need find only two solutions

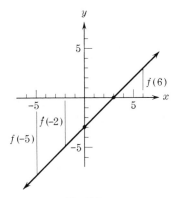

Fig. 7.9

of such an equation to determine its graph. In practice, the two solutions easiest to find are usually those with first and second components respectively zero—that is, the solutions $(x, 0)$ and $(0, y)$. Setting $y = 0$ in

$$Ax + By + C = 0,$$

it follows that

$$Ax + C = 0,$$

from which

$$x = -\frac{C}{A} \quad (A \neq 0),$$

and $(-C/A, 0)$ is one point on the graph. Similarly, for $x = 0$,

$$By + C = 0$$

and

$$y = -\frac{C}{B} \quad (B \neq 0),$$

and $(0, -C/B)$ is another point on the graph. Since these two points are the points where the graph crosses the x- and y-axes, respectively, they are easy to locate. The numbers $-C/A$ and $-C/B$ are called the **x-** and **y-intercepts** of the graph, and are usually denoted by a and b. As an example, consider the function defined by

$$3x + 4y = 12. \qquad (3)$$

If $y = 0$,

$$3x = 12$$

$$x = 4,$$

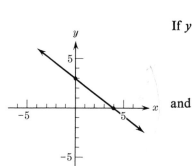

Fig. 7.10

and the x-intercept is 4. If $x = 0$,

$$4y = 12$$

$$y = 3,$$

and the y-intercept is 3. Thus the graph of the function defined by (3) appears as in Figure 7.10.

If the graph intersects the axes at or near the origin, the intercepts either do not represent two separate points, or the points are too close together to be of much use in drawing the graph. It is then necessary to plot at least one other point at a distance far enough removed from the origin to establish the line with accuracy.

There are two special cases of linear equations worth noting. First, an equation such as

$$y = 4$$

in $R \times R$ is an equation in two variables,

$$0x + y = 4.$$

For each x, this equation assigns $y = 4$. That is, any ordered pair of the form $(x, 4)$ is a solution of the equation. For instance,

$$(-1, 4), (2, 4), (4, 4), \text{ etc.}$$

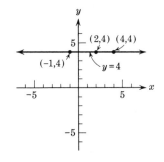

Fig. 7.11

are all solutions of the equation. If we graph these points and connect them with a straight line, we have Figure 7.11. Because the equation

$$y = a$$

assigns to each x the same value for y, a function defined by such an equation is called a **constant function.**

The other special case of the linear equation is of the type

$$x = 3,$$

which, in $R \times R$, may be looked upon as an equation in two variables,

$$x + 0y = 3.$$

Here, only one value is permissible for x, namely 3, while any value may be assigned to y.   That is, any ordered pair of the form $(3, y)$ is a solution of this equation.   If we choose two solutions, say $(3, 1)$ and $(3, 3)$ and graph the equation, we have Figure 7.12.

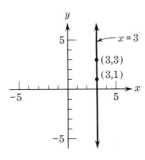

Fig. 7.12

It is clear that this equation does *not* define a function (why?), and accounts for the restriction $B \neq 0$ on equation (2).

EXERCISE 7.3

Graph.

Example: $3x + 4y = 24$

   Determine the intercepts.

   If $x = 0$, $y = 6$; if $y = 0$, $x = 8$

   6 is the y-intercept;
   8 is the x-intercept.

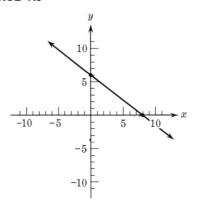

1. $y = 3x + 1$ 2. $y = x - 5$ 3. $y = -2x$
4. $2x + y = 3$ 5. $3x - y = -2$ 6. $3x = 2y$

7. $2x + 3y = 6$ **8.** $3x - 2y = 8$ **9.** $2x + 5y = 10$

10. $y = 5$ **11.** $x = -2$ **12.** $x = -3$

13. $y = -x$ **14.** $y - 10 = 0$ **15.** $x - 50 = 0$

16. $2x - 25 = 0$ **17.** $2 + 2x = 3y$ **18.** $3x - 2 = 4y$

19. $2y + 3 = -x$ **20.** $5y - 2 = 4x$ **21.** $2y = 5(2 + x)$

22. $3y = 4(x - 1)$ **23.** $4x = 3(2 - y)$ **24.** $2x = 5(y - 3)$

Example: Graph $f(x) = x - 1$. Represent $f(5)$ and $f(3)$ by drawing line segments from $(5, 0)$ to $[5, f(5)]$ and from $(3, 0)$ to $[3, f(3)]$.

$f(5)$ is the ordinate at $x = 5$.

$f(3)$ is the ordinate at $x = 3$.

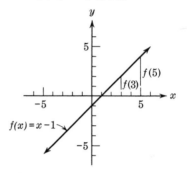

25. Graph $f(x) = 2x + 1$. Represent $f(3)$ and $f(-2)$ by drawing line segments from $(3, 0)$ to $[3, f(3)]$ and from $(-2, 0)$ to $[-2, f(-2)]$.

26. Graph $f(x) = 2x - 5$. Represent $f(4)$ and $f(0)$ by drawing line segments from $(4, 0)$ to $[4, f(4)]$ and from $(0, 0)$ to $[0, f(0)]$.

27. Graph $f(x) = 4 + x$. Represent $f(5)$ and $f(3)$ by drawing line segments from $(5, 0)$ to $[5, f(5)]$ and from $(3, 0)$ to $[3, f(3)]$.

28. Graph $f(x) = 3x - 6$. Represent $f(6)$ and $f(-3)$ by drawing line segments from $(6, 0)$ to $[6, f(6)]$ and from $(-3, 0)$ to $[-3, f(-3)]$.

State a defining equation and specify a meaningful domain for a function relating:

Example: The area (A) of a triangle and the length of the base (b), if the altitude is 6 inches in length.

Since $A = \frac{1}{2}bh$,

$A = \frac{1}{2}b(6)$.

Ans. $A = 3b$, $\{b \mid b > 0\}$

29. The circumference (C) and length of radius (r) of a circle.

30. The perimeter (P) and length of side (s) of a square.

31. The perimeter (P) of a rectangle with one side of length 5 and an adjacent side of length w.

32. The distance (d) traveled by a car moving at a constant rate of 40 mph and the time (t) it has traveled.

33. We observe that $x(y + 1) = xy + x$ is an identity for x and y real numbers. Describe the graph of this equation. Does it define a function? *Hint:* What ordered pairs satisfy the equation?

34. Graph $x + y = 6$ and $5x - y = 0$ on the same set of axes. Estimate the coordinates of the point of intersection. What can you say about the coordinates of this point in relation to the two linear equations?

Show that the graph of each of the following is not a straight line, but two half-lines.

35. $y = |x|$ **36.** $y = -|x|$ **37.** $y = |x + 2|$

38. $y = |x - 2|$ **39.** $y = |x| + 2$ **40.** $y = |x| - 2$

41. Use the results of Problems 35–40 to infer a quick means for sketching $y - b = |x - a|$ for any given values of a and b.

7.4 Distance and Slope Formulas

Any two distinct points in a plane can be looked upon as the end points of a line segment (Figure 7.13). Letters with subscripts x_1, y_1, x_2, and y_2 are

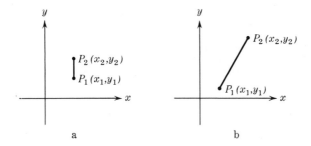

Fig. 7.13

used to indicate specific numbers—numbers that are to be considered fixed during a discussion.

We shall discuss two fundamental properties of a line segment—its **length** and its **inclination** with respect to the x-axis. We first observe that any two distinct points lie either on the same vertical line or one is to the right of the other, the one on the right having a larger x-coordinate. Let us first consider only the latter case. If we construct through P_2 a line parallel to the y-axis and through P_1 a line parallel to the x-axis, the lines will meet at a point P_3 as shown in either Figure 7.14-a or 7.14-b. The x-coordinate of P_3 is evidently the same as the x-coordinate of P_2, while the y-coordinate of P_3 is the same as that of P_1; hence the coordinates of P_3 are (x_2, y_1). By inspection, we observe that the distance between P_2 and P_3 is simply the difference in the y-coordinates of the two points $(y_2 - y_1)$ and the distance between P_1 and P_3 is the difference of the x-coordinates of these points $(x_2 - x_1)$.

In general, since $y_2 - y_1$ is positive or negative as $y_2 > y_1$ or $y_2 < y_1$, respectively, and $x_2 - x_1$ is positive or negative as $x_2 > x_1$ or $x_2 < x_1$, respectively, it is also convenient to designate the distances represented by $x_2 - x_1$ and $y_2 - y_1$ as positive or negative. For this reason distances measured parallel to the axes are frequently called **directed distances.**

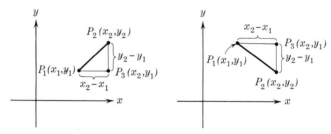

Fig. 7.14

The Pythagorean theorem can be used to find the length of the line segment from P_1 to P_2. This theorem asserts that the square of the length of the hypotenuse of any right triangle is equal to the sum of the squares of the lengths of the legs. Thus

$$d^2 = (x_2 - x_1)^2 + (y_2 - y_1)^2$$

and, by considering only the positive square root of the right-hand member,

$$d = \sqrt{(x_2 - x_1)^2 + (y_2 - y_1)^2}. \tag{1}$$

Since the distances $(x_2 - x_1)$ and $(y_2 - y_1)$ are squared, it makes no difference whether they are positive or negative—the result is the same. Equation (1) is a formula for the distance between any two points in the plane in terms of the coordinates of the points. The distance is always taken as positive. If the points P_1 and P_2 lie on the same horizontal line, we have observed that the directed distance between them is

$$d = x_2 - x_1$$

and, if they lie on the same vertical line,

$$d = y_2 - y_1.$$

If we are concerned only with distance and not direction, then these become $d = |x_2 - x_1|$ and $d = |y_2 - y_1|$, respectively.

The second useful property of the line segment joining two points is that of its inclination. The inclination of a line segment can be measured by comparing the *rise* of the segment with a given *run* (Figure 7.15).

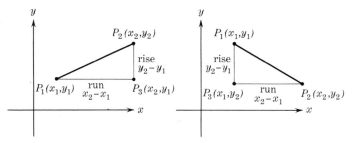

Fig. 7.15

The ratio of *rise to run* is called the **slope** of the line segment and is designated by the letter m. Thus

$$m = \frac{\text{rise}}{\text{run}}.$$

Since the rise is simply $y_2 - y_1$ and the run is $x_2 - x_1$, the slope of the line segment joining P_1 and P_2 is given by

$$m = \frac{y_2 - y_1}{x_2 - x_1} \quad (x_2 \neq x_1). \tag{2}$$

Taking P_2 to the right of P_1, $x_2 - x_1$ will necessarily be positive and the slope will be positive or negative as $y_2 - y_1$ is positive or negative—that is, according to whether the line slopes upward or downward from P_1 to P_2. A positive slope indicates that a line is rising to the right; a negative slope indicates that it is falling to the right. Since

$$\frac{y_2 - y_1}{x_2 - x_1} = \frac{-(y_1 - y_2)}{-(x_1 - x_2)} = \frac{y_1 - y_2}{x_1 - x_2},$$

the restriction that P_2 be to the right of P_1 is not necessary, and the order in which the points are considered is immaterial.

If a segment is parallel to the x-axis, $y_2 - y_1 = 0$ and it will have the slope 0, while if it is parallel to the y-axis, $x_2 - x_1 = 0$ and its slope is not defined (Figure 7.16).

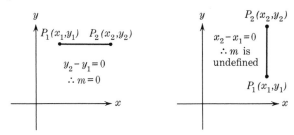

Fig. 7.16

EXERCISE 7.4

Find the distance between each of the given pairs of points, and find the slope of the line segment joining them.

Example: $(3, -5)$, $(2, 4)$

Consider $(3, -5)$ as P_1 and $(2, 4)$ as P_2.

$$d = \sqrt{(x_2 - x_1)^2 + (y_2 - y_1)^2} \qquad m = \frac{y_2 - y_1}{x_2 - x_1}$$

$$= \sqrt{[2 - 3]^2 + [4 - (-5)]^2} \qquad\quad = \frac{4 - (-5)}{2 - 3}$$

$$= \sqrt{1 + 81} \qquad\qquad\qquad\qquad = \frac{9}{-1}$$

Ans.   Distance, $\sqrt{82}$;   slope, -9

1. $(1, 1)$, $(4, 5)$
2. $(-1, 1)$, $(5, 9)$
3. $(-3, 2)$, $(2, 14)$
4. $(-4, -3)$, $(1, 9)$
5. $(2, 1)$, $(1, 0)$
6. $(-3, 2)$, $(0, 0)$
7. $(5, 4)$, $(-1, 1)$
8. $(2, -3)$, $(-2, -1)$
9. $(3, 5)$, $(-2, 5)$
10. $(2, 0)$, $(-2, 0)$
11. $(0, 5)$, $(0, -5)$
12. $(-2, -5)$, $(-2, 3)$

Find the length of the sides of the triangle whose vertices are given.

13. $(10, 1)$, $(3, 1)$, $(5, 9)$
14. $(0, 6)$, $(9, -6)$, $(-3, 0)$
15. $(5, 6)$, $(11, -2)$, $(-10, -2)$
16. $(-1, 5)$, $(8, -7)$, $(4, 1)$

17. Show that the triangle described in Problem 14 is a right triangle. *Hint:* Use the converse of the Pythagorean theorem; that is, if $c^2 = a^2 + b^2$, the triangle is a right triangle.

18. The two line segments whose end points are $(0, -7)$, $(8, -5)$ and $(5, 7)$ $(8, -5)$ are perpendicular. Find the slope of each line segment. Compare the slopes. Do the same for the perpendicular line segments whose end points are $(8, 0)$, $(6, 6)$ and $(-3, 3)$, $(6, 6)$. Can you make a conjecture about the slopes of perpendicular line segments?

19. Use the fact that two lines are parallel if and only if their slopes are equal to show that the points $(2, 4)$, $(3, 8)$, $(5, 1)$, and $(4, -3)$ are the vertices of a parallelogram.

20. Using the fact from Problem 19, show that the points $(-5, 4)$, $(7, -11)$, $(12, 25)$, and $(0, 40)$ are the vertices of a parallelogram.

7.5 Point-Slope and Slope-Intercept Forms

We have previously used the equation

$$Ax + By + C = 0 \quad (B \neq 0) \tag{1}$$

to define a linear function.   Let us designate (1) as **standard form** for a linear
equation, and then consider two alternative forms that display useful aspects.

Point-Slope Form

Assuming that the slope of the line segment joining any two points on a
line does not depend upon the points, consider a line on the plane with given
slope m and passing through a given point
(x_1, y_1) (Figure 7.17).   If we choose any
other point on the line and assign to it the
coordinates (x, y), it is evident that the
slope of the line is given by

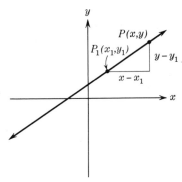

$$\frac{y - y_1}{x - x_1} = m \quad (x \neq x_1), \tag{2}$$

from which

$$y - y_1 = m(x - x_1) \quad (x \neq x_1). \tag{3}$$

Notice that (2) and (3) are equivalent
for all values of x except x_1, in which
case the left-hand member of (2) is not

Fig. 7.17

defined.   Since (x_1, y_1) is a point on the line, and since the coordinates of
(x_1, y_1) also satisfy (3), the graph of (3) contains all those points in the graph
of (2) and, in addition, the point (x_1, y_1).   Since x and y are the coordinates
of *any* point on the line, equation (3), with the restriction that $x \neq x_1$ removed,
is the equation of the line passing through (x_1, y_1) with slope m.   Thus,

$$y - y_1 = m(x - x_1)$$

is called the **point-slope** form for a linear equation.

Slope-Intercept Form

Now consider the equation of the line passing through a given point on
the y-axis whose coordinates are $(0, b)$ and having
slope m (Figure 7.18).   Substituting $(0, b)$ in the
point-slope form of a linear equation

$$y - y_1 = m(x - x_1),$$

we obtain

$$y - b = m(x - 0),$$

from which

$$y = mx + b. \tag{4}$$

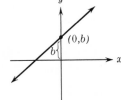

Fig. 7.18

Equation (4) is called the **slope-intercept form** for the equation of a straight line. Any equation in standard form, such as

$$2x + 3y - 6 = 0,$$

can be written in the slope-intercept form by solving for y in terms of x. Thus

$$3y = -2x + 6$$

and

$$y = -\frac{2}{3}x + 2.$$

The slope of the line, $-2/3$, and the y-intercept, 2, can now be read directly from the last form of the equation.

EXERCISE 7.5

Find the equation of the line through each of the given points and having the given slope; write in standard form.

Example: $(3, -5)$, $m = -2$

Substitute given values in the point-slope form of the linear equation.

$$y - y_1 = m(x - x_1)$$
$$y - (-5) = -2(x - 3)$$
$$y + 5 = -2x + 6$$

Ans. $2x + y - 1 = 0$

1. $(2, 1)$, $m = 4$ 2. $(-2, 3)$, $m = 5$ 3. $(5, 5)$, $m = -1$

4. $(-3, -2)$, $m = \frac{1}{2}$ 5. $(0, 0)$, $m = 3$ 6. $(-1, 0)$, $m = 1$

7. $(0, -1)$, $m = -\frac{1}{2}$ 8. $(2, -1)$, $m = \frac{3}{4}$ 9. $(-2, -2)$, $m = -\frac{3}{4}$

10. $(2, -3)$, $m = 0$ 11. $(-4, 2)$, $m = 0$ 12. $(-1, -2)$, parallel to y-axis

Write each of the equations in slope-intercept form; specify the slope of the line and the y-intercept.

Example: $2x - 3y = 5$

Solve explicitly for y.

$$-3y = 5 - 2x$$
$$3y = 2x - 5$$
$$y = \frac{2}{3}x - \frac{5}{3}$$

Compare with the general slope-intercept form $y = mx + b$.

Ans. $y = \frac{2}{3}x - \frac{5}{3}$; slope, $\frac{2}{3}$; y-intercept, $-\frac{5}{3}$

13. $x + y = 3$ **14.** $2x + y = -1$ **15.** $3x + 2y = 1$

16. $3x - y = 7$ **17.** $x - 3y = 2$ **18.** $2x - 3y = 0$

19. $8x - 3y = 0$ **20.** $-x = 2y - 5$ **21.** $2x = 5 - 3y$

22. Write the equation of the line with the same slope as $x - 2y = 5$ and passing through the origin. Draw the graph of this equation.

23. Write the equation of the line through $(0, 5)$ with the same slope as $2y - 3x = 5$. Draw the graph of this equation.

24. Show that

$$y - y_1 = \left(\frac{y_2 - y_1}{x_2 - x_1}\right)(x - x_1)$$

is the equation of the line joining the points (x_1, y_1) and (x_2, y_2). *Hint:* Use the point-slope form and the slope formula from Section 7.4.

25. Using the form

$$y - y_1 = \left(\frac{y_2 - y_1}{x_2 - x_1}\right)(x - x_1),$$

find the equation of the lines through the points

a. $(2, 1)$ and $(-1, 3)$.   b. $(3, 0)$ and $(5, 0)$.

c. $(-2, 1)$ and $(3, -2)$.   d. $(-1, -1)$ and $(1, 1)$.

26. Consider the linear function

$$F = \{(x, y) \mid y = F(x)\}.$$

If $(2, 3)$ and $(-1, 4)$ are known to be in F, find $F(x)$ in terms of x.

7.6 Graphs of First-Degree Relations

An open sentence of the form

$$Ax + By + C \leq 0,$$

where A, B, and C are real numbers, is an inequality of the first degree, and defines a first-degree relation in $R \times R$. Such inequalities can be graphed on the plane, but the graph will be a region of the plane rather than a straight line. For example, consider the inequality

$$2x + y - 3 < 0. \tag{1}$$

Rewritten in the form

$$y < -2x + 3, \tag{2}$$

we have that, for each x, y is less than $-2x + 3$. The graph of the equation

$$y = -2x + 3 \tag{3}$$

is simply a straight line, as illustrated in Figure 7.19.   Therefore, to graph (2), we need only observe that any point below this line has x- and y-coordinates that satisfy (2), and consequently the solution set of (2) corresponds to the entire region below the line.   The region is indicated on the graph with shading.   That the line itself is not in the solution set is shown by means of a broken line, as in Figure 7.20.   Had the inequality been

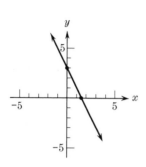

$$2x + y - 3 \leq 0,$$

the line would be a part of the solution set and would be shown as a solid line on the graph.

Fig. 7.19

In general,

$$Ax + By + C < 0 \quad \text{or} \quad Ax + By + C > 0$$

will have as a solution set the coordinates of all points in a half-plane either above or below the line

$$Ax + By + C = 0,$$

depending upon the inequality symbols involved.   We can determine which of the half-planes should be shaded by substituting the coordinates of any point not on the line and noting whether or not they satisfy the inequality. If they do, then the half-plane containing the point is shaded; if the co-ordinates do not satisfy the inequality, then the other half-plane is shaded. A good point to use in this process is the origin with the coordinates $(0, 0)$.

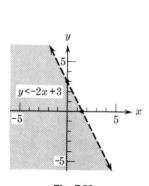

Fig. 7.20

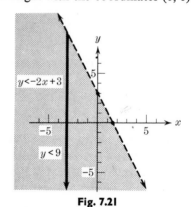

Fig. 7.21

Inequalities do not define functions according to our definition in Section 7.2, because each element of the replacement set for the independent variable is not associated with a unique element in the replacement set of the dependent variable.   For example, in the inequality

$$y < -2x + 3,$$

if $x = -3$,

$$y < -2(-3) + 3,$$

$$y < 9,$$

which is certainly not a unique value for the dependent variable. The infinite number of values for the dependent variable $y < 9$ is indicated by the heavy vertical line in Figure 7.21.

EXERCISE 7.6

Graph the solution set of the inequality.

Example: $2x + y \geq 4$

     Solve explicitly for y. $y \geq 4 - 2x$

     Graph the equality $y = 4 - 2x$.

     Substitute 0 for x and y in the inequality.

         $0 \geq 4 - 2(0)$

     Since this is not a true statement, shade the half-plane not containing the origin.

     Line is included in graph.

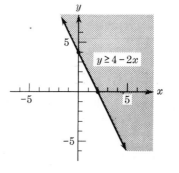

1. $y < x$	**2.** $y > x$	**3.** $y \leq x + 2$	**4.** $y \geq x - 2$
5. $x + y < 5$	**6.** $2x + y < 2$	**7.** $x - y < 3$	**8.** $x - 2y < 5$
9. $x \leq 2y - 4$	**10.** $2x \leq y + 1$	**11.** $3 \geq 2x - 2y$	**12.** $0 \geq x + y$

Graph each set of ordered pairs.

Example: $\{(x, y) \mid x > 2\}$

     Graph the equality $x = 2$.

     Shade area to the right of the line representing $x = 2$.

     Line is excluded from graph.

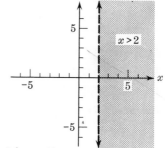

13. $\{(x, y) \mid x > 0\}$ **14.** $\{(x, y) \mid y < 0\}$

15. $\{(x, y) \mid x < 0\}$ **16.** $\{(x, y) \mid x < -2\}$

17. $\{(x, y) \mid -1 < x < 5\}$ **18.** $\{(x, y) \mid 0 \leq y \leq 1\}$

19. $\{(x, y) \mid |x| < 3\}$ **20.** $\{(x, y) \mid |y| > 1\}$

Graph each of the following using double shading.

21. $\{(x, y) \mid x \geq 4\} \cap \{(x, y) \mid y \leq 2\}$

22. $\{(x, y) \mid |x| \leq 2\} \cap \{(x, y) \mid |y| \leq 2\}$

23. $\{(x, y) \mid x + y \leq 6\} \cap \{(x, y) \mid x + y \geq 4\}$

24. $\{(x, y) \mid y \geq x\} \cup \{(x, y) \mid y \leq -x\}$

25. $\{(x, y) \mid y \leq -|x|\} \cup \{(x, y) \mid |x| \leq 1\}$

26. $\{(x, y) \mid y \leq 2 - |x|\} \cap \{(x, y) \mid y > |x| - 2\}$

CHAPTER REVIEW

1. Given $A = \{a, b, c\}$ and $B = \{x, y\}$, what is $A \times B$?

2. What is the solution set of $2x - 3y = 1$ over $A \times A$, if $A = \{-2, -1, 0, 1, 2\}$?

3. If $f(x) = 2x^2 - 3x + 1$:

   a. find $f(3) - f(0)$.

   b. find $\dfrac{f(x + h) - f(x)}{h}$.

4. State the domain and range of the relation defined by $y < 3x - 1$ over $\{2, 3, 4\} \times \{1, 2, 3\}$.

5. Graph $2x - 3y = 18$ over $R \times R$ and state the intercepts of the graph.

6. Find k if $(3, 2)$ is a solution of the equation $2x - ky = 6$.

7. a. Find the distance between the points $(3, -5)$ and $(6, 8)$.
   b. Find the slope of the line segment joining the points.

8. Find the equation in standard form of the line through $(3, 5)$ with slope 2.

9. Find the equation in standard form of the line containing $(-2, 7)$ and $(3, 5)$.

10. Write $2x + 3y = 6$ in slope-intercept form and specify the slope and the y-intercept of its graph.

11. Write the equation of the line through $(-1, 1)$ parallel to the graph of $2x = 5 - 3y$.

12. Graph $\{(x, y) \mid y > x + 2\}$.

13. Graph $\{(x, y) \mid y \leq 4x + 4\}$.

14. Graph $\{(x, y) \mid y \leq 4\} \cap \{(x, y) \mid x \geq 1\}$.

15. Graph $\{(x, y) \mid x + y \leq 4\} \cap \{(x, y) \mid x \geq 0\}$.

8

FUNCTIONS AND GRAPHS II

8.1 The Graph of a Quadratic Function

Consider the quadratic equation in two variables,

$$y = x^2 - 4. \tag{1}$$

As with linear equations in two variables, solutions of this equation must be ordered pairs. We need replacements for both x and y in order to obtain a statement we may adjudge to be true or false. As before, such ordered pairs can be found by arbitrarily assigning values to x and computing related values for y. For instance, assigning the value -3 to x, we have from (1),

$$y = (-3)^2 - 4,$$

$$y = 5,$$

and $(-3, 5)$ is a solution. Similarly, we find that

$$(-2, 0), (-1, -3), (0, -4),$$
$$(1, -3), (2, 0), \text{ and } (3, 5)$$

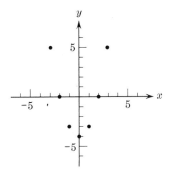

Fig. 8.1

are also solutions of (1).   Plotting the corresponding points on the plane, we have the graph in Figure 8.1.   Clearly, these points do not lie on a straight line, and we might reasonably inquire whether the graph of the solution set of (1),

$$S = \{(x, y) \mid y = x^2 - 4\},$$

forms any kind of a meaningful pattern on the plane.   By plotting additional solutions of (1)—solutions with x-components between those already found—we may be able to obtain a clearer picture.   Accordingly, we find the solutions

$$\left(\frac{-5}{2}, \frac{9}{4}\right), \left(\frac{-3}{2}, \frac{-7}{4}\right), \left(\frac{-1}{2}, \frac{-15}{4}\right),$$

$$\left(\frac{1}{2}, \frac{-15}{4}\right), \left(\frac{3}{2}, \frac{-7}{4}\right), \left(\frac{5}{2}, \frac{9}{4}\right),$$

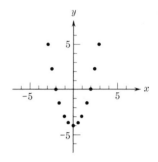

Fig. 8.2

and by plotting these points in addition to those found earlier, we have the graph in Figure 8.2.   It now appears reasonable to connect these points in sequence from left to right, by a smooth curve as in Figure 8.3, and to assume that the curve is a good approximation to the graph of (1). This curve is an example of a **parabola**.   Note that, regardless of the number of individual points we plot in graphing (1), we have no absolute assurance that connecting these points with a smooth curve will produce the correct graph, although the more points we plot and locate, the more reasonable it should seem that connecting them will do this.   Proving that the graph is indeed a parabola requires the use of concepts from the calculus and is not attempted herein.

More generally, the graph of any quadratic equation of the form

$$y = ax^2 + bx + c, \tag{2}$$

where a, b, and c are real and $a \neq 0$, is a parabola.   Since with each x an equation of the form (2) will associate only one y, such an equation defines a function whose domain is the set of real numbers and whose range is some subset of the real numbers.   For example, by inspecting the graph (Figure 8.3) we observe that the range of the function defined by (1) is the set of real numbers

$$\{y \mid y \geq -4\}.$$

To show that there is a lowest (or else a highest) point on the graph of (2), we can proceed as follows, by completing the square:

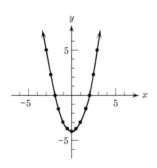

Fig. 8.3

$$y = ax^2 + bx + c \quad (a \neq 0)$$

$$= a\left(x^2 + \frac{b}{a}x + \frac{c}{a}\right)$$

$$= a\left(x^2 + \frac{b}{a}x + \frac{b^2}{4a^2} - \frac{b^2}{4a^2} + \frac{c}{a}\right)$$

$$= a\left(x^2 + \frac{b}{a}x + \frac{b^2}{4a^2}\right) - \frac{b^2 - 4ac}{4a}$$

$$= a\left(x + \frac{b}{2a}\right)^2 - \frac{b^2 - 4ac}{4a}. \tag{3}$$

Now if $a > 0$, then the first term on the right is 0 at $x = -b/2a$, and otherwise this term is positive; hence the lowest point on the graph is

$$\left(\frac{-b}{2a}, -\frac{b^2 - 4ac}{4a}\right). \tag{4}$$

Similarly, if $a < 0$, then the first term on the right in (3) is negative except at $x = -b/2a$, and accordingly (4) gives the highest point on the graph in this case.

In graphing a quadratic equation it is desirable to select first components for the ordered pairs that will ensure that the more significant parts of the parabola will be displayed. These parts include the intercepts and the maximum or minimum (highest or lowest) point on the curve.

In locating the x-intercepts of the graph of the function

$$\{[x, f(x)] \mid f(x) = ax^2 + bx + c\},$$

we identify those values of x for which $f(x) = 0$. For any function f, values of x for which $f(x) = 0$ are called **zeros** of the function. Moreover, if $f(x) = ax^2 + bx + c$, and if $f(x_1) = 0$ for any real number x_1, then

$$ax_1^2 + bx_1 + c = 0$$

and x_1 is a solution of the quadratic equation $ax^2 + bx + c = 0$. Thus, we have three different names for a single idea:

1. The elements of the solution set of the equation $ax^2 + bx + c = 0$.
2. The zeros of the function $\{(x, y) \mid y = ax^2 + bx + c\}$.
3. The x-intercepts of the graph of the function $\{(x, y) \mid y = ax^2 + bx + c\}$.

Regarding this idea, we should recall from Chapter 6 that a quadratic equation may have no real solution, one real solution, or two real solutions. If the equation has no real solutions, we find that the graph of the related quadratic equation in two variables does not touch the x-axis; if there is one solution, the graph will be tangent to the x-axis; if there are two real solutions, the graph will cross the x-axis at two distinct points (Figure 8.4).

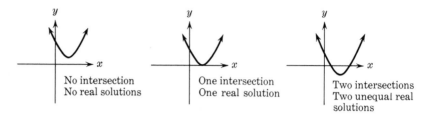

No intersection   One intersection   Two intersections
No real solutions   One real solution   Two unequal real
                                                   solutions

Fig. 8.4

As in Section 7.3, the ordinate of a point on the curve can be represented as a line segment drawn from a point on the curve perpendicular to the x-axis. Graphing the equation

$$f(x) = -x^2 + 16,$$

we obtain Figure 8.5, where a few representative ordinates are shown.

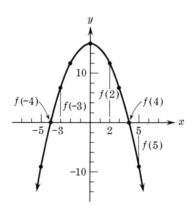

Fig. 8.5

EXERCISE 8.1

In each of the Problems 1–16,
(a) find solutions of the equation using integral values for x where $-4 \le x \le 4$;
(b) use the solutions to graph the function in $R \times R$ defined by the equation.

Example: $y = -x^2 + 3x$

Ans.   (a) $(-4, -28)$ **Ans.** (b)
          $(-3, -18)$
          $(-2, -10)$
          $(-1, -4)$
          $(0, 0)$
          $(1, 2)$
          $(2, 2)$
          $(3, 0)$
          $(4, -4)$

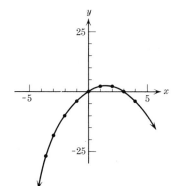

1. $y = x^2 + 1$ **2.** $y = x^2 + 4$

3. $f(x) = x^2 - 3$ **4.** $f(x) = -x^2 + 1$

5. $y = -x^2 + 4$ **6.** $y = -x^2 - 3$

7. $f(x) = 2x^2 - x + 3$ **8.** $f(x) = -2x^2 + x - 3$

9. $y = -3x^2 + x$ **10.** $y = 3x^2 - x$

11. $y = x^2 + 2x + 1$ **12.** $y = -x^2 - 2x - 1$

13. $f(x) = x^2 - 2x + 1$ **14.** $f(x) = -x^2 + 2x - 1$

15. $f(x) = -x^2 + x + 1$ **16.** $f(x) = 3x^2 + x - 2$

Use analytic methods to obtain the x-intercepts and the coordinates of the maximum or minimum point for the graph of the given equation.

Example: $y = x^2 - 7x + 6$

Since the solution set of $x^2 - 7x + 6 = 0$ is $\{1, 6\}$, the x-intercepts are 1 and 6. By completing the square in the right-hand member of

$$y = x^2 - 7x + 6,$$

we obtain

$$y = (x^2 - 7x + \tfrac{49}{4}) - \tfrac{49}{4} + 6,$$

or

$$y = (x - \tfrac{7}{2})^2 - \tfrac{25}{4}.$$

For $x = \tfrac{7}{2}$, y has a minimum value $-\tfrac{25}{4}$. Therefore, the minimum point is at $(\tfrac{7}{2}, -\tfrac{25}{4})$.

Ans. x-intercepts: 1 and 6; minimum point: $(\tfrac{7}{2}, -\tfrac{25}{4})$

17. $g(x) = x^2 - 3x + 2$ **18.** $f(x) = -x^2 + 5x - 4$

19. $y = -x^2 + 3x - 2$ **20.** $y = x^2 - 6x - 7$

21. $f(x) = -x^2 - 8x + 9$ **22.** $g(x) = \frac{1}{2}x^2 + 2x$

23. $y = -\frac{1}{2}x^2 - 2x$ **24.** $f(x) = -x^2 - \frac{3}{2}x$

25. $y = x^2 + \frac{3}{2}x$ **26.** $y = x^2 - 6x + 9$

Use the information obtained about the intercepts and the maximum and minimum points in the appropriate problems above to sketch the graph of:

27. Problem 17.   **28.** Problem 18.   **29.** Problem 19.

30. Problem 20.   **31.** Problem 21.   **32.** Problem 22.

33. Graph the equation $f(x) = x^2 + 1$. Represent $f(0)$ and $f(4)$ by drawing line segments from $(0, 0)$ to $[0, f(0)]$ and from $(4, 0)$ to $[4, f(4)]$.

34. Graph the equation $f(x) = x^2 - 1$. Represent $f(-3)$ and $f(2)$ by drawing line segments from $(-3, 0)$ to $[-3, f(-3)]$ and from $(2, 0)$ to $[2, f(2)]$.

Solve Problems 35–37 analytically and check the solution with a graph.

Example:

Find two numbers whose sum is 18 and whose product is as large as possible.

Let x represent a number; then $18 - x$ represents the second number.

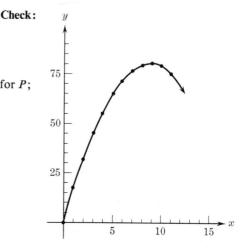

$P = x(18 - x)$ **Check:**

$P = -x^2 + 18x$

$P = -1(x^2 - 18x + 81) + 81$

$P = -1(x - 9)^2 + 81$

$x = 9$ yields the maximum value for P; therefore $18 - x = 9$.

Ans. 9 and 9

35. Find two numbers whose sum is 8 and whose product is as large as possible.

36. Find two numbers whose sum is 12 and whose product is as large as possible.

37. Find the maximum area of a rectangle whose perimeter is 100 inches. *Hint:* Let x represent the length, then $50 - x$ represents the width and $A = x(50 - x)$.

38. Graph the equation $y^2 = 4$.   *Hint:* Consider the equation $0x + y^2 = 4$.

39. Does the equation $y^2 = 4$ define a function? Why or why not?

40. Graph each of the following equations on a separate coordinate system.

     a. $y = \sqrt{4 - x^2}$ b. $y = -\sqrt{4 - x^2}$ c. $y = \pm\sqrt{4 - x^2}$

     Which of these equations does not define a function? Why not?

41. If, for each x, $f(x) = f(-x)$, the graph of f is said to be symmetric with respect to the y-axis. Which of the following have graphs that are symmetric with respect to the y-axis?

     a. $f(x) = x$ b. $f(x) = x^2$ c. $f(x) = \sqrt{x^2 + 1}$ d. $f(x) = |x|$

8.2   Conic Sections

In addition to $y = ax^2 + bx + c$, there are three other types of quadratic equations in two variables whose graphs are of particular interest. We shall discuss each of them separately.

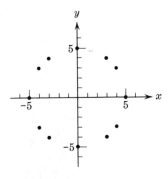   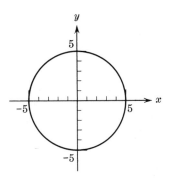

Fig. 8.6   **Fig. 8.7**

First, consider the equation

$$x^2 + y^2 = 25. \tag{1}$$

Solving this equation explicitly for y, we have

$$y = \pm\sqrt{25 - x^2}. \tag{2}$$

Assigning values to x, we find the following ordered pairs in the solution set:

$$(-5, 0), (-4, 3), (-3, 4), (0, 5), (3, 4), (4, 3), (5, 0),$$
$$(-4, -3), (-3, -4), (0, -5), (3, -4), (4, -3).$$

Plotting these points on the plane, we have the graph in Figure 8.6. Connecting these points with a smooth curve, we have the graph in Figure 8.7, a circle with radius 5 and center at the origin.

Since the number 25 in the right-hand member of (1) is clearly the determining factor in the length of the radius of the circle, we can generalize and observe that any equation in the form

$$x^2 + y^2 = r^2$$

will graph into a circle with radius r and with center at the origin. (See Problem 31, Exercise 8.2 for a more general approach.)

Note that in the preceding example it is not necessary to assign any values $|x| > 5$, because y is imaginary for these values of x. Since, except for -5 and $+5$, each permissible value for x is associated with two values for y —one positive and one negative—(1) and (2) do not define functions. We could represent the relationship (2) by two equations,

$$y = f(x) = \sqrt{25 - x^2} \tag{3}$$

and

$$y = f(x) = -\sqrt{25 - x^2}, \tag{3a}$$

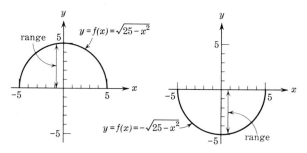

Fig. 8.8

whose graphs would appear as in Figure 8.8. These equations do define functions. In both cases, the domain of the function in $R \times R$ is

$$\{x \mid |x| \le 5\},$$

while the ranges differ. By inspecting the graph, we observe that the ranges of the functions defined by (3) and (3a) are

$$\{y \mid 0 \le y \le 5\} \quad \text{and} \quad \{y \mid -5 \le y \le 0\},$$

respectively.

The second quadratic equation in two variables of interest is that typified by

$$4x^2 + 9y^2 = 36. \tag{4}$$

We obtain solutions of (4) by first solving explicitly for y,

$$y = \pm\frac{2}{3}\sqrt{9 - x^2}, \tag{5}$$

and assigning to x values $-3 \leq x \leq 3$. (Why these values only?)   We obtain, for example,

$$(-3, 0), \ (-2, \tfrac{2}{3}\sqrt{5}), \ (-1, \tfrac{4}{3}\sqrt{2}), \ (0, 2), \ (1, \tfrac{4}{3}\sqrt{2}), \ (2, \tfrac{2}{3}\sqrt{5}), \ (3, 0),$$
$$(-2, -\tfrac{2}{3}\sqrt{5}), \ (-1, -\tfrac{4}{3}\sqrt{2}), \ (0, -2), \ (1, -\tfrac{4}{3}\sqrt{2}), \ (2, -\tfrac{2}{3}\sqrt{5}).$$

Locating the corresponding points on the plane and connecting them with a smooth curve, we have the graph in Figure 8.9.   This curve is called an **ellipse.**

The graph of any equation of the form

$$Ax^2 + By^2 = C \quad (A, B, C > 0, A \neq B)$$

is an ellipse with center at the origin, x-intercepts $\pm \sqrt{C/A}$, and y-intercepts $\pm \sqrt{C/B}$.

The third quadratic equation with which we are presently concerned is typified by

$$x^2 - y^2 = 9.$$

Solving this equation for y, we obtain

$$y = \pm \sqrt{x^2 - 9},$$

which has as a part of its solution set the ordered pairs

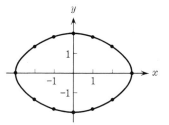

Fig. 8.9

$$(-5, 4), \ (-4, \sqrt{7}), \ (-3, 0), \ (3, 0), \ (4, \sqrt{7}), \ (5, 4),$$
$$(-5, -4), \ (-4, -\sqrt{7}), \ (4, -\sqrt{7}), \ (5, -4).$$

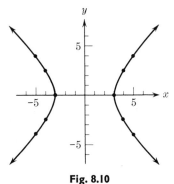

Fig. 8.10

Plotting the corresponding points and connecting them with a smooth curve, we obtain Figure 8.10.   This curve is called a **hyperbola.**

Any equation of the form

$$Ax^2 - By^2 = C \quad (A, B, C > 0)$$

graphs into a hyperbola with center at the origin and x-intercepts $\pm\sqrt{C/A}$. Any equation of the form

$$By^2 - Ax^2 = C \quad (A, B, C > 0)$$

graphs into a hyperbola with center at the origin and y-intercepts at $\pm\sqrt{C/B}$.

The graphs of the equations dealt with in this section, together with the parabola of the preceding section, are called **conic sections** or **conics** because such curves result from the intersection of a plane and a cone (Figure 8.11).

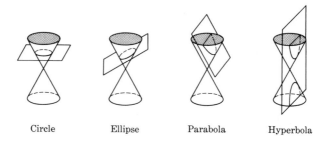

Circle   Ellipse   Parabola   Hyperbola

Fig. 8.11

EXERCISE 8.2

(a) Rewrite each of the following equations with y as the left-hand member.
(b) Write each equation equivalently as two separate equations, each of which defines a function.
(c) State the domain of each of the functions defined in (b) in $R \times R$.

Example: $4x^2 + y^2 = 36$

$y^2 = 36 - 4x^2$

Ans. (a) $y = \pm 2\sqrt{9 - x^2}$ **Ans.** (c) Domain $= \{x \mid -3 \le x \le 3\}$

Ans. (b) $y = 2\sqrt{9 - x^2}$
$ y = -2\sqrt{9 - x^2}$

1. $x^2 + y^2 = 4$ 2. $x^2 + y^2 = 9$ 3. $9x^2 + y^2 = 36$

4. $4x^2 + y^2 = 4$ 5. $x^2 + 4y^2 = 16$ 6. $x^2 + 9y^2 = 4$

7. $x^2 - y^2 = 1$ 8. $4x^2 - y^2 = 1$ 9. $y^2 - x^2 = 9$

10. $4y^2 - 9x^2 = 36$ 11. $2x^2 + 3y^2 = 24$ 12. $4x^2 + 3y^2 = 12$

Graph the equation.

Example: $4x^2 + y^2 = 36$

$y^2 = 36 - 4x^2$

$y = \pm 2\sqrt{9 - x^2}$

Solutions are:

$(3, 0)$ $(-3, 0)$

$(2, \pm 2\sqrt{5})$ $(-2, \pm 2\sqrt{5})$

$(1, \pm 4\sqrt{2})$ $(-1, \pm 4\sqrt{2})$

$(0, \pm 6)$

13. Problem 1 of this set.   14. Problem 2.   15. Problem 3.

16. Problem 4.   17. Problem 5.   18. Problem 6.

19. Problem 7.   20. Problem 8.   21. Problem 9.

22. Problem 10.   23. Problem 11.   24. Problem 12.

25. Graph $xy = 4$ and $xy = 12$ on the same set of axes. (These curves are also hyperbolas.)

26. Graph $xy = -4$ and $xy = -12$ on the same set of axes.

27. Graph $x^2 + y^2 = 25$ and $4x^2 + y^2 = 36$ on the same set of axes. What is the significance of the coordinates of the points of intersection?

28. Graph $y^2 - x^2 = 0$. Discuss the graph in relation to Figure 8.11.

29. Graph $4x^2 - y^2 = 0$. Generalize from the result and discuss the graph of any equation of the form $Ax^2 - By^2 = C$, where $C = 0$.

30. Graph $4x^2 + y^2 = 0$. Generalize from the result and discuss the graph of any equation of the form $Ax^2 + By^2 = C$, where $A, B > 0$ and $C = 0$.

31. Use the distance formula to show that the graph of $\{(x, y) \mid x^2 + y^2 = r^2\}$ is the set of all points located a distance r from the origin.

8.3 Sketching Graphs of Conic Sections

We should make use of the form of the equation to aid in graphing quadratic equations in two variables. With this in mind, the ideas developed in Sections 8.1 and 8.2 may be summarized as follows:

1. A quadratic equation of the form

$$y = ax^2 + bx + c \tag{1}$$

has a graph that is a parabola, opening upward if $a > 0$ and downward if $a < 0$.

2. A quadratic equation of the form

$$Ax^2 + By^2 = C \quad (A^2 + B^2 \neq 0) \tag{2}$$

has a graph that is

(a) a circle if $A = B$, and A, B, and C have like signs;

(b) an ellipse if $A \neq B$ and A, B, and C have like signs;

(c) a hyperbola if A and B are opposite in sign and $C \neq 0$;

(d) two distinct lines through the origin if A and B are opposite in sign and $C = 0$ (see Problem 29, Exercise 8.2);

(e) a point if A and B are both ≥ 0 or both ≤ 0 and $C = 0$ (see Problem 30, Exercise 8.2);

(f) imaginary if A and B are both ≥ 0 and $C < 0$, or if A and B are both ≤ 0 and $C > 0$.

After recognizing the general form of the curve, the graph of a few points should suffice to sketch the graph. The intercepts, for instance, are always easy to locate. Consider the equation

$$x^2 + 4y^2 = 8. \tag{3}$$

By comparing this equation with 2(b), we note immediately that its graph is an ellipse. If $y = 0$, $x = \pm\sqrt{8}$, and if $x = 0$, $y = \pm\sqrt{2}$. We can then sketch the graph of (3) as in Figure 8.12.

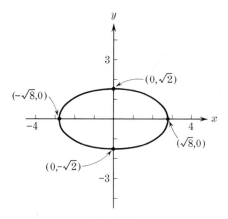

Fig. 8.12

As another example, consider the equation

$$x^2 - y^2 = 3. \tag{4}$$

By comparing this equation with 2(c), we see that its graph is a hyperbola. If $y = 0$, $x = \pm\sqrt{3}$, and if $x = 0$, y is imaginary (the graph will not cross the *y*-axis). By assigning a few other arbitrary values to one of the variables, say *x*, e.g., (4,) and (−4,), we can find the additional ordered pairs

$$(4, \sqrt{13}), \ (4, -\sqrt{13}), \ (-4, \sqrt{13}), \ (-4, -\sqrt{13})$$

which satisfy (4). The graph can then be sketched as shown in Figure 8.13.

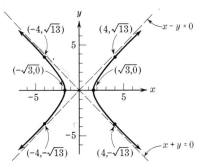

Fig. 8.13

The dashed lines shown in the figure are called **asymptotes** of the graph, and themselves comprise the graph of $x^2 - y^2 = 0$. While we will not discuss the notion in detail here, it is true that, in general, the graph of $Ax^2 - By^2 = C$ will "approach" the two straight lines in the graph of $Ax^2 - By^2 = 0$ for each $A, B, C > 0$. (See Problems 27 and 28, page 190.)

EXERCISE 8.3

Name and sketch the graph of each of the following equations.

Example: $4x^2 = 36 - 9y^2$

    Rewrite in standard form.

$$4x^2 + 9y^2 = 36$$

    By inspection, the graph is an ellipse.

    Intercepts are
      $(0, 2), (0, -2), (3, 0), (-3, 0)$.

1. $x^2 + y^2 = 49$ 2. $x^2 + y^2 = 64$ 3. $x^2 + 9y = 0$

4. $2x^2 - y = 0$ 5. $4x^2 + 25y^2 = 100$ 6. $x^2 + 2y^2 = 8$

7. $x^2 = 9 + y^2$ 8. $-2y^2 = 8 - x^2$ 9. $4x^2 - 4y^2 = 0$

10. $x^2 - 9y^2 = 0$ 11. $y = x^2 - 4$ 12. $y = 4 - 2x^2$

13. $4x^2 + 4y^2 = 1$ 14. $9x^2 + 9y^2 = 2$ 15. $3x^2 = 12 - 4y^2$

16. $4x^2 = 12 - 3y^2$ 17. $y = 4 + 3x - x^2$ 18. $y = x^2 - 3x + 2$

19. $y - 4 = -x^2 - 5x$ 20. $y + x^2 = 2 + x$

21. Sketch the family of four curves $y = x^2 + k$ $(k = -2, 0, 2, 4)$ on a single set of axes. What effect does varying k have on the graph?

22. Graph the set of points satisfying *both* $x^2 + y^2 = 25$ *and* $y = x^2$.

23. Graph the set of points satisfying *either* $y = 4 - x^2$ *or* $y = x^2 - 4$.

24. Graph $\{(x, y) \mid y = 2\} \cap \{(x, y) \mid x = 3\}$.

25. Graph $\{(x, y) \mid y = x + 2\} \cap \{(x, y) \mid 4x^2 + y^2 = 36\}$.

26. Graph $\{(x, y) \mid y = x + 2\} \cup \{(x, y) \mid 4x^2 + y^2 = 36\}$.

27. Show that the ordinates to the graph of $Ax^2 - By^2 = C$ for any value of x are given by

$$y = \pm \sqrt{\frac{A}{B}} x \left(\sqrt{1 - \frac{C}{Ax^2}} \right).$$

28. Explain why, for large values of x, the value of the expression

$$\sqrt{1 - \frac{C}{Ax^2}}$$

approaches 1, and hence explain why $y = \pm \sqrt{\dfrac{A}{B}} x$ are equations for the asymptotes to the graph of $Ax^2 - By^2 = C$.

8.4 Variation as a Functional Relationship

There are two types of functional relationships, widely used in the sciences, to which custom has assigned special names. First, any function defined by the equation

$$y = kx \quad (k \text{ a nonzero constant}) \tag{1}$$

is an example of **direct variation.** The variable y is said to **vary directly** as the variable x. Another example of direct variation is

$$y = kx^2 \quad (k \text{ a nonzero constant}), \tag{1a}$$

where we say that y varies directly as the square of x and, in general,

$$y = kx^n \quad (k \text{ a nonzero constant and } n > 0) \tag{1b}$$

asserts that y varies directly as the nth power of x.

We find examples of such variation in the relationships existing between the radius of a circle and the circumference and area. Thus

$$C = 2\pi r \tag{2}$$

asserts that the circumference of a circle varies directly as the radius, while

$$A = \pi r^2 \tag{3}$$

expresses the fact that the area of a circle varies directly as the square of the radius. Since for each r, (2) and (3) associate only one value of C or A, both of these equations define functions, (2) a linear function and (3) a quadratic function.

The second important type of variation arises from the equation

$$xy = k \quad (k \text{ a nonzero constant}), \tag{4}$$

where x and y are said to **vary inversely**. When (4) is written in the form

$$y = \frac{k}{x}, \tag{5}$$

y is said to vary inversely as x. Similarly, if

$$y = \frac{k}{x^2}, \tag{5a}$$

y is said to vary inversely as the square of x, etc. As an example of inverse variation, consider the set of rectangles with area 24 square units. Since the area of a rectangle is given by

$$lw = A,$$

we have

$$lw = 24,$$

and the length and width of the rectangle can be seen to vary inversely.

Since (5) or (5a) associates only one y with each x ($x \neq 0$), an inverse variation defines a function, with domain

$$\{x \mid x \neq 0\}.$$

The names "direct" and "inverse" as applied to variation arise from the facts that in direct variation an assignment of increasing absolute values to x results in an association with increasing absolute values of y, whereas in inverse variation an assignment of increasing absolute values to x results in an association with decreasing absolute values of y.

The constant involved in equations describing direct or inverse variation is called the **constant of variation**. If we know that one variable varies directly or inversely as another, and if we have one set of associated values for the variables, we can find the constant of variation involved. For example, suppose we know that y varies directly as x^2, and that $y = 4$ when $x = 7$. The fact that y varies directly as x^2 tells us that

$$y = kx^2, \tag{6}$$

and the fact that $y = 4$ when $x = 7$ tells us that $(7, 4)$ is a solution of (6), and hence that

$$4 = k(49),$$

from which

$$k = \frac{4}{49}.$$

The equation specifically expressing the direct variation is

$$y = \frac{4}{49} x^2.$$

In the event that one variable varies as the product of two or more other variables, we refer to the relationship as **joint variation.** Thus, if y varies jointly as u, v, and w, we have

$$y = kuvw. \tag{7}$$

Also, direct and inverse variation may take place concurrently. That is, y may vary directly as x and inversely as z, giving rise to the equation

$$y = k\frac{x}{z}.$$

It should be pointed out that the way in which the word "variation" is used herein is a technical one, and when the ideas of direct, inverse, or joint variation are encountered, we should always think of equations of the form (1), (5), or (7). For instance, the equations

$$y = 2x + 1,$$

$$y = \frac{1}{x} - 2,$$

and

$$y = xz + 2$$

do not describe examples of variation within our meaning of the word.

There is an alternative term used to describe the variation relationships discussed in this section. The word "proportional" is frequently used in this sense. To say that "y is directly proportional to x" or "y is inversely proportional to x" is another way of describing direct and inverse variation. The use of the word "proportion" arises from the fact that any two solutions (a, b) and (c, d) of an equation expressing a direct variation satisfy an equation of the form

$$\frac{a}{b} = \frac{c}{d},$$

which is commonly called a **proportion.** For example, consider the problem in which the volume of a gas varies directly with the absolute temperature and inversely with the pressure and which can be represented by the relationship

$$V = \frac{kT}{P}. \tag{8}$$

For any set of values T_1, P_1, and V_1,

$$k = \frac{V_1 P_1}{T_1}, \tag{8a}$$

and for any other set of values T_2, P_2, and V_2,

$$k = \frac{V_2 P_2}{T_2}. \tag{8b}$$

Equating the right-hand members of (8a) and (8b),

$$\frac{V_1 P_1}{T_1} = \frac{V_2 P_2}{T_2}, \tag{8c}$$

from which the value of any variable can be determined if the values of the other variables are known.

EXERCISE 8.4

Write an equation expressing the relationship between the variables, using k as the constant of variation.

Example: At a constant temperature, the volume (V) of a gas varies inversely as the pressure (P).

Ans. $V = \dfrac{k}{P}$

1. The distance (d) traveled by a car moving at a constant rate varies directly as the time (t).

2. The tension (T) on a spring varies directly as the distance (s) it is stretched.

3. The current (I) in an electrical circuit with constant voltage varies inversely as the resistance (R) of the circuit.

4. The time (t) required by a car to travel a fixed distance varies inversely as the rate (r) at which it travels.

5. The volume (V) of a rectangular box of fixed depth varies jointly as its length (l) and width (w).

6. The power (P) in an electric circuit varies jointly as the resistance (R) and the square of the current (I).

Find the constant of variation:

Example: If V varies inversely as P and $V = 100$ when $P = 30$.

Write an equation expressing the relationship between the variables.

$$V = \frac{k}{P}$$

Substitute the known values for the variables and solve for k.

$$100 = \frac{k}{30}$$

$$3000 = k$$

Ans.   3000

7. If y varies directly as x and $y = 6$ when $x = 2$.

8. If y varies directly as x and $y = 2$ when $x = 5$.

9. If u varies inversely as the square of v and $u = 2$ when $v = 10$.

10. If r varies inversely as the cube of t and $r = 8$ when $t = 10$.

11. If z varies jointly as x and y and $z = 8$ when $x = 2$ and $y = 2$.

12. If p varies jointly as q and r and $p = 5$ when $q = 2$ and $r = 7$.

Example: If V varies directly as T and inversely as P and $V = 40$ when $T = 300$ and $P = 30$, find V when $T = 324$ and $P = 24$.

Write an equation expressing the relationship between the variables.

$$V = \frac{kT}{P} \tag{1}$$

Substitute the initially known values for V, T, and P.   Solve for k.

$$40 = \frac{k300}{30}$$

$$4 = k$$

Rewrite equation (1) with k replaced by 4.

$$V = \frac{4T}{P}$$

Substitute second set of values for T and P and solve for V.

$$V = \frac{4(324)}{24}$$

Ans.   54

13. If y varies directly as x^2 and $y = 9$ when $x = 3$, find y when $x = 4$.

14. If r varies directly as s and inversely as t and $r = 12$ when $s = 8$ and $t = 2$, find r when $s = 3$ and $t = 6$.

15. The distance a particle falls in a certain medium is directly proportional to the square of the length of time it falls.   If the particle falls 16 feet in 2 seconds, how far will it fall in 10 seconds?

16. In Problem 15, how far will the body fall *during* the seventh second?

17. The pressure exerted by a liquid at a given point varies directly as the depth of the point beneath the surface of the liquid.   If a certain liquid exerts a pressure of 40 pounds per square foot at a depth of 10 feet, what would be the pressure at 40 feet?

18. The volume (V) of a gas varies directly as its temperature (T) and inversely as its pressure (P).   A gas occupies 20 cubic feet at a temperature of 300° A (absolute) and a pressure of 30 pounds per square inch.   What will the volume be if the temperature is raised to 360° A and the pressure decreased to 20 pounds per square inch?

19. The maximum-safe uniformly distributed load (L) for a horizontal beam varies jointly as its breadth (b) and square of the depth (d) and inversely as the length (l).   An 8-foot beam with $b = 2$ and $d = 4$ will safely support

a uniformly distributed load of up to 750 pounds. How many uniformly distributed pounds will an 8-foot beam support if $b = 2$ and $d = 6$?

20. The resistance (R) of a wire varies directly as the length (l) and inversely as the square of its diameter (d). 50 feet of wire of diameter 0.012 inches has a resistance of 10 ohms. What is the resistance of 50 feet of the same type of wire if the diameter is increased to 0.015 inches?

Represent the relationship as a proportion by eliminating the constant of variation and then solve for the required variable.

Example: If V varies directly as T and inversely as P, and $V = 40$ when $T = 300$ and $P = 30$, find V when $T = 324$ and $P = 24$.

Write an equation expressing the relationship between the variables.

$$V = \frac{kT}{P}$$

Solve for k.

$$k = \frac{VP}{T}$$

Write a proportion relating the variables for two different sets of conditions.

$$\frac{V_1 P_1}{T_1} = \frac{V_2 P_2}{T_2}$$

Substitute the known values of the variables.

$$\frac{(40)(30)}{300} = \frac{V_2(24)}{324}$$

Solve for V_2.

$$V_2 = \frac{(324)(40)(30)}{300(24)}$$

Ans. 54

21. Problem 13 of this set.   **22.** Problem 14.   **23.** Problem 15.

24. Problem 16.   **25.** Problem 17.   **26.** Problem 18.

27. Problem 19.   **28.** Problem 20.

29. From the formula for the circumference of a circle, $C = \pi D$, show that the ratio of the circumference of two circles equals the ratio of their respective diameters.

30. From the formula for the area of a circle, $A = \pi r^2$, show that the ratio of the areas of two circles equals the ratio of the squares of their respective radii.

31. Graph on the same set of axes the linear functions defined by $y = kx$, $x \geq 0$, when $k = -3, -2, -1, 1, 2,$ and 3, respectively. Note that the constant of variation and the slope of the graph of the equation are the same. What can you say about the x- and y-intercepts in each case?

32. Graph on the same set of axes the quadratic function defined by $y = kx^2$, $x \geq 0$, when $k = 1$, 2, and 3, respectively.   What effect does a variation in k have on the graph of $y = kx^2$?

33. Graph on the same set of axes the equations $y = kx$, $y = kx^2$, and $y = kx^3$ where $k = 2$ and $x \geq 0$.   What effect does increasing the degree of the equation $y = kx^n$ have on the graph of the equation?

34. Graph on the same set of axes the function defined by $xy = k$, for $k = 1$, 2, and $x > 0$.   What effect does a variation in k have on the graph of the function?

35. Graph on the same set of axes the functions defined by $xy = k$, $x^2y = k$, and $x^3y = k$ for $k = 2$ and $x > 0$.   What effect does increasing n have on the graph of $x^ny = k$?

36. If y varies directly as x and z varies directly as x, show that $y + z$ varies directly as x.

37. If y varies directly as x and z varies directly as x, show that $\sqrt{yz}$ varies directly as x.

8.5 Graphs of Quadratic Inequalities

Quadratic inequalities of the form

$$y < ax^2 + bx + c \tag{1}$$

or

$$y > ax^2 + bx + c, \tag{2}$$

which define quadratic relations, can be graphed in the same manner in which we graphed linear inequalities in two variables. We first graph the equation having the same members and then shade an appropriate region as required. For instance, to graph

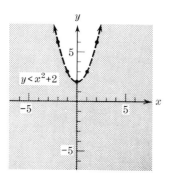

$$y < x^2 + 2, \tag{3}$$

we first graph

$$y = x^2 + 2, \tag{4}$$

and then shade the area below the curve. As we did in Section 7.6, we can determine which part of the plane should be shaded by substituting the coordinates of the origin

Fig. 8.14

$(0, 0)$ in the inequality and noting whether or not the result is true. Substituting $(0, 0)$ in (3), we obtain $0 < 0 + 2$, which is true, and the part of the plane including the origin is shaded. Since the graph of (4) is not part of the graph of (3), a broken curve is used (Figure 8.14).

EXERCISE 8.5

Graph.

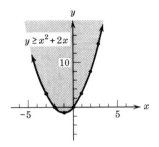

Example: $y \geq x^2 + 2x$

Graph $y = x^2 + 2x$.

Shade portion of plane above the graph of $y = x^2 + 2x$.

1. $y > x^2$ **2.** $y < x^2$ **3.** $y \geq x^2 + 3$

4. $y \leq x^2 + 3$ **5.** $y < 3x^2 + 2x$ **6.** $y > 3x^2 + 2x$

7. $y \leq x^2 + 3x + 2$ **8.** $y \geq x^2 + 3x + 2$ **9.** $y \geq 2x^2 - 5x + 1$

10. $y \leq 2x^2 - 5x + 1$ **11.** $3x^2 + 4x + 1 \leq y$ **12.** $2x^2 - 3x - 1 \geq y$

13. Graph the inequality $x^2 + y^2 \leq 25$ by observing that the graph of the equation $x^2 + y^2 = a^2$ is a circle of radius a and examining what $a \leq 5$ implies for $x^2 + y^2$.

Graph.

14. $\{(x, y) \mid 4x^2 + 9y^2 \leq 36\}$

15. $\{(x, y) \mid 16 \leq x^2 + y^2 \leq 25\}$

16. $\{(x, y) \mid y \leq 1 - x^2\} \cup \{(x, y) \mid y \geq -1\}$

17. $\{(x, y) \mid y \leq 4 - x^2\} \cup \{(x, y) \mid y \geq x^2 - 4\}$

18. $\{(x, y) \mid x \geq 2\} \cap \{(x, y) \mid y \leq 3\}$

19. $\{(x, y) \mid y \geq 2x\} \cap \{(x, y) \mid y \leq 2x\}$

20. $\{(x, y) \mid y > 2x\} \cup \{(x, y) \mid y < 2x\}$

CHAPTER REVIEW

1. Find the coordinates of the minimum point on the graph of
$$\{[x, f(x)] \mid f(x) = x^2 - 6x + 5\}.$$

2. Graph $\{(x, y) \mid y = -2x^2 + 5x\}$.

3. Write $x + 9y^2 = 26$ as two separate equations, each of which defines a function; state the domain of each function over $R \times R$.

4. Name the graph of each of the following equations.

    a. $x^2 - 3y^2 = 8$ b. $x^2 = 4 - y^2$

    c. $x^2 - y + 4 = 0$ d. $2y^2 = 4 - x^2$

5. a. Graph $\{(x, y) \mid x^2 + y^2 = 36\}$.   b. Graph $\{(x, y) \mid 4x^2 + y^2 = 36\}$.

6. a. Graph $\{(x, y) \mid 4x^2 - y^2 = 16\}$.   b. Graph $\{(x, y) \mid y^2 - 4x^2 = 16\}$.

7. Find k if $(2, -1)$ is a solution of $kx^2 - 3y = 6$.

8. a. Graph $\{(x, y) \mid xy = 8\}$.   b. Graph $\{(x, y) \mid xy = -8\}$.

9. Graph $\{(x, y) \mid y = kx^2\}$ $(k = -4, -2, 2, 4)$ on the same set of axes.

10. If y varies inversely as t^2, and $y = 16$ when $t = 3$, find y when $t = 4$.

11. The weight of a body above the surface of the earth varies inversely as the square of its distance from the center of the earth. If we assume the radius of the earth to be 4000 miles, how much would a man weigh 500 miles above the earth's surface if he weighed 200 pounds on the surface?

12. Graph $\{(x, y) \mid y \geq x^2 + 1\}$.

13. Graph $\{(x, y) \mid y \leq \sqrt{25 - x^2}\}$.

14. Graph $\{(x, y) \mid y > x^2\} \cup \{(x, y) \mid y \leq -x^2\}$.

15. Graph $\{(x, y) \mid y > x^2 - 4x\} \cap \{(x, y) \mid y \leq 2\}$.

9

SYSTEMS OF EQUATIONS
AND INEQUALITIES

In Chapter 7, we observed that the solution set of an open sentence in two variables, such as

$$ax + by + c = 0$$

or

$$ax + by + c \leq 0,$$

might contain infinitely many ordered pairs of numbers. It is often necessary to consider pairs of such sentences and to inquire whether or not the solution sets of the sentences contain ordered pairs in common. More specifically, we are interested in determining the members of the intersection of their solution sets.

9.1 Systems of Linear Equations in Two Variables

We shall begin by considering the system

$$a_1 x + b_1 y + c_1 = 0 \quad (a_1, b_1 \text{ not both } 0)$$

$$a_2 x + b_2 y + c_2 = 0 \quad (a_2, b_2 \text{ not both } 0)$$

and studying $A \cap B$, where

$$A = \{(x, y) \mid a_1x + b_1y + c_1 = 0\}$$

and

$$B = \{(x, y) \mid a_2x + b_2y + c_2 = 0\}.$$

In a geometric sense, because the graphs of both A and B are straight lines, we are confronted with three possibilities, as illustrated in Figure 9.1:

a. The graphs are the same line.
b. The graphs are parallel but distinct lines.
c. The graphs intersect in one and only one point.

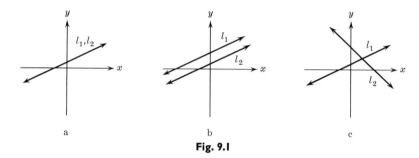

Fig. 9.1

These possibilities lead, correspondingly, to the conclusion that one and only one of the following is true for any given system of two such linear equations in x and y:

a. The solution sets of the equations are equal, and their intersection contains all those ordered pairs found in either one of the given solution sets.
b. The intersection of the two solution sets is the null set.
c. The intersection of the two solution sets contains one and only one ordered pair.

In case (a), the left-hand members of the two linear equations in x and y are said to be **linearly dependent**, and the equations are **consistent**; in case (b), the left-hand members are **linearly independent**, and the equations are **inconsistent**; and in case (c), the left-hand members are **linearly independent** and the equations are **consistent**. If the two left-hand members are linearly dependent, then one of them can be obtained from the other through multiplication by a constant. Thus

$$2x + 4y - 8 \quad \text{and} \quad 6x + 12y - 24$$

are linearly dependent, but

$$2x + 4y - 8 \quad \text{and} \quad 6x + 12y - 23$$

are not.

For example, from the graphs of the system

$$x + y = 5$$

$$x - y = 1$$

in Fig. 9.2, it is evident that the ordered pair (3, 2) is common to the solution sets of both equations. That is,

$$\{(x, y) \mid x + y = 5\} \cap \{(x, y) \mid x - y = 1\} = \{(3, 2)\}.$$

This can be verified by substituting (3, 2) into each equation in turn and observing that a true statement results in each case.

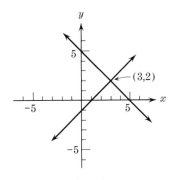

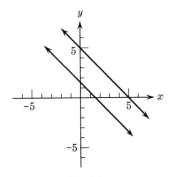

           Fig. 9.2   **Fig. 9.3**

As another example, consider the system

$$x + y = 5$$

$$2x + 2y = 3$$

and the graphs of these equations in Figure 9.3, where the lines appear to be parallel. We conclude that the solution set of this system is $\emptyset$. That is,

$$\{(x, y) \mid x + y = 5\} \cap \{(x, y) \mid 2x + 2y = 3\} = \emptyset.$$

This brings us to a very important consideration regarding the use of graphs to solve such systems. The results obtained by means of a graph are, in general, only approximations, because of the limitations placed on us by the nature of the instruments we use to construct graphs. Also, in cases where one or both of the components of the ordered pair in the solution are nonintegral, we must *estimate* its graph. In the case of the system above, the lines appear to be parallel, but we can never be sure by confining our attention to the graph.

Because graphing equations is a time-consuming process, and, more importantly, because graphical results are not always precise, solutions to systems of linear equations are usually sought by analytic methods.

One such method depends on the following theorem.

Any ordered pair (x, y) *that satisfies the equations*

$$a_1x + b_1y + c_1 = 0 \tag{1}$$

$$a_2x + b_2y + c_2 = 0 \tag{2}$$

will also satisfy the equation

$$A(a_1x + b_1y + c_1) + B(a_2x + b_2y + c_2) = 0 \tag{3}$$

for every real A and B.

This is true because the replacement of the variables in (3) with the components of any ordered pair (x, y) that satisfies both (1) and (2) results in

$$A(0) + B(0) = 0,$$

which is clearly true for any values of A and B. The left-hand member of equation (3) is called a **linear combination** of the left-hand members of equations (1) and (2). The foregoing italicized statement asserts that any ordered pair satisfying both (1) and (2) must also satisfy the sum of any real-number multiples of (1) and (2). This fact can be used to identify any such ordered pairs.

Consider the system

$$2x + y - 4 = 0 \tag{4}$$

$$x - 3y + 5 = 0. \tag{5}$$

We can multiply each member of (4) by 1 and each member of (5) by -2 to obtain

$$2x + y - 4 = 0 \tag{4'}$$

$$-2x + 6y - 10 = 0. \tag{5'}$$

The sum of the left-hand members of (4′) and (5′) is a linear combination of the left-hand members of (4) and (5), and the result,

$$0x + 7y - 14 = 0 \tag{6}$$

or

$$y = 2, \tag{6'}$$

must contain in its solution set any solution common to the solution sets of the two original equations. But any solution of (6) must be of the form $(x, 2)$—that is, have y-component 2. Now, substituting 2 for y in either (4) or (5), the x-component for the ordered pair $(x, 2)$ that satisfies (4) and (5) can be determined. If (4) is used, we have

$$2x + (2) - 4 = 0$$

$$x = 1$$

and, if (5) is used, we have

$$x - 3(2) + 5 = 0$$

$$x = 1.$$

Since the ordered pair $(1, 2)$ satisfies both (4) and (5), the required solution set is $\{(1, 2)\}$. That is,

$$\{(x, y) \mid 2x + y - 4 = 0\} \cap \{(x, y) \mid x - 3y + 5 = 0\} = \{(1, 2)\}.$$

Notice that $(1, 2)$ also satisfies (6) and (6').

Observe how the concept of a linear combination is used. Multipliers A and B are chosen so that the resulting linear equation is free of one of the variables—which one is immaterial.

The argument proceeds in exactly the same manner when the constant terms are written as the right-hand members of the two equations. As an example, consider the system

$$2x - y = 5 \tag{7}$$

$$3x + 2y = 4. \tag{8}$$

We can mentally multiply each member of equation (7) by 2 and each member of equation (8) by 1 and add the resulting equations member by member, yielding

$$7x = 14,$$

from which we obtain 2 as the x-component of a solution of (7) and (8). Thus $(2, y)$ is the form of the required solution, and, upon substituting 2 for x in (7), we have

$$2(2) - y = 5,$$

from which

$$y = -1.$$

The solution set of the system (7) and (8) is, therefore, $\{(2, -1)\}$. In this case, we chose multipliers 2 and 1 to eliminate y from the resulting equation.

If the coefficients of the variables in one equation in a system are proportional to the coefficients in the other equation, the equations are either dependent or inconsistent. For example, consider the system

$$2x + 3y = 2 \tag{9}$$

$$4x + 6y = 7. \tag{10}$$

Since the coefficients of x and y in (9) and (10) are such that

$$\frac{2}{4} = \frac{3}{6},$$

it follows that any attempt to form a linear combination of the left-hand members of these equations free of one variable will result in an equation free of both variables. Thus, if we multiply -2 times equation (9) and 1 times equation (10), we have

$$-4x - 6y = -4$$

$$4x + 6y = 7,$$

which, upon adding left-hand members and right-hand members, yields

$$0 = 3.$$

Since this equation is not true for any values of x and y, the solution set of the system is $\emptyset$ and the equations are inconsistent. Now, consider the system

$$2x + 3y = 2 \qquad\qquad (11)$$

$$4x + 6y = 4, \qquad\qquad (12)$$

where the coefficients of the variables and the constant terms are proportional. The result of adding -2 times equation (11) to 1 times equation (12) is

$$0 = 0.$$

Because this equation is true for any values of x and y, the solution sets of the given equations must be identical and the equations are dependent.

Systems of equations are quite useful in expressing relationships in practical applications. By assigning separate variables to represent separate physical quantities, the difficulty encountered in symbolically representing these relationships can usually be decreased. In writing systems of equations, we must be careful that the conditions giving rise to one equation are independent of the conditions giving rise to any other equation.

EXERCISE 9.1

Find the solution set for each of the following systems by analytic methods. Check your solutions of Problems 1–14 by graphical methods. If the equations are inconsistent or dependent, so state.

Example: $\frac{2}{3}x - y = 2$ (1)

         $x + \frac{1}{2}y = 7$ (2)

Multiply each member of equation (1) by 3 and each member of equation (2) by 2.

   $2x - 3y = 6$ (1′)

    $2x + y = 14$ (2′)

Add -1 times (1′) to 1 times (2′) and solve for y.

      $4y = 8$

      $y = 2$

Substitute 2 for y in either (1), (2), (1'), or (2') and solve for x. In this example, equation (2) is used.

$$x + \tfrac{1}{2}(2) = 7$$
$$x = 6$$

Ans. $\{(6, 2)\}$

1. $x - y = 1$
$x + y = 5$

2. $2x - 3y = 6$
$x + 3y = 3$

3. $3x + y = 7$
$2x - 5y = -1$

4. $2x - y = 7$
$3x + 2y = 14$

5. $5x - y = -29$
$2x + 3y = 2$

6. $6x + 4y = 12$
$3x + 2y = 12$

7. $5x + 2y = 3$
$x = 0$

8. $2x - y = 0$
$x = -3$

9. $3x - 2y = 4$
$y = -1$

10. $x + 2y = 6$
$x = 2$

11. $\tfrac{1}{4}x - \tfrac{1}{3}y = -\tfrac{5}{12}$
$\tfrac{1}{10}x + \tfrac{1}{5}y = \tfrac{1}{2}$

12. $\tfrac{2}{3}x - y = 4$
$x - \tfrac{3}{4}y = 6$

13. $\tfrac{1}{7}x - \tfrac{3}{7}y = 1$
$2x - y = -4$

14. $\tfrac{1}{4}x - \tfrac{2}{3}y = 2$
$x - 2y = 6$

In Problems 15–18, solve for $1/x$ or $1/y$ and then for x and y.

15. $\dfrac{1}{x} + \dfrac{1}{y} = 7$

$\dfrac{2}{x} + \dfrac{3}{y} = 16$

16. $\dfrac{1}{x} + \dfrac{2}{y} = -\dfrac{11}{12}$

$\dfrac{1}{x} + \dfrac{1}{y} = -\dfrac{7}{12}$

17. $\dfrac{5}{x} - \dfrac{6}{y} = -3$

$\dfrac{10}{x} + \dfrac{9}{y} = 1$

18. $\dfrac{1}{x} + \dfrac{2}{y} = 11$

$\dfrac{1}{x} - \dfrac{2}{y} = -1$

19. $\dfrac{1}{x} - \dfrac{1}{y} = 4$

$\dfrac{2}{x} - \dfrac{1}{2y} = 11$

20. $\dfrac{2}{3x} + \dfrac{3}{4y} = \dfrac{7}{12}$

$\dfrac{4}{x} - \dfrac{3}{4y} = \dfrac{7}{4}$

Problems 21–32 that follow have previously been solved by means of a single equation in one variable. Each of these should now be solved using systems of equations.

Example: The sum of two numbers is 17 and one of the numbers is four less than twice the other. Find the numbers.

Represent each number by a separate variable.

Let x and y represent numbers.

Represent two independent conditions stated in the problem by two equations.

$x + y = 17$

$x = 2y - 4$

Rewrite the equations in standard form.

$x + y = 17$

$x - 2y = -4$

Solve the resulting system.

Ans.   The numbers are 10 and 7.   **Check:** Does $(10) + (7) = 17$?   Yes.

Does $(10) = 2(7) - 4$?   Yes.

21. Problem 3   **22.** Problem 4.   **23.** Problem 5.
of Exercise 5.6.

24. Problem 6.   **25.** Problem 9.   **26.** Problem 14.

27. Problem 17.   **28.** Problem 18.   **29.** Problem 19.

30. Problem 20.   **31.** Problem 21.   **32.** Problem 22.

33. Find a and b so that the graph of $ax + by + 3 = 0$ passes through the points $(-1, 2)$ and $(-3, 0)$.

34. Find a and b so that the solution set of the system

$$ax + by = 4$$

$$bx - ay = -3$$

is $\{(1, 2)\}$.

35. Recall that the slope-intercept form of a straight line is given by $y = mx + b$. Find the equation of the line that passes through the points $(0, 2)$ and $(3, -8)$.

36. Find the equation of the line that passes through the points $(-6, 2)$ and $(4, 1)$.

37. Find the linear relationship between centigrade temperature C and Fahrenheit temperature F, given the fact that $F = 32°$ when $C = 0°$, and $F = 212°$ when $C = 100°$.

38. Show that if the equations in the system

$$a_1x + b_1y = c_1$$

$$a_2x + b_2y = c_2$$

have identical solution sets, then

$$\frac{a_1}{a_2} = \frac{b_1}{b_2} = \frac{c_1}{c_2}.$$

Hint: Write the equations in slope-intercept form and argue from the fact that equal slopes and equal intercepts imply identical solution sets.

39. Show that if

$$\frac{a_1}{a_2} = \frac{b_1}{b_2} \neq \frac{c_1}{c_2},$$

then the equations in the system

$$a_1 x + b_1 y = c_1$$

$$a_2 x + b_2 y = c_2$$

are either dependent or inconsistent.

9.2 Linear Systems in Two Variables—Solution by Determinants

A square array of numbers written between vertical lines,

$$\begin{vmatrix} a_1 & b_1 \\ a_2 & b_2 \end{vmatrix},$$

is called a **determinant.** The numbers a_1, b_1, a_2, and b_2 are called **elements** of the determinant. Because this determinant has two rows and two columns of elements, it is called a two-by-two (2×2) determinant or a determinant of order two.

We define the value of the determinant to be

$$a_1 b_2 - a_2 b_1.$$

This value is obtained by multiplying the elements on the diagonals, and adding the negative of the second product to the first product. This process can be shown schematically as

$$\begin{vmatrix} a_1 & b_1 \\ a_2 & b_2 \end{vmatrix} = a_1 b_2 - a_2 b_1.$$

For example,

$$\begin{vmatrix} 1 & 2 \\ -1 & 3 \end{vmatrix} = 3 - (-2) = 5,$$

$$\begin{vmatrix} 0 & -1 \\ -1 & 7 \end{vmatrix} = 0 - 1 = -1.$$

A determinant, therefore, is simply another way to represent a single number.

Determinants can be used to solve linear systems. In this section we will confine our attention to linear systems of two equations in two variables of the form

$$a_1 x + b_1 y = c_1 \tag{1}$$

$$a_2 x + b_2 y = c_2. \tag{2}$$

If this system is solved by means of a linear combination, we have, upon multiplication of equation (1) by $-a_2$ and equation (2) by a_1, the equations

$$-a_1a_2x - a_2b_1y = -a_2c_1 \tag{1'}$$

$$a_1a_2x + a_1b_2y = a_1c_2, \tag{2'}$$

the sum of whose members is

$$a_1b_2y - a_2b_1y = a_1c_2 - a_2c_1.$$

Now, factoring y from each term in the left-hand member, we have

$$(a_1b_2 - a_2b_1)y = a_1c_2 - a_2c_1,$$

and

$$y = \frac{a_1c_2 - a_2c_1}{a_1b_2 - a_2b_1}. \tag{3}$$

But the numerator of (3) is just the value of the determinant

$$\begin{vmatrix} a_1 & c_1 \\ a_2 & c_2 \end{vmatrix},$$

which we designate as D_y, and the denominator is the value of the determinant

$$\begin{vmatrix} a_1 & b_1 \\ a_2 & b_2 \end{vmatrix},$$

which we designate as D, so that (3) can be written

$$y = \frac{D_y}{D} = \frac{\begin{vmatrix} a_1 & c_1 \\ a_2 & c_2 \end{vmatrix}}{\begin{vmatrix} a_1 & b_1 \\ a_2 & b_2 \end{vmatrix}}. \tag{4}$$

The elements of the determinant in the denominator of (4) are the coefficients of the variables in (1) and (2). The elements of the determinant in the numerator of (4) are identical to those in the denominator, except that the elements in the column containing the coefficients of y have been replaced by the constant terms of (1) and (2).

By exactly the same procedure, we can show that

$$x = \frac{D_x}{D} = \frac{\begin{vmatrix} c_1 & b_1 \\ c_2 & b_2 \end{vmatrix}}{\begin{vmatrix} a_1 & b_1 \\ a_2 & b_2 \end{vmatrix}}, \tag{5}$$

and (4) and (5) together yield the components of the ordered pair in the solution set of the system. The use of determinants in this way is known as *Cramer's rule* for the solution of a system of linear equations.

As an example of the use of Cramer's rule, consider the system

$$2x + y = 4$$
$$x - 3y = -5.$$

We have

$$D = \begin{vmatrix} 2 & 1 \\ 1 & -3 \end{vmatrix} = (-6 - 1) = -7,$$

$$D_x = \begin{vmatrix} 4 & 1 \\ -5 & -3 \end{vmatrix} = (-12 + 5) = -7,$$

and

$$D_y = \begin{vmatrix} 2 & 4 \\ 1 & -5 \end{vmatrix} = (-10 - 4) = -14.$$

Therefore,

$$x = \frac{D_x}{D} = \frac{-7}{-7} = 1,$$

$$y = \frac{D_y}{D} = \frac{-14}{-7} = 2,$$

and the solution set is $\{(1, 2)\}$.

If $D = 0$ in this procedure, the equations in the system are either dependent or inconsistent as D_y and D_x are zero or not zero.

EXERCISE 9.2

Evaluate.

Example:

$$\begin{vmatrix} 2 & -3 \\ 1 & 4 \end{vmatrix} = (2)(4) - (1)(-3) = 11$$

Ans. 11

1. $\begin{vmatrix} 1 & 0 \\ 2 & 1 \end{vmatrix}$ **2.** $\begin{vmatrix} 3 & -2 \\ 4 & 1 \end{vmatrix}$ **3.** $\begin{vmatrix} -5 & -1 \\ 3 & \frac{3}{5} \end{vmatrix}$ **4.** $\begin{vmatrix} 1 & -2 \\ -1 & 2 \end{vmatrix}$

5. $\begin{vmatrix} -1 & 6 \\ 0 & -2 \end{vmatrix}$ **6.** $\begin{vmatrix} 20 & 3 \\ -20 & -2 \end{vmatrix}$ **7.** $\begin{vmatrix} \frac{2}{3} & \frac{3}{5} \\ \frac{2}{5} & -\frac{4}{3} \end{vmatrix}$ **8.** $\begin{vmatrix} \frac{3}{4} & \frac{1}{3} \\ -\frac{2}{3} & \frac{1}{4} \end{vmatrix}$

Find the solution set of each of the following systems by Cramer's rule.

Example: $2x - 3y = 6$
$$2x + y = 14$$

$$D = \begin{vmatrix} 2 & -3 \\ 2 & 1 \end{vmatrix} = (2)(1) - (2)(-3) = 8$$

The elements in D_x are obtained from the elements in D by replacing the elements in the column containing the coefficients of x with the constant terms 6 and 14.

$$D_x = \begin{vmatrix} 6 & -3 \\ 14 & 1 \end{vmatrix} = (6)(1) - (14)(-3) = 48$$

The elements in D_y are obtained from the elements in D by replacing the elements in the column containing the coefficients of y with the constant terms 6 and 14.

$$D_y = \begin{vmatrix} 2 & 6 \\ 2 & 14 \end{vmatrix} = (2)(14) - (2)(6) = 16$$

x and y can now be determined by Cramer's rule.

$$x = \frac{D_x}{D} = \frac{48}{8} = 6$$

$$y = \frac{D_y}{D} = \frac{16}{8} = 2$$

Ans. $\{(6, 2)\}$

9. $2x - 3y = -1$
   $x + 4y = 5$

10. $3x - 4y = -2$
    $x - 2y = 0$

11. $3x - 4y = -2$
    $6x + 12y = 36$

12. $2x - 4y = 7$
    $x - 2y = 1$

13. $\frac{1}{3}x - \frac{1}{2}y = 0$
    $\frac{1}{2}x + \frac{1}{4}y = 4$

14. $\frac{2}{3}x + y = 1$
    $x - \frac{4}{3}y = 0$

15. $x - 2y = 5$
    $\frac{2}{3}x - \frac{4}{3}y = 6$

16. $\frac{1}{2}x + y = 3$
    $-\frac{1}{4}x - y = -3$

17. $x - 3y = 1$
    $y = 1$

18. $2x - 3y = 12$
    $x = 4$

19. $ax + by = 1$
    $bx + ay = 1$

20. $x + y = a$
    $x - y = b$

Show that for every real value of the variables:

21. $\begin{vmatrix} a & a \\ b & b \end{vmatrix} = 0.$

22. $\begin{vmatrix} a_1 & b_1 \\ a_2 & b_2 \end{vmatrix} = -\begin{vmatrix} a_2 & b_2 \\ a_1 & b_1 \end{vmatrix}.$

23. $\begin{vmatrix} a_1 & b_1 \\ a_2 & b_2 \end{vmatrix} = -\begin{vmatrix} b_1 & a_1 \\ b_2 & a_2 \end{vmatrix}.$

24. $\begin{vmatrix} ka_1 & b_1 \\ ka_2 & b_2 \end{vmatrix} = k\begin{vmatrix} a_1 & b_1 \\ a_2 & b_2 \end{vmatrix}.$

25. $\begin{vmatrix} a_1 + ka_2 & b_1 + kb_2 \\ a_2 & b_2 \end{vmatrix} = \begin{vmatrix} a_1 & b_1 \\ a_2 & b_2 \end{vmatrix}.$

26. Show that if both $D_y = 0$ and $D_x = 0$, it follows that $D = 0$ when c_1 and c_2 are not both 0, and the equations in the system

$$a_1x + b_1y + c_1 = 0$$
$$a_2x + b_2y + c_2 = 0$$

are dependent. *Hint:* Show that the first two determinant equations imply that $a_1c_2 = a_2c_1$ and $b_1c_2 = b_2c_1$ and that the rest follows from the formation of a proportion with these equations.

27. Show that if $D = 0$ and $D_x = 0$, then $D_y = 0$.

9.3 Linear Systems in Three Variables—Analytic Solution

A solution of an equation in three variables, such as

$$x + 2y - 3z + 4 = 0, \tag{1}$$

is an ordered triple of numbers (x, y, z), because all three of the variables in (1) must be replaced by numerals before we can decide whether the result is an equality. Thus $(0, -2, 0)$ and $(-1, 0, 1)$ are solutions of (1), while $(1, 1, 1)$ is not. There are, of course, infinitely many members in the solution set of (1).

The solution set of a system of three linear equations in three variables, such as

$$x + 2y - 3z + 4 = 0 \tag{1}$$

$$2x - y + z - 3 = 0 \tag{2}$$

$$3x + 2y + z - 10 = 0, \tag{3}$$

is the intersection of the solution sets of all three of the equations in the system. That is,

$$S = \{(x, y, z) \mid x + 2y - 3z + 4 = 0\} \cap \{(x, y, z) \mid 2x - y + z - 3 = 0\}$$
$$\cap \{(x, y, z) \mid 3x + 2y + z - 10 = 0\}.$$

We seek solution sets of systems such as (1), (2), and (3) by methods analogous to those used in solving linear systems in two variables. Since graphical treatments would be three-dimensional (linear equations in three variables can be represented by planes, and their common intersection, if any, would represent the solution set), we will consider analytic solutions only. In the foregoing system, we might begin by multiplying equation (1) by -2 and adding the result to 1 times equation (2) to produce

$$-5y + 7z - 11 = 0, \tag{4}$$

which is satisfied by any ordered triple (x, y, z) that satisfies (1) and (2). Similarly, we can add -3 times equation (1) to 1 times equation (3) to obtain

$$-4y + 10z - 22 = 0, \tag{5}$$

which is satisfied by any ordered triple (x, y, z) that satisfies both (1) and (3). We can now argue that any ordered triple satisfying the system

$$-5y + 7z - 11 = 0 \tag{4}$$

$$-4y + 10z - 22 = 0 \tag{5}$$

will also satisfy (1), (2), and (3). Since the system (4) and (5) does not depend on x, the problem has been reduced to one of finding the y- and

z-components of the solution only. The system (4) and (5) can be solved by the methods of Section 9.2 or Section 9.3. Either procedure will lead to the values $y = 2$ and $z = 3$. Since any solution of (1), (2), and (3) must be of the form $(x, 2, 3)$, 2 can be substituted for y and 3 for z in (1) to obtain $x = 1$, so that the desired solution set is

$$\{(1, 2, 3)\}.$$

If at any step in the procedure outlined above the resulting linear combination vanishes or yields a contradiction, the system contains linearly dependent equations or else two or three inconsistent equations, and either has no members in its solution set or else an infinite number of members.

The process of solving a system of consistent and independent equations can be reduced to a series of mechanical procedures as illustrated by the example in Exercise 9.3.

EXERCISE 9.3

Solve. If the equations in the system are inconsistent or dependent, so state.

Example:

$x + 2y - z + 1 = 0$	(1)
$x - 3y + z - 2 = 0$	(2)
$2x + y + 2z - 6 = 0$	(3)

Multiply (1) by -1 and add the result to 1 times (2); multiply (1) by -2 and add the result to 1 times (3).

$-5y + 2z - 3 = 0$	(4)
$-3y + 4z - 8 = 0$	(5)

Multiply (4) by -2 and add the result to 1 times (5).

$7y - 2 = 0$	(6)
$y = \tfrac{2}{7}$	

Substitute $\tfrac{2}{7}$ for y in either (4) or (5), say (4).

$$-5(\tfrac{2}{7}) + 2z - 3 = 0$$
$$z = \tfrac{31}{14}$$

Substitute $\tfrac{2}{7}$ for y and $\tfrac{31}{14}$ for z in either (1), (2), or (3), say (1).

$$x + 2(\tfrac{2}{7}) - \tfrac{31}{14} + 1 = 0$$
$$x = \tfrac{9}{14}$$

Ans. $\{(\tfrac{9}{14}, \tfrac{2}{7}, \tfrac{31}{14})\}$

1. $x + y + z = 2$
$2x - y + z = -1$
$x - y - z = 0$

2. $x + y + z = 1$
$2x - y + 3z = 2$
$2x - y - z = 2$

3. $x + y + 2z = 0$
$2x - 2y + z = 8$
$3x + 2y + z = 2$

4. $5y - 8z = -19$
    $5x - 8z = 6$
    $3x - 2y = 12$

5. $x - 2y + z = -1$
    $2x + y - 3z = 3$
    $3x + 3y - 2z = 10$

6. $x - 2y + 4z = -3$
    $3x + y - 2z = 12$
    $2x + y - 3z = 11$

7. $x - 2y + 3z = 4$
    $2x - y + z = 1$
    $3x - 3y + 4z = 5$

8. $x + 5y - z = 2$
    $3x - 9y + 3z = 6$
    $x - 3y + z = 4$

9. $2x + z = 7$
    $y - z = -2$
    $x + y = 2$

10. $2x - 3y + z = 3$
    $x - y - 2z = -1$
    $-x + 2y - 3z = -4$

11. $x - \frac{1}{2}y - \frac{1}{2}z = 4$
    $x - \frac{3}{2}y - 2z = 3$
    $\frac{1}{4}x + \frac{1}{4}y - \frac{1}{4}z = 0$

12. $x + 2y + \frac{1}{2}z = 0$
    $x + \frac{3}{5}y - \frac{2}{5}z = \frac{1}{5}$
    $4x - 7y - 7z = 6$

Example: The sum of three numbers is 12. Twice the first number is equal to the second, and the third is equal to the sum of the other two. Find the numbers.

Represent each number by a separate variable.

Let x, y, and z represent numbers.

Write the three independent conditions stated in the problem as three equations.

$x + y + z = 12$

     $2x = y$

   $x + y = z$

Rewrite equations in standard form.

$x + y + z = 12$

     $2x - y = 0$

$x + y - z = 0$

Find the solution set of the system by any convenient means.

Ans. The numbers are 2, 4, and 6.

13. The sum of three numbers is 15. The second equals two times the first and the third equals the second. Find the numbers.

14. The sum of three numbers is 2. The first number is equal to the sum of the other two, and the third number is the result of subtracting the first from the second. Find the numbers.

15. A box contains \$6.25 in nickels, dimes, and quarters. There are 85 coins in all with three times as many nickels as dimes. How many coins of each kind are there?

16. The perimeter of a triangle is 155 inches. The side x is 20 inches shorter than the side y, and the side y is 5 inches longer than the side z. Find the lengths of the sides of the triangle.

17. A man had \$446 in ten-dollar, five-dollar, and one-dollar bills. There were 94 bills in all and 10 more five-dollar bills than ten-dollar bills. How many bills of each kind did he have?

18. Find values for a, b, and c so that the graph of $x^2 + y^2 + ax + by + c = 0$ will contain the points $(0, 0)$, $(6, 0)$, and $(0, 8)$.

19. The equation for a circle can be written $x^2 + y^2 + ax + by + c = 0$. Find the equation of the circle whose graph contains the points $(2, 3)$, $(3, 2)$, and $(-4, -5)$.

20. Find values for a, b, and c so that the graph of $y = ax^2 + bx + c$ will contain the points $(-1, 2)$, $(1, 6)$, and $(2, 11)$.

21. Show that the system

$$x + y + 2z = 2$$
$$2x - y + z = 3$$

has an infinite number of members in its solution set. *Hint:* Express x in terms of z alone, then express y in terms of z alone. List two ordered triples that are solutions.

22. Use an argument similar to that used in Problem 21 to show that any system of two consistent equations in three variables has an infinite number of members in its solution set.

23. Show that the system

$$x + y + z = 3 \quad \text{(a)}$$
$$x - 2y - z = -2 \quad \text{(b)}$$
$$x + y + 2z = 4 \quad \text{(c)}$$
$$2x - y + 2z = 4 \quad \text{(d)}$$

has $\emptyset$ as a solution set. *Hint:* Does the solution set of the system (a), (b), and (c) have any members that satisfy (d)?

9.4 Third-Order Determinants

A determinant of the form

$$\begin{vmatrix} a_1 & b_1 & c_1 \\ a_2 & b_2 & c_2 \\ a_3 & b_3 & c_3 \end{vmatrix}$$

is said to be a three-by-three (3×3) or third-order determinant. The value of a third-order determinant is defined to be

$$\begin{vmatrix} a_1 & b_1 & c_1 \\ a_2 & b_2 & c_2 \\ a_3 & b_3 & c_3 \end{vmatrix} = a_1b_2c_3 - a_1b_3c_2 + a_3b_1c_2 - a_2b_1c_3 + a_2b_3c_1 - a_3b_2c_1. \quad (1)$$

Again, we note that a 3×3 determinant is simply another way of writing a single number, namely, that number represented by the expression in the right-hand member of (1).

The **minor** of an element in a determinant is defined to be the determinant that remains after deleting the row and column in which the element appears. In the determinant (1):

the minor of the element a_1 is $\begin{vmatrix} b_2 & c_2 \\ b_3 & c_3 \end{vmatrix}$;

the minor of the element b_1 is $\begin{vmatrix} a_2 & c_2 \\ a_3 & c_3 \end{vmatrix}$;

the minor of the element c_1 is $\begin{vmatrix} a_2 & b_2 \\ a_3 & b_3 \end{vmatrix}$; etc.

If, by suitably factoring pairs of terms in the right-hand member, (1) is rewritten in the form

$$\begin{vmatrix} a_1 & b_1 & c_1 \\ a_2 & b_2 & c_2 \\ a_3 & b_3 & c_3 \end{vmatrix} = a_1(b_2c_3 - b_3c_2) - b_1(a_2c_3 - a_3c_2) + c_1(a_2b_3 - a_3b_2), \quad (2)$$

we observe that the sums enclosed in parentheses in the right-hand member of (2) are the respective minors (second-order determinants) of the elements a_1, b_1, and c_1. Therefore, (2) can be written

$$\begin{vmatrix} a_1 & b_1 & c_1 \\ a_2 & b_2 & c_2 \\ a_3 & b_3 & c_3 \end{vmatrix} = a_1 \begin{vmatrix} b_2 & c_2 \\ b_3 & c_3 \end{vmatrix} - b_1 \begin{vmatrix} a_2 & c_2 \\ a_3 & c_3 \end{vmatrix} + c_1 \begin{vmatrix} a_2 & b_2 \\ a_3 & b_3 \end{vmatrix}. \quad (3)$$

The right-hand member of (3) is called the **expansion** of the determinant by minors about the first row.

Suppose, instead of factoring the right-hand member of (1) into the right-hand member of (2), we factor it as

$$\begin{vmatrix} a_1 & b_1 & c_1 \\ a_2 & b_2 & c_2 \\ a_3 & b_3 & c_3 \end{vmatrix} = a_1(b_2c_3 - b_3c_2) - a_2(b_1c_3 - b_3c_1) + a_3(b_1c_2 - b_2c_1). \quad (4)$$

Then we have the expansion of the determinant by minors about the first column,

$$\begin{vmatrix} a_1 & b_1 & c_1 \\ a_2 & b_2 & c_2 \\ a_3 & b_3 & c_3 \end{vmatrix} = a_1 \begin{vmatrix} b_2 & c_2 \\ b_3 & c_3 \end{vmatrix} - a_2 \begin{vmatrix} b_1 & c_1 \\ b_3 & c_3 \end{vmatrix} + a_3 \begin{vmatrix} b_1 & c_1 \\ b_2 & c_2 \end{vmatrix}. \quad (5)$$

With the proper use of signs it is possible to expand a determinant by minors about *any* row or *any* column and obtain an expression equivalent to a

factored form of the right-hand member of (1).   A helpful device for determining the signs of the terms in an expansion of a third-order determinant
by minors is the array of alternating signs

$$+ \quad - \quad +$$
$$- \quad + \quad -$$
$$+ \quad - \quad +$$

which we will call the **sign array** for the determinant.   To obtain an expansion
of (1) about a given row or column, the appropriate sign from the sign array
is prefixed to each term in the expansion.

As an example, let us expand the determinant

$$\begin{vmatrix} 1 & 2 & -3 \\ 0 & 2 & -1 \\ 1 & 1 & 0 \end{vmatrix}$$

about the second row.   We have

$$\begin{vmatrix} 1 & 2 & -3 \\ 0 & 2 & -1 \\ 1 & 1 & 0 \end{vmatrix} = -(0)\begin{vmatrix} 2 & -3 \\ 1 & 0 \end{vmatrix} + (2)\begin{vmatrix} 1 & -3 \\ 1 & 0 \end{vmatrix} - (-1)\begin{vmatrix} 1 & 2 \\ 1 & 1 \end{vmatrix}$$

$$= 0 + 2(0 + 3) + 1(1 - 2)$$

$$= 6 - 1$$

$$= 5.$$

The student should expand this determinant about each row and about each
column to verify that the result is the same in each expansion.

The expansion of a higher-order determinant by minors can be accomplished in the same way.   By continuing the pattern of alternating signs used
for third-order determinants, the sign array extends to higher-order determinants.   The determinants in each term in the expansion will be of
order one less than the order of the original determinant.

EXERCISE 9.4

Evaluate.

Example: $\begin{vmatrix} 1 & 2 & 0 \\ 3 & -1 & 4 \\ -2 & 1 & 3 \end{vmatrix}$

Expand about any row or column; the first row is used here.

$$\begin{vmatrix} 1 & 2 & 0 \\ 3 & -1 & 4 \\ -2 & 1 & 3 \end{vmatrix} = 1 \begin{vmatrix} -1 & 4 \\ 1 & 3 \end{vmatrix} - 2 \begin{vmatrix} 3 & 4 \\ -2 & 3 \end{vmatrix} + 0 \begin{vmatrix} 3 & -1 \\ -2 & 1 \end{vmatrix}$$

$$= 1[(-1)(3) - (1)(4)] - 2[(3)(3) - (-2)(4)] + 0$$
$$= [-3 - 4] - 2[9 + 8]$$
$$= -7 - 34 = -41$$

Ans. -41

1. $\begin{vmatrix} 2 & 0 & 1 \\ 1 & 1 & 2 \\ -1 & 0 & 1 \end{vmatrix}$

2. $\begin{vmatrix} 1 & 3 & 1 \\ -1 & 2 & 1 \\ 0 & 2 & 0 \end{vmatrix}$

3. $\begin{vmatrix} 2 & -1 & 0 \\ -3 & 1 & 2 \\ 1 & -3 & 1 \end{vmatrix}$

4. $\begin{vmatrix} 2 & 4 & -1 \\ -1 & 3 & 2 \\ 4 & 0 & 2 \end{vmatrix}$

5. $\begin{vmatrix} 1 & 2 & 3 \\ 3 & -1 & 2 \\ 2 & 0 & 2 \end{vmatrix}$

6. $\begin{vmatrix} 1 & 0 & 0 \\ 0 & 1 & 2 \\ 0 & 3 & 4 \end{vmatrix}$

7. $\begin{vmatrix} -1 & 0 & 2 \\ -2 & 1 & 0 \\ 0 & 1 & -3 \end{vmatrix}$

8. $\begin{vmatrix} 2 & 1 & 4 \\ 3 & 2 & 6 \\ 5 & -3 & 10 \end{vmatrix}$

9. $\begin{vmatrix} 2 & 5 & -1 \\ 1 & 0 & 2 \\ 0 & 0 & 1 \end{vmatrix}$

10. $\begin{vmatrix} 2 & 3 & 1 \\ 0 & 1 & 0 \\ -4 & 2 & 1 \end{vmatrix}$

11. $\begin{vmatrix} a & b & 1 \\ a & b & 1 \\ 1 & 1 & 1 \end{vmatrix}$

12. $\begin{vmatrix} a & a & a \\ 1 & 2 & 3 \\ 4 & 5 & 6 \end{vmatrix}$

13. $\begin{vmatrix} x & 0 & 0 \\ 0 & x & 0 \\ 0 & 0 & x \end{vmatrix}$

14. $\begin{vmatrix} 0 & 0 & x \\ 0 & x & 0 \\ x & 0 & 0 \end{vmatrix}$

15. $\begin{vmatrix} x & y & 0 \\ x & y & 0 \\ 0 & 0 & 1 \end{vmatrix}$

16. $\begin{vmatrix} 0 & a & b \\ a & 0 & a \\ b & a & 0 \end{vmatrix}$

17. $\begin{vmatrix} a & b & 0 \\ b & 0 & b \\ 0 & b & a \end{vmatrix}$

18. $\begin{vmatrix} 0 & b & 0 \\ b & a & b \\ 0 & b & 0 \end{vmatrix}$

Solve for x.

19. $\begin{vmatrix} x & 0 & 0 \\ 2 & 1 & 3 \\ 0 & 1 & 4 \end{vmatrix} = 3$

20. $\begin{vmatrix} x^2 & 0 & 1 \\ 2 & -1 & 3 \\ 3 & 2 & 0 \end{vmatrix} = 1$

21. $\begin{vmatrix} x^2 & x & 1 \\ 0 & 2 & 1 \\ 3 & 1 & 4 \end{vmatrix} = 28$

22. $\begin{vmatrix} x & 1 & 1 \\ 0 & x & 1 \\ 0 & x & 0 \end{vmatrix} = -4$

23. Show that

$$\begin{vmatrix} x & x & a \\ y & y & b \\ z & z & c \end{vmatrix} = 0$$

for all values of x, y, and z. What have you proved about determinants containing two identical columns?

24. Show that

$$\begin{vmatrix} 0 & 0 & 0 \\ a & b & c \\ d & e & f \end{vmatrix} = 0$$

for any values of a, b, c, d, e, f. What have you proved about determinants containing a row of zero elements?

25. Show that

$$\begin{vmatrix} 1 & 2 & 3 \\ 4 & 5 & 6 \\ 0 & 0 & 1 \end{vmatrix} = - \begin{vmatrix} 4 & 5 & 6 \\ 1 & 2 & 3 \\ 0 & 0 & 1 \end{vmatrix}.$$

Make a conjecture about the result of interchanging any two rows of a determinant.

26. Show that

$$\begin{vmatrix} 2 & 0 & 1 \\ 4 & 1 & -2 \\ 6 & 1 & 1 \end{vmatrix} = 2 \begin{vmatrix} 1 & 0 & 1 \\ 2 & 1 & -2 \\ 3 & 1 & 1 \end{vmatrix}.$$

Make a conjecture about the result of factoring a common factor from each element of a column in a determinant.

Extend the procedure in the text and evaluate.

27. $\begin{vmatrix} 0 & 1 & 0 & 0 \\ 1 & 0 & 3 & 2 \\ 5 & -1 & 2 & 1 \\ 1 & 0 & 1 & 1 \end{vmatrix}$

28. $\begin{vmatrix} 1 & 2 & 0 & -1 \\ 1 & 0 & -1 & 2 \\ 0 & 1 & 1 & 1 \\ 2 & -1 & 0 & 1 \end{vmatrix}$

29. $\begin{vmatrix} 2 & -1 & 3 & 1 \\ 1 & 1 & 3 & 1 \\ 0 & 0 & 2 & 0 \\ 2 & -1 & 5 & 2 \end{vmatrix}$

30. $\begin{vmatrix} 1 & 0 & -3 & 5 \\ -1 & 1 & 0 & -1 \\ -2 & 2 & 1 & 0 \\ 0 & 3 & 2 & 1 \end{vmatrix}$

9.5 Linear Systems in Three Variables—Solution by Determinants

Consider the linear system in three variables

$$a_1 x + b_1 y + c_1 z = d_1 \tag{1}$$

$$a_2 x + b_2 y + c_2 z = d_2 \tag{2}$$

$$a_3 x + b_3 y + c_3 z = d_3. \tag{3}$$

By solving this system by the methods of Section 9.3, it can be shown that Cramer's rule is applicable to such systems and, in fact, to all similar systems as well as to linear systems in two variables. That is,

$$x = \frac{D_x}{D}, \quad y = \frac{D_y}{D}, \quad z = \frac{D_z}{D},$$

where

$$D = \begin{vmatrix} a_1 & b_1 & c_1 \\ a_2 & b_2 & c_2 \\ a_3 & b_3 & c_3 \end{vmatrix}, \quad D_x = \begin{vmatrix} d_1 & b_1 & c_1 \\ d_2 & b_2 & c_2 \\ d_3 & b_3 & c_3 \end{vmatrix},$$

$$D_y = \begin{vmatrix} a_1 & d_1 & c_1 \\ a_2 & d_2 & c_2 \\ a_3 & d_3 & c_3 \end{vmatrix}, \quad D_z = \begin{vmatrix} a_1 & b_1 & d_1 \\ a_2 & b_2 & d_2 \\ a_3 & b_3 & d_3 \end{vmatrix}.$$

Note that the elements of the determinant D in each denominator are the coefficients of the variables in (1), (2), and (3), and that the numerators are formed from D by replacing the elements in the x, y, or z column, respectively, by d_1, d_2, and d_3. We illustrate the application of Cramer's rule by example. Consider the system

$$x + 2y - 3z = -4$$

$$2x - y + z = 3$$

$$3x + 2y + z = 10.$$

The determinant D, whose elements are the coefficients of the variables, is given by

$$D = \begin{vmatrix} 1 & 2 & -3 \\ 2 & -1 & 1 \\ 3 & 2 & 1 \end{vmatrix}.$$

This determinant can perhaps be expanded most easily about the first column, yielding

$$D = \begin{vmatrix} 1 & 2 & -3 \\ 2 & -1 & 1 \\ 3 & 2 & 1 \end{vmatrix} = 1 \begin{vmatrix} -1 & 1 \\ 2 & 1 \end{vmatrix} - 2 \begin{vmatrix} 2 & -3 \\ 2 & 1 \end{vmatrix} + 3 \begin{vmatrix} 2 & -3 \\ -1 & 1 \end{vmatrix}$$

$$= -3 - 16 - 3$$

$$= -22.$$

Replacing the first column in D with -4, 3, and 10, we obtain

$$D_x = \begin{vmatrix} -4 & 2 & -3 \\ 3 & -1 & 1 \\ 10 & 2 & 1 \end{vmatrix}.$$

Expanding D_x about the third column, we have

$$D_x = \begin{vmatrix} -4 & 2 & -3 \\ 3 & -1 & 1 \\ 10 & 2 & 1 \end{vmatrix} = -3 \begin{vmatrix} 3 & -1 \\ 10 & 2 \end{vmatrix} - 1 \begin{vmatrix} -4 & 2 \\ 10 & 2 \end{vmatrix} + 1 \begin{vmatrix} -4 & 2 \\ 3 & -1 \end{vmatrix}$$

$$= -48 + 28 - 2$$

$$= -22.$$

D_y and D_z can be computed in similar fashion.

$$D_y = \begin{vmatrix} 1 & -4 & -3 \\ 2 & 3 & 1 \\ 3 & 10 & 1 \end{vmatrix} = -44, \quad D_z = \begin{vmatrix} 1 & 2 & -4 \\ 2 & -1 & 3 \\ 3 & 2 & 10 \end{vmatrix} = -66.$$

We then have

$$x = \frac{D_x}{D} = \frac{-22}{-22} = 1,$$

$$y = \frac{D_y}{D} = \frac{-44}{-22} = 2,$$

$$z = \frac{D_z}{D} = \frac{-66}{-22} = 3,$$

and the solution set of the system is

$$\{(1, 2, 3)\}.$$

If $D = 0$ for a linear system in three variables, the system either has an empty solution set or a solution set with infinitely many members, depending upon whether D_x, D_y, and D_z are not zero or are zero, respectively.

EXERCISE 9.5

Solve by Cramer's rule. If the solution set has no members or an infinite number of members, so state.

Example:

$$4x + 10y - z = 2$$

$$2x + 8y + z = 4$$

$$x - 3y - 2z = 3$$

Determine values for D, D_x, D_y, and D_z. The elements of D are the coefficients of the variables in the order they occur. For D_x, D_y, and D_z, the respective column of elements in D is replaced by the constants 2, 4, and 3.

$$D = \begin{vmatrix} 4 & 10 & -1 \\ 2 & 8 & 1 \\ 1 & -3 & -2 \end{vmatrix} = 12; \quad D_x = \begin{vmatrix} 2 & 10 & -1 \\ 4 & 8 & 1 \\ 3 & -3 & -2 \end{vmatrix} = 120;$$

$$D_y = \begin{vmatrix} 4 & 2 & -1 \\ 2 & 4 & 1 \\ 1 & 3 & -2 \end{vmatrix} = -36; \quad D_z = \begin{vmatrix} 4 & 10 & 2 \\ 2 & 8 & 4 \\ 1 & -3 & 3 \end{vmatrix} = 96.$$

Use Cramer's rule to determine x, y, and z.

$$x = \frac{D_x}{D} = \frac{120}{12} = 10, \quad y = \frac{D_y}{D} = \frac{-36}{12} = -3, \quad z = \frac{D_z}{D} = \frac{96}{12} = 8$$

Ans. $\{(10, -3, 8)\}$

1. $x + y = 2$
$2x - z = 1$
$2y - 3z = -1$

2. $2x - 6y + 3z = -12$
$3x - 2y + 5z = -4$
$4x + 5y - 2z = 10$

3. $x - 2y + z = -1$
$3x + y - 2z = 4$
$y - z = 1$

4. $2x + 5z = 9$
$4x + 3y = -1$
$3y - 4z = -13$

5. $2x + 2y + z = 1$
$x - y + 6z = 21$
$3x + 2y - z = -4$

6. $4x + 8y + z = -6$
$2x - 3y + 2z = 0$
$x + 7y - 3z = -8$

7. $x + y + z = 0$
$2x - y - 4z = 15$
$x - 2y - z = 7$

8. $x + y - 2z = 3$
$3x - y + z = 5$
$3x + 3y - 6z = 9$

9. $x - 2y + 2z = 3$
$2x - 4y + 4z = 1$
$3x - 3y - 3z = 4$

10. $3x - 2y + 5z = 6$
$4x - 4y + 3z = 0$
$5x - 4y + z = -5$

11. $x - 4z = -1$
$3x + 3y = 2$
$3x + 4z = 5$

12. $2x - \frac{2}{3}y + z = 2$
$\frac{1}{2}x - \frac{1}{3}y - \frac{1}{4}z = 0$
$4x + 5y - 3z = -1$

13. $x + 4z = 3$
$y + 3z = 9$
$2x + 5y - 5z = -5$

14. $2x + y = 18$
$y + z = -1$
$3x - 2y - 5z = 38$

15. $2x + z = 2$
$3y - 2z = 22$
$2x - y = 13$

16. $x - 3y = -1$
$3y - z = -9$
$x - 4y = 1$

17. $x + y + z = 0$
$w + 2y - z = 4$
$2w - y + 2z = 3$
$-2w + 2y - z = -2$

18. $x + y + z = 0$
$x + z + w = 0$
$x + y + w = 0$
$y + z + w = 0$

9.6 Properties of Determinants

Problems 21–25 in Exercise 9.2 developed certain properties for second-order determinants. Problems 23 and 24 in Exercise 9.4 also developed two properties for third-order determinants and Problems 25 and 26 suggested some conjectures about two other properties. These properties also hold for higher-order determinants. Although we shall not prove them here, let us state them for the general $n \times n$ determinant and take a more detailed look at several examples of these statements as they apply to 3×3 determinants.

Property 1. *If each entry in any row (or column) of a determinant is 0, then the determinant is equal to 0.*

For example,

$$\begin{vmatrix} 1 & 1 & 0 \\ 3 & 5 & 0 \\ 2 & 7 & 0 \end{vmatrix} = 0 \quad \text{and} \quad \begin{vmatrix} 3 & -2 & 4 \\ 0 & 0 & 0 \\ 1 & 2 & 0 \end{vmatrix} = 0.$$

Property 2. *If any two rows (or columns) of a determinant are interchanged, the resulting determinant is the negative of the original determinant.*

For example,

$$\begin{vmatrix} 1 & 3 & 4 \\ 2 & 5 & 6 \\ 7 & 8 & 9 \end{vmatrix} = - \begin{vmatrix} 3 & 1 & 4 \\ 5 & 2 & 6 \\ 8 & 7 & 9 \end{vmatrix} \quad \text{and} \quad \begin{vmatrix} 1 & 3 & 4 \\ 2 & 5 & 6 \\ 7 & 8 & 9 \end{vmatrix} = - \begin{vmatrix} 7 & 8 & 9 \\ 2 & 5 & 6 \\ 1 & 3 & 4 \end{vmatrix}.$$

In the first example, the first and second columns were interchanged and in the second the first and third rows were interchanged.

Property 3. *If two rows (or two columns) of a determinant have corresponding entries that are equal, the determinant is 0.*

For example,

$$\begin{vmatrix} 1 & 2 & 1 \\ 4 & 5 & 6 \\ 1 & 2 & 1 \end{vmatrix} = 0 \quad \text{and} \quad \begin{vmatrix} 7 & 4 & 4 \\ 2 & -3 & -3 \\ -1 & 5 & 5 \end{vmatrix} = 0.$$

Property 4. *If each of the entries of one row (or column) of a determinant is multiplied by k, the determinant is multiplied by k.*

For example,

$$\begin{vmatrix} 1 & 0 & 0 \\ 2 & 1 & 3 \\ 1 \times 2 & 3 \times 2 & 4 \times 2 \end{vmatrix} = 2 \begin{vmatrix} 1 & 0 & 0 \\ 2 & 1 & 3 \\ 1 & 3 & 4 \end{vmatrix} \quad \text{and} \quad \begin{vmatrix} 4 & 5 & 8 \\ 1 & 1 & 2 \\ 3 & 1 & 6 \end{vmatrix} = 2 \begin{vmatrix} 4 & 5 & 4 \\ 1 & 1 & 1 \\ 3 & 1 & 3 \end{vmatrix}.$$

Property 5. *If each entry in a row (or column) of a determinant is written as the sum of two terms, the determinant can be written as the sum of two determinants as follows:*

$$\begin{vmatrix} 1 & 3 & 6 \\ a_2 + d_2 & b_2 + e_2 & c_2 + f_2 \\ 2 & 5 & 4 \end{vmatrix} = \begin{vmatrix} 1 & 3 & 6 \\ a_2 & b_2 & c_2 \\ 2 & 5 & 4 \end{vmatrix} + \begin{vmatrix} 1 & 3 & 6 \\ d_2 & e_2 & f_2 \\ 2 & 5 & 4 \end{vmatrix}$$

and

$$\begin{vmatrix} 2 & 4 & c_1 + d_1 \\ 3 & 1 & c_2 + d_2 \\ 6 & 5 & c_3 + d_3 \end{vmatrix} = \begin{vmatrix} 2 & 4 & c_1 \\ 3 & 1 & c_2 \\ 6 & 5 & c_3 \end{vmatrix} + \begin{vmatrix} 2 & 4 & d_1 \\ 3 & 1 & d_2 \\ 6 & 5 & d_3 \end{vmatrix}.$$

Property 6. *If each entry of one row (or column) of a determinant is multiplied by a real number k and the resulting product is added to the corresponding entry in another row (or column, respectively) in the determinant, the resulting determinant is equal to the original determinant.*

For example,

$$\begin{vmatrix} 1 & 2 & 3 \\ 4 & 5 & 6 \\ 7 & 8 & 9 \end{vmatrix} = \begin{vmatrix} 1 + 2(3) & 2 & 3 \\ 4 + 2(6) & 5 & 6 \\ 7 + 2(9) & 8 & 9 \end{vmatrix} = \begin{vmatrix} 7 & 2 & 3 \\ 16 & 5 & 6 \\ 25 & 8 & 9 \end{vmatrix}$$

and

$$\begin{vmatrix} 1 & 2 & 3 \\ 4 & 5 & 6 \\ 7 & 8 & 9 \end{vmatrix} = \begin{vmatrix} 1 + 4(4) & 2 + 4(5) & 3 + 4(6) \\ 4 & 5 & 6 \\ 7 & 8 & 9 \end{vmatrix} = \begin{vmatrix} 17 & 22 & 27 \\ 4 & 5 & 6 \\ 7 & 8 & 9 \end{vmatrix}.$$

The preceding statements can be used to write sequences of equal determinants, leading from one form to another and more useful form. For example, we may wish to expand

$$D = \begin{vmatrix} 2 & -1 & 1 \\ 1 & 3 & -4 \\ 3 & -1 & 5 \end{vmatrix}.$$

As a step toward expanding the determinant, we shall use Property 6 to produce an equal determinant with a row or a column containing zero entries in all but one place. Let us arbitrarily select the second column for this role. Multiplying elements of the first row by 3 and adding the result to elements of the second row, we obtain

$$D = \begin{vmatrix} 2 & -1 & 1 \\ 1 + 3(2) & 3 + 3(-1) & -4 + 3(1) \\ 3 & -1 & 5 \end{vmatrix} = \begin{vmatrix} 2 & -1 & 1 \\ 7 & 0 & -1 \\ 3 & -1 & 5 \end{vmatrix}.$$

Next, multiplying elements of the first row by -1 and adding the result to elements of the third row, we find that

$$D = \begin{vmatrix} 2 & -1 & 1 \\ 7 & 0 & -1 \\ 3 - 1(2) & -1 - 1(-1) & 5 - 1(1) \end{vmatrix} = \begin{vmatrix} 2 & -1 & 1 \\ 7 & 0 & -1 \\ 1 & 0 & 4 \end{vmatrix}.$$

If we now expand the determinant about the second column, we have

$$D = \begin{vmatrix} 2 & -1 & 1 \\ 7 & 0 & -1 \\ 1 & 0 & 4 \end{vmatrix} = -(-1)\begin{vmatrix} 7 & -1 \\ 1 & 4 \end{vmatrix} + 0 + 0.$$

We can now expand directly and obtain

$$D = [28 - (-1)] = 29.$$

EXERCISE 9.6

Without evaluating, state (using Properties 1–6 in this section) why each statement is true. Verify selected examples by expansion.

1. $\begin{vmatrix} 2 & 3 & 1 \\ 0 & 0 & 0 \\ -1 & 2 & 0 \end{vmatrix} = 0$

2. $\begin{vmatrix} 3 & 1 & 3 \\ 0 & 1 & 0 \\ 1 & 2 & 1 \end{vmatrix} = 0$

3. $\begin{vmatrix} 3 & 1 & -1 \\ 0 & 1 & 2 \\ 3 & 1 & -1 \end{vmatrix} = 0$

4. $\begin{vmatrix} 3 & 2 & 0 \\ -1 & 2 & 0 \\ 1 & 1 & 0 \end{vmatrix} = 0$

5. $\begin{vmatrix} -2 & 1 & 0 \\ 3 & 4 & 1 \\ -4 & 2 & 0 \end{vmatrix} = 0$

6. $\begin{vmatrix} 0 & 1 & 4 \\ 6 & 1 & 2 \\ 0 & 2 & 8 \end{vmatrix} = 0$

7. $\begin{vmatrix} 2 & 3 \\ 1 & -1 \end{vmatrix} = -\begin{vmatrix} 3 & 2 \\ -1 & 1 \end{vmatrix}$

8. $\begin{vmatrix} -2 & 3 & 1 \\ -1 & 0 & 1 \\ -2 & 1 & 0 \end{vmatrix} = -\begin{vmatrix} 2 & 3 & 1 \\ 1 & 0 & 1 \\ 2 & 1 & 0 \end{vmatrix}$

9. $\begin{vmatrix} 4 & 2 & 1 \\ 0 & -1 & -2 \\ 1 & 0 & 2 \end{vmatrix} = -\begin{vmatrix} 4 & 2 & 1 \\ 0 & 1 & 2 \\ 1 & 0 & 2 \end{vmatrix}$

10. $\begin{vmatrix} 3 & 1 & 0 \\ -2 & 1 & 1 \\ 0 & 2 & -1 \end{vmatrix} = -\begin{vmatrix} 0 & 1 & 3 \\ 1 & 1 & -2 \\ -1 & 2 & 0 \end{vmatrix}$

11. $2\begin{vmatrix} 1 & 0 & 2 \\ -1 & 2 & 0 \\ 1 & 1 & 1 \end{vmatrix} = \begin{vmatrix} 1 & 0 & 2 \\ -1 & 2 & 0 \\ 2 & 2 & 2 \end{vmatrix}$

12. $\begin{vmatrix} 3 & -4 & 2 \\ 1 & -2 & 0 \\ 0 & 8 & 1 \end{vmatrix} = -2\begin{vmatrix} 3 & 2 & 2 \\ 1 & 1 & 0 \\ 0 & -4 & 1 \end{vmatrix}$

13. $\begin{vmatrix} 3 & 0 & 6 \\ 2 & 1 & 2 \\ 0 & 1 & -2 \end{vmatrix} = 6 \begin{vmatrix} 1 & 0 & 1 \\ 2 & 1 & 1 \\ 0 & 1 & -1 \end{vmatrix}$

14. $\begin{vmatrix} 1 & 2 & 1 \\ -1 & 0 & -2 \\ 2 & 4 & 1 \end{vmatrix} = -2 \begin{vmatrix} 1 & 1 & 1 \\ 1 & 0 & 2 \\ 2 & 2 & 1 \end{vmatrix}$

15. $\begin{vmatrix} 3 & 5 \\ 1 & 4 \end{vmatrix} = \begin{vmatrix} 3 & 3 \\ 1 & 2 \end{vmatrix} + \begin{vmatrix} 3 & 2 \\ 1 & 2 \end{vmatrix}$

16. $\begin{vmatrix} 3 & 1 & 4 \\ 2 & 2 & 2 \\ 1 & 0 & -1 \end{vmatrix} = \begin{vmatrix} 3 & 1 & 4 \\ 1 & 1 & 1 \\ 1 & 0 & -1 \end{vmatrix} + \begin{vmatrix} 3 & 1 & 4 \\ 1 & 1 & 1 \\ 1 & 0 & -1 \end{vmatrix}$

17. $\begin{vmatrix} 1 & 2 \\ 3 & 4 \end{vmatrix} = \begin{vmatrix} 1+2 & 2 \\ 3+4 & 4 \end{vmatrix}$

18. $\begin{vmatrix} 1 & 2 \\ 3 & 4 \end{vmatrix} = \begin{vmatrix} 1+4 & 2 \\ 3+8 & 4 \end{vmatrix}$

19. $\begin{vmatrix} 1 & 2 \\ 3 & 4 \end{vmatrix} = \begin{vmatrix} 1 & 2 \\ 3-3 & 4-6 \end{vmatrix}$

20. $\begin{vmatrix} 1 & 2 \\ 3 & 4 \end{vmatrix} = \begin{vmatrix} 1 & 2-2 \\ 3 & 4-6 \end{vmatrix}$

21. $\begin{vmatrix} 1 & 2 & 1 \\ 0 & 2 & 3 \\ 2 & -1 & 2 \end{vmatrix} = \begin{vmatrix} 1 & 2 & 1 \\ 0 & 2 & 3 \\ 0 & -5 & 0 \end{vmatrix}$

22. $\begin{vmatrix} -1 & 1 & 0 \\ 2 & 3 & -1 \\ 2 & 1 & 2 \end{vmatrix} = \begin{vmatrix} 0 & 1 & 0 \\ 5 & 3 & -1 \\ 3 & 1 & 2 \end{vmatrix}$

One of the properties of determinants was used on the left-hand member of each of the following equalities to produce the elements in the right-hand member. Complete the entries. (*Note:* Solutions for statements 25–30 are not unique.)

23. $\begin{vmatrix} 1 & 3 \\ 2 & 2 \end{vmatrix} = \begin{vmatrix} 1 & 3 \\ 0 & \end{vmatrix}$

24. $\begin{vmatrix} 2 & -1 \\ 3 & 1 \end{vmatrix} = \begin{vmatrix} & 0 \\ 3 & 1 \end{vmatrix}$

25. $\begin{vmatrix} 1 & -2 & 1 \\ 3 & 1 & 4 \\ 0 & 2 & 1 \end{vmatrix} = \begin{vmatrix} 1 & -2 & 1 \\ 0 & & 1 \\ 0 & 2 & 1 \end{vmatrix}$

26. $\begin{vmatrix} 3 & -1 & 0 \\ 1 & 2 & 1 \\ 2 & 3 & 1 \end{vmatrix} = \begin{vmatrix} 3 & -1 & 0 \\ 1 & 2 & 1 \\ & 1 & 0 \end{vmatrix}$

27. $\begin{vmatrix} 2 & 3 & 1 & 4 \\ 0 & 2 & 1 & 2 \\ 1 & 1 & 2 & 3 \\ 0 & 1 & 1 & 1 \end{vmatrix} = \begin{vmatrix} 0 & 1 & -3 & \\ 0 & 2 & 1 & 2 \\ 1 & 1 & 2 & 3 \\ 0 & 1 & 1 & 1 \end{vmatrix}$

28. $\begin{vmatrix} 2 & 1 & 1 & 0 \\ 1 & 2 & 0 & 2 \\ 3 & 1 & 0 & 3 \\ 2 & -1 & 4 & 2 \end{vmatrix} = \begin{vmatrix} 2 & 1 & 1 & 0 \\ 1 & 2 & 0 & 2 \\ 3 & 1 & 0 & 3 \\ & -5 & 0 & 2 \end{vmatrix}$

29. $\begin{vmatrix} 1 & 2 & 3 & 1 \\ 2 & 0 & 1 & 2 \\ 3 & -1 & 2 & 1 \\ 0 & 1 & 1 & 1 \end{vmatrix} = \begin{vmatrix} 1 & 1 & 2 & 1 \\ 2 & -2 & -1 & 2 \\ 3 & & 1 & 1 \\ 0 & 0 & 0 & 1 \end{vmatrix}$

30. $\begin{vmatrix} 1 & 2 & -1 & 3 \\ 2 & 1 & 2 & 1 \\ 4 & 2 & 3 & 4 \\ 2 & 1 & 2 & 1 \end{vmatrix} = \begin{vmatrix} -3 & 2 & -5 & 1 \\ 0 & 1 & 0 & 0 \\ 0 & 2 & -1 & \\ 0 & 1 & 0 & 0 \end{vmatrix}$

First reduce each determinant to an equal 2 × 2 determinant and then evaluate.

31. $\begin{vmatrix} 2 & 1 & 0 \\ 3 & 2 & 1 \\ -1 & 2 & 0 \end{vmatrix}$

32. $\begin{vmatrix} 1 & 2 & 1 \\ 2 & -1 & 2 \\ 0 & 1 & 0 \end{vmatrix}$

33. $\begin{vmatrix} 1 & 0 & 3 \\ 2 & -1 & 1 \\ 1 & 2 & 1 \end{vmatrix}$

34. $\begin{vmatrix} 1 & 2 & -1 \\ 2 & 1 & 3 \\ 0 & 1 & 2 \end{vmatrix}$ **35.** $\begin{vmatrix} 1 & 2 & 1 \\ -1 & 2 & 3 \\ 2 & -1 & 1 \end{vmatrix}$ **36.** $\begin{vmatrix} 3 & -1 & 2 \\ 1 & 2 & 1 \\ -2 & 1 & 3 \end{vmatrix}$

37. $\begin{vmatrix} 2 & 3 & -1 \\ 1 & -2 & 1 \\ 2 & 3 & 4 \end{vmatrix}$ **38.** $\begin{vmatrix} 2 & 2 & 1 \\ 3 & -1 & 2 \\ 2 & 1 & 3 \end{vmatrix}$

39. $\begin{vmatrix} 0 & 0 & 1 & 2 \\ 6 & 0 & 0 & 1 \\ 6 & 1 & 0 & -1 \\ 6 & 1 & 0 & 2 \end{vmatrix}$ **40.** $\begin{vmatrix} 4 & 2 & 0 & 2 \\ -1 & 0 & 2 & 1 \\ 3 & 0 & -1 & 1 \\ 0 & 0 & 2 & 1 \end{vmatrix}$

9.7 Second-Degree Systems in Two Variables—Solution by Substitution

Real solutions of systems of equations in two variables, where one or both of the equations are quadratic, can often be found by graphing both equations and estimating the coordinates of any points they have in common. For example, to find the solution set of the system

$$x^2 + y^2 = 26 \tag{1}$$

$$x + y = 6, \tag{2}$$

we graph the equations on the same set of axes, as shown in Figure 9.4,

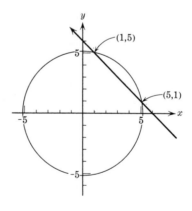

Fig. 9.4

and observe that the graphs intersect at the points (1, 5) and (5, 1). Thus the solution set of the system (1) and (2) is

$$\{(1,\ 5),\ (5,\ 1)\}.$$

However, solving second-degree systems graphically on the real plane may produce only approximations to such real solutions as exist; and furthermore, we cannot expect to locate solutions among the complex numbers. It is, therefore, more practical to concentrate on analytic methods of solution, since the results are exact, and we can obtain complex solutions. It is suggested, however, that you sketch the graphs of the equations as a rough check on an analytic solution. We can expect to find at most four and as few as no points of intersection in graphing second-degree systems, depending upon the types of equations involved and upon the coefficients and constants in the given equations.

One of the most useful techniques available for finding solution sets for systems of equations is that of **substitution.** Consider the system above,

$$x^2 + y^2 = 26 \tag{1}$$

$$x + y = 6. \tag{2}$$

Equation (2) can be written in the form

$$y = 6 - x \tag{3}$$

and we can argue that for any ordered pair (x, y) in the solution set of both (1) and (2), x and y in (1) represent the same numbers as x and y in (3), and hence the substitution axiom can be invoked to replace y in (1) by its equal $(6 - x)$ from (3). This will produce

$$x^2 + (6 - x)^2 = 26, \tag{4}$$

which will have as a solution set those values of x for which the ordered pair (x, y) is a common solution of (1) and (2). We can now find the solution set of (4):

$$x^2 + 36 - 12x + x^2 = 26,$$

$$2x^2 - 12x + 10 = 0,$$

$$x^2 - 6x + 5 = 0,$$

$$(x - 5)(x - 1) = 0,$$

from which x is either 1 or 5. Now by replacing x in (3) by each of these numbers in turn,

$$y = 6 - 1 = 5$$

and

$$y = 6 - 5 = 1,$$

so that the solution set of the system (1) and (2) is

$$\{(1, 5), (5, 1)\}.$$

Check this solution and notice that these ordered pairs are also solutions of (1). Using equation (1) rather than equation (2) or (3) to obtain values for the y-component, we would have

$$1^2 + y^2 = 26 \qquad\qquad 5^2 + y^2 = 26$$
$$y = \pm 5 \qquad\qquad y = \pm 1$$

and the solutions obtained are $(1, 5)$, $(1, -5)$, $(5, 1)$, and $(5, -1)$. However, $(1, -5)$ and $(5, -1)$ are not solutions of (2). Therefore the solution set is again $\{(1, 5), (5, 1)\}$. This example suggests that if the degrees of equations differ, one component of a solution should be substituted in the equation of lower degree in order to find *only* those ordered pairs that are solutions of *both* equations.

The technique of solution by substitution can be used very easily with systems containing two first-degree equations, or one first-degree and one higher-degree equation, but is less satisfactory for systems where both of the equations are of degree greater than one in both variables.

EXERCISE 9.7

Solve by the method of substitution. In Problems 1–10, check the solutions by sketching the graphs of the equations and estimating the coordinates of any points of intersection.

Example: $y = x^2 + 2x + 1$ (1)   **Check:**

$y - x = 3$ (2)

    Solve equation (2) explicitly for y.

$y = x + 3$ (2′)

    Substitute $(x + 3)$ for y in (1).

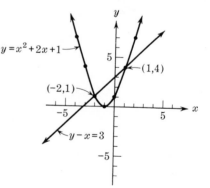

$x + 3 = x^2 + 2x + 1$ (3)

    Solve for x.

$x^2 + x - 2 = 0$

$(x + 2)(x - 1) = 0$

$x = -2, x = 1$

    Substitute each of these values in turn in (2′) to determine values for y.

If $x = -2$, $y = 1$; if $x = 1$, $y = 4$.

Ans. $\{(-2, 1), (1, 4)\}$

1. $y = x^2 - 5$ 2. $y = x^2 - 2x + 1$ 3. $x^2 + y^2 = 13$
    $y = 4x$ $y + x = 3$ $x + y = 5$

4. $x^2 + 2y^2 = 12$ 5. $x + y = 1$ 6. $2x - y = 9$
$2x - y = 2$ $xy = -12$ $xy = -4$

7. $xy = 4$ 8. $x^2 - y^2 = 35$ 9. $x^2 + y^2 = 9$
$x^2 + y^2 = 8$ $xy = 6$ $y = 4$

10. $2x^2 - 4y^2 = 12$ 11. $x^2 - xy - 2y^2 = 4$ 12. $x^2 - 2x + y^2 = 3$
$x = 4$ $x - y = 2$ $2x + y = 4$

13. $2x^2 - 5xy + 2y^2 = 5$ 14. $2x^2 + xy + y^2 = 9$
$2x - y = 1$ $-x + 3y = 9$

15. $x^2 - 2x + y^2 - 1 = 0$ 16. $2x^2 - xy - y^2 = 20$
$2x - 3y = 3$ $2x + y = 4$

17. The sum of the squares of two positive numbers is 13. If twice the first number is added to the second, the sum is 7. Find the numbers.

18. The sum of two numbers is 6 and their product is $\frac{35}{4}$. Find the numbers.

19. The perimeter of a rectangle is 26 inches and the area is 12 square inches. Find the dimensions of the rectangle.

20. The area of a rectangle is 216 square feet. If the perimeter is 60 feet, find the dimensions of the rectangle.

21. A rectangle has a perimeter of 18 feet. If the length is decreased by 5 feet and the width increased by 12 feet, the area is doubled. Find the dimensions of the original rectangle.

22. The annual income from an investment is $32. If the amount invested were $200 more and the rate $\frac{1}{2}\%$ less, the annual income would be $35. What is the amount and rate of the investment?

23. At a constant temperature the pressure (P) and volume (V) of a gas are related by the equation $PV = K$. The product of the pressure (in pounds per square inch) and the volume (in cubic inches) of a certain gas is 30 inch-pounds. If the temperature remains constant as the pressure is increased 4 pounds per square inch, the volume is decreased by 2 cubic inches. Find the original pressure and volume of the gas.

24. What relationship must exist between the numbers a and b so that the solution set of the system
$$x^2 + y^2 = 25$$
$$y = ax + b$$
will have two ordered pairs of real numbers? One ordered pair of real numbers? No ordered pairs of real numbers? *Hint:* Use substitution and consider the nature of the roots of the resulting quadratic equation.

25. Consider the system
$$x^2 + y^2 = 8 \tag{1}$$
$$xy = 4. \tag{2}$$
We can solve this system by substituting $4/x$ for y in (1) to obtain
$$x^2 + \frac{16}{x^2} = 8,$$

from which we have $x = 2$ or $x = -2$. Now if we obtain the y-components of the solution from (2), we find that for $x = 2$, $y = 2$, and for $x = -2$, $y = -2$. But if we seek y-components from (1), we have that for $x = 2$, $y = \pm 2$ and for $x = -2$, $y = \pm 2$. Discuss the fact that we seem to obtain two more solutions from (1) than from (2). What is the solution set of the system?

9.8 Second-Degree Systems in Two Variables—Solution by Other Methods

If both of the equations in a system are of second degree in both variables, the use of linear combinations of members of the equations often provides a simpler means of solution than does substitution. For example, consider the system

$$4x^2 + y^2 = 25 \tag{1}$$

$$x^2 - y^2 = -5. \tag{2}$$

By forming a linear combination using 1 times equation (1) and 1 times equation (2), we have

$$5x^2 = 20,$$

from which

$$x = 2, \; x = -2,$$

and we have the x-components of the members of the solution set of the system (1) and (2). Substituting 2 for x in either (1) or (2), say (1),

$$4(2)^2 + y^2 = 25,$$

$$y^2 = 25 - 16,$$

$$y^2 = 9,$$

and

$$y = 3 \quad \text{or} \quad y = -3.$$

That is, the ordered pairs $(2, 3)$ and $(2, -3)$ are in the solution set of the system. Substituting -2 for x in (1) or (2) [this time we shall use (2)] gives us

$$(-2)^2 - y^2 = -5,$$

$$-y^2 = -5 - 4,$$

$$y^2 = 9,$$

so that

$$y = 3 \quad \text{or} \quad y = -3.$$

This tells us that the ordered pairs $(-2, 3)$ and $(-2, -3)$ are solutions of the system, and the complete solution set is

$$\{(2, 3), \; (2, -3), \; (-2, 3), \; (-2, -3)\}.$$

For an example of a slightly different procedure, consider the system

$$x^2 + y^2 = 5 \tag{3}$$

$$x^2 - 2xy + y^2 = 1. \tag{4}$$

By forming a linear combination using 1 times equation (3) and -1 times equation (4), we have

$$2xy = 4,$$

$$xy = 2, \tag{5}$$

whose solution set contains all of the ordered pairs that satisfy both (3) and (4). Therefore, forming the new system

$$x^2 + y^2 = 5 \tag{3}$$

$$xy = 2, \tag{5}$$

we can be sure that the solution set of this system will contain the solution set of the system (3) and (4). This latter system can be solved by substitution. We have from (5)

$$y = \frac{2}{x}.$$

Replacing y in (3) by $\frac{2}{x}$, we find

$$x^2 + \left(\frac{2}{x}\right)^2 = 5,$$

$$x^2 + \frac{4}{x^2} = 5. \tag{6}$$

Multiplying each member by x^2, we have

$$x^4 + 4 = 5x^2, \tag{7}$$

$$x^4 - 5x^2 + 4 = 0, \tag{7'}$$

which is quadratic in x^2. The left-hand member of (7') factors, and

$$(x^2 - 1)(x^2 - 4) = 0,$$

from which

$$x^2 - 1 = 0 \quad \text{or} \quad x^2 - 4 = 0,$$

and

$$x = 1, \quad x = -1, \quad x = 2, \quad x = -2.$$

Since the step from (6) to (7) was a nonelementary transformation, we are careful to note that these all satisfy (6). [What value for x would have to be excluded if it appeared as a solution of (7)?] Now substituting 1, -1, 2, and -2 in turn for x in (5), we have

for $x = 1$, $y = 2$;

for $x = -1$, $y = -2$;

for $x = 2$, $y = 1$;

for $x = -2$, $y = -1$;

and the solution set of the system (3) and (4) is

$$\{(1, 2), (-1, -2), (2, 1), (-2, -1)\}.$$

There are other techniques involving substitution in conjunction with linear combinations that are useful in handling systems of higher-degree equations, but they all bear similarity to those illustrated. Each system should be scrutinized for some means of finding an equivalent system that will lend itself to solution by linear combination or substitution.

EXERCISE 9.8

Solve analytically.

Example: $4x^2 + y^2 = 25$ (1)

           $x^2 + 4y^2 = 40$ (2)

Obtain a linear combination using 1 times equation (1) and -4 times equation (2) and solve for y.

$$-15y^2 = -135$$
$$y^2 = 9$$
$$y = 3; \ y = -3$$

Substitute values for y in (1) or (2), say (1), to obtain associated values for x.

$4x^2 + (3)^2 = 25$ $4x^2 + (-3)^2 = 25$

    $4x^2 + 9 = 25$ $4x^2 + 9 = 25$

        $4x^2 = 16$ $4x^2 = 16$

          $x^2 = 4$ $x^2 = 4$

          $x = \pm 2$ $x = \pm 2$

Ans. $\{(2, 3), (2, -3), (-2, 3), (-2, -3)\}$

1. $x^2 + y^2 = 10$
    $9x^2 + y^2 = 18$

2. $x^2 + 4y^2 = 52$
    $x^2 + y^2 = 25$

3. $x^2 + 4y^2 = 17$
    $3x^2 - y^2 = -1$

4. $9x^2 + 16y^2 = 100$
    $x^2 + y^2 = 8$

5. $x^2 - y^2 = 7$
    $2x^2 + 3y^2 = 24$

6. $x^2 + 4y^2 = 25$
    $4x^2 + y^2 = 25$

7. $3x^2 + 4y^2 = 16$
    $x^2 - y^2 = 3$

8. $4x^2 + 3y^2 = 12$
    $x^2 + 3y^2 = 12$

9. $4x^2 - 9y^2 + 132 = 0$
    $x^2 + 4y^2 - 67 = 0$

10. $16y^2 + 5x^2 - 26 = 0$
    $25y^2 - 4x^2 - 17 = 0$

11. $x^2 - xy + y^2 = 7$
    $x^2 + y^2 = 5$

12. $3x^2 - 2xy + 3y^2 = 43$
    $x^2 + y^2 = 17$

13. $2x^2 + xy - 4y^2 = -12$
    $x^2 - 2y^2 = -4$

14. $x^2 + 2xy - y^2 = 14$
    $x^2 - y^2 = 8$

15. $x^2 + 3xy - y^2 = -3$
$x^2 + xy - y^2 = 1$

16. $2x^2 + xy - 2y^2 = 16$
$x^2 + 2xy - y^2 = 17$

17. $3x^2 + 3xy - y^2 = 35$
$x^2 - xy - 6y^2 = 0$

18. $x^2 - xy + y^2 = 21$
$x^2 + 2xy - 8y^2 = 0$

Hint: Factor second equation.

19. How many *real* solutions are possible for simultaneous systems of independent equations that consist of:

(a) two linear equations in two variables?
(b) one linear equation and one quadratic equation in two variables?
(c) two quadratic equations in two variables?
Support each of your answers with sketches.

CHAPTER REVIEW

Solve each system by substitution or linear combinations.

1. $x + 5y = 18$
$x - y = -3$

2. $x + 5y = 11$
$2x + 3y = 8$

3. $\frac{1}{2}x + 3y - \frac{1}{2}z = 8$
$2x - \frac{1}{3}y + z = -11$
$\frac{1}{4}x + \frac{2}{3}y + 3z = -6$

4. $x + y + z = 2$
$3x - y + z = 4$
$2x + y + 2z = 3$

5. $x^2 + y = 3$
$5x + y = 7$

6. $x^2 + 2y^2 + 3xy + x = 2$
$2x + 5y = -4$

7. $2x^2 + 5y^2 - 53 = 0$
$4x^2 + 3y^2 - 43 = 0$

8. $x^2 - 3xy + y^2 + 1 = 0$
$x^2 + y^2 - 5 = 0$

Evaluate.

9. $\begin{vmatrix} 3 & -2 \\ 1 & -5 \end{vmatrix}$

10. $\begin{vmatrix} 2 & 1 & 3 \\ 0 & 4 & -1 \\ 2 & 0 & 3 \end{vmatrix}$

Solve each system by Cramer's rule.

11. $2x + 3y = -2$
$x - 8y = -39$

12. $2x + 3y - z + 2 = 0$
$x - y + z - 6 = 0$
$3x - y + z - 10 = 0$

13. State whether each system is dependent, inconsistent, or consistent and independent.

a. $2x - 3y = 4$
$x + 2y = 7$

b. $2x - 3y = 4$
$6x - 9y = 12$

c. $2x - 3y = 4$
$6x - 9y = 4$

Each of the following statements, 14–17, is a result of one or more of the properties in Section 9.6.   State the property (or properties) applicable in each case.

14. $\begin{vmatrix} 2 & 4 & 1 \\ 3 & 2 & 2 \\ -2 & 0 & 10 \end{vmatrix} = -2 \begin{vmatrix} 2 & 4 & 1 \\ 3 & 2 & 2 \\ 1 & 0 & -5 \end{vmatrix}$

15. $\begin{vmatrix} 3 & -1 & 2 \\ 0 & 0 & 0 \\ 2 & 1 & -3 \end{vmatrix} = 0$

16. $\begin{vmatrix} 2 & 4 & 0 \\ 1 & -2 & 3 \\ 0 & 1 & 2 \end{vmatrix} = \begin{vmatrix} 0 & 8 & -6 \\ 1 & -2 & 3 \\ 0 & 1 & 2 \end{vmatrix}$

17. $\begin{vmatrix} 0 & 4 & 0 \\ -2 & 0 & -6 \\ 1 & 0 & 3 \end{vmatrix} = 0$

18. Show that

$$\begin{vmatrix} a & d & g \\ b & e & h \\ c & f & i \end{vmatrix} = -\begin{vmatrix} d & a & g \\ e & b & h \\ f & c & i \end{vmatrix}.$$

19. Reduce to an equal 2×2 determinant and evaluate:

$$\begin{vmatrix} -1 & 0 & 2 & 1 \\ 0 & 3 & -1 & 1 \\ 2 & 1 & 0 & -2 \\ -1 & 1 & 1 & -1 \end{vmatrix}.$$

20. Use determinants to solve the system

$$2x - y + 3z = 4$$
$$x + y - 2z = 0$$
$$4x - 2y + 6z = 3.$$

Is there a solution or solutions?   Explain.

10

SEQUENCES AND SERIES

10.1 Sequences

A function whose domain is a set of successive positive integers, for example, the function defined by

$$s(n) = n + 3, \quad n \in \{1, 2, 3, \cdots\}, \tag{1}$$

is called a **sequence function.** The elements in the range of such a function arranged in the order

$$s(1), s(2), s(3), s(4), \cdots$$

are said to form a **sequence.** Thus the sequence associated with (1) is found by successively substituting the numbers 1, 2, 3, $\cdots$ for n:

$$s(1) = (1) + 3 = 4,$$
$$s(2) = (2) + 3 = 5,$$
$$s(3) = (3) + 3 = 6,$$
$$s(4) = (4) + 3 = 7,$$

and the first four terms are 4, 5, 6, and 7. The nth term or **general term** is $n + 3$. As another example, the first five terms of the sequence defined by the equation

$$s(n) = \frac{3}{2n - 1}, \quad n \in \{1, 2, 3, \cdots\},$$

are 3/1, 3/3, 3/5, 3/7, and 3/9, and the twenty-fifth term is

$$s(25) = \frac{3}{2(25) - 1} = \frac{3}{49}.$$

Given several terms in a sequence, it is sometimes possible to find an expression for a general term. Thus, if the first four terms in a sequence are

$$2, 4, 6, 8, \cdots, \tag{2}$$

we may, by a process of trial and error, or simply by inspection, find an expression for a general term,

$$s(n) = 2n.$$

As another example, consider the parlor pastime of tearing in half a sheet from the daily newspaper, placing the two halves together, and then repeating the process. How long can a person expect to continue this procedure? The answer to this question clearly depends upon the person doing the tearing, but we can determine the magnitude of the undertaking at any given step by noting that the number of sheets of newspaper to be torn is a term in the sequence

$$1, 2, 4, 8, 16, \cdots. \tag{3}$$

If a general term that agrees with the physical reality of the situation can be found for this sequence, we can immediately write the number of sheets of paper involved in the eighth tear, or any other tear. In this example, of course, we have the advantage of knowing how the sequence is being generated. Since each term in the sequence (3) results from doubling the preceding term, we observe that

$$s(1) = 1 = 2^0,$$
$$s(2) = 2 = 2^1,$$
$$s(3) = 4 = 2^2,$$
$$s(4) = 8 = 2^3.$$

At this point it appears that the nth term in the sequence could be obtained by raising 2 to the $(n - 1)$st power. We find that

$$s(n) = 2^{n-1}$$

does indeed generate the sequence (3).

The process by which we obtained a general term for each of the sequences (2) and (3) may be called *informal induction*. The reasoning process is inductive because we generalize from a number of special cases, and it is informal because we do not prove that the general term will hold for all positive integers n.

If only a finite number of successive terms are known for a sequence, and no rule is given for determining the general term, then a *unique* general term cannot be obtained. For example, both

$$s(n) = 3n$$

and

$$s(n) = 3n + (n - 1)(n - 2)(n - 3)$$

generate the sequence 3, 6, 9, but they will produce different sequences for terms following the third. In general, we seek the simplest such expression.

A sequence is called **finite** or **infinite** as its domain of definition contains a finite or infinite number of members.

The notation ordinarily used for the terms in a sequence is not function notation as such. It is customary to denote a term in a sequence by means of a subscript. Thus, we will use s_n rather than $s(n)$, and the sequence $s(1), s(2), s(3), \cdots$ will appear as $s_1, s_2, s_3, \cdots$.

In the exercise in this section, you will be asked to find general terms by trial and error or by inspection. You will be introduced to more formal methods for special sequences in later sections.

EXERCISE 10.1

Find the first four terms in a sequence with the general term as given.

Examples:

a. $s_n = \dfrac{n(n + 1)}{2}$

$s_1 = \dfrac{1(1 + 1)}{2} = 1$

$s_2 = \dfrac{2(2 + 1)}{2} = 3$

$s_3 = \dfrac{3(3 + 1)}{2} = 6$

$s_4 = \dfrac{4(4 + 1)}{2} = 10$

Ans. 1, 3, 6, 10

b. $s_n = (-1)^n 2^n$

$s_1 = (-1)^1 2^1 = -2$

$s_2 = (-1)^2 2^2 = 4$

$s_3 = (-1)^3 2^3 = -8$

$s_4 = (-1)^4 2^4 = 16$

Ans. $-2, 4, -8, 16$

1. $s_n = n - 5$ $\qquad$ **2.** $s_n = 2n - 3$ $\qquad$ **3.** $s_n = \dfrac{n^2 - 2}{2}$

4. $s_n = \dfrac{3}{n^2 + 1}$ $\qquad$ **5.** $s_n = 1 + \dfrac{1}{n}$ $\qquad$ **6.** $s_n = \dfrac{n}{2n - 1}$

7. $s_n = \dfrac{n(n - 1)}{2}$ $\qquad$ **8.** $s_n = \dfrac{5}{n(n + 1)}$ $\qquad$ **9.** $s_n = (-1)^n$

10. $s_n = (-1)^{n+1}$ $\qquad$ **11.** $s_n = \dfrac{(-1)^n(n - 2)}{n}$ $\qquad$ **12.** $s_n = (-1)^{n-1}\, 3^{n+1}$

Find a general term for a sequence with the first four terms as given.

Examples:

a. $2, \dfrac{3}{2}, \dfrac{4}{3}, \dfrac{5}{4}$ $\qquad\qquad\qquad$ b. $x, \dfrac{-x^2}{2}, \dfrac{x^3}{3}, \dfrac{-x^4}{4}$

There are no unique solutions; answers are obtained by trial and error or by inspection.

Ans. $\dfrac{n + 1}{n}$ $\qquad\qquad\qquad$ Ans. $(-1)^{n+1}\dfrac{x^n}{n}$

13. 4, 8, 12, 16, $\cdots$ $\qquad$ **14.** 5, 10, 15, 20, $\cdots$ $\qquad$ **15.** 2, 5, 8, 11, $\cdots$

16. 1, 3, 5, 7, $\cdots$ $\qquad$ **17.** $-1, 1, -1, 1, \cdots$ $\qquad$ **18.** 1, $-1, 1, -1, \cdots$

19. $-3, 5, -7, 9, \cdots$ $\qquad$ **20.** 3, $-7, 11, -15, \cdots$ $\qquad$ **21.** $\frac{1}{2}, \frac{2}{3}, \frac{3}{4}, \frac{4}{5}, \cdots$

22. $\frac{1}{3}, \frac{1}{4}, \frac{1}{5}, \frac{1}{6}, \cdots$ $\qquad$ **23.** 2, 5, 10, 17, $\cdots$ $\qquad$ **24.** $\frac{1}{2}, \frac{1}{4}, \frac{1}{8}, \frac{1}{16}, \cdots$

25. $x^2, x^3, x^4, x^5, \cdots$ $\qquad\qquad$ **26.** $x^2, x^4, x^6, x^8, \cdots$

27. $-x, x^3, -x^5, x^7, \cdots$ $\qquad\qquad$ **28.** 1, $-x, x^2, -x^3, \cdots$

29. A culture of bacteria doubles every hour. If there were 10 bacteria in the culture originally, how many are there after 2 hours? 4 hours? n hours?

30. A ball rebounds one half of the distance it falls. When dropped from 8 feet, how high does it rebound on the first bounce? On the second bounce? On the nth bounce?

31. A certain radioactive substance has a half-life of 2400 years. (50% of the original material is present at the end of 2400 years.) If 100 grams were produced today, how many grams would be present in 4800 years? In 9600 years?

10.2 Series

Associated with any sequence is a **series,** the series being defined as the indicated sum of the terms in the sequence. Thus, associated with the sequence

$$4, 7, 10, \cdots, 3n + 1 \tag{1}$$

is the series

$$S_n = 4 + 7 + 10 + \cdots + (3n + 1), \tag{2}$$

and associated with the sequence

$$x, x^2, x^3, x^4, \cdots, x^n \tag{3}$$

is the series

$$S_n = x + x^2 + x^3 + x^4 + \cdots + x^n. \tag{4}$$

Since the terms in the series are the same as those in the sequence, we can refer to the first term or the second term or the general term of a series in the same manner as we do for a sequence.

A series whose general term is known can be represented in a very convenient, compact way by means of what is called **sigma** or **summation notation.** The Greek letter Σ (sigma) is used to denote a sum. For example, series (2) can be written

$$S_n = \sum_{i=1}^{n} (3i + 1), \tag{5}$$

where we understand that S_n is the series whose terms are obtained by replacing i in the expression $3i + 1$ with the numbers 1, 2, 3, $\cdots$, n, successively. Thus

$$S_6 = \sum_{i=1}^{6} (3i + 1)$$

appears in expanded form as

$$S_6 = 4 + 7 + 10 + 13 + 16 + 19.$$

The variable used in conjunction with summation notation is called the **index of summation** and the set of integers over which we sum (in this case $\{1, 2, 3, 4, 5, 6\}$) is called the **range of summation.**

To show that a series has an infinite number of terms—that is, has no last term—we shall adopt the notation

$$S_\infty = \sum_{i=4}^{\infty} (3i + 1). \tag{6}$$

Writing (6) in expanded form, we have

$$S_\infty = 13 + 16 + 19 + 22 + \cdots,$$

where in this case i has been replaced by 4, 5, 6, 7, $\cdots$. Notice that the first replacement for i is 4.

EXERCISE 10.2

Write in expanded form.

Examples:

a. $\sum_{i=2}^{4} (i^2 + 1)$ b. $\sum_{k=1}^{\infty} (-1)^k 2^{k+1}$

  i takes values 2, 3, 4. k takes values 1, 2, 3 $\cdots$.

  $i = 2$, $(2)^2 + 1 = 5$ $k = 1$, $(-1)^1 2^{1+1} = (-1)(4) = -4$

  $i = 3$, $(3)^2 + 1 = 10$ $k = 2$, $(-1)^2 2^{2+1} = (1)(8) = 8$

  $i = 4$, $(4)^2 + 1 = 17$ $k = 3$, $(-1)^3 2^{3+1} = (-1)(16) = -16$

  Ans. $5 + 10 + 17$ **Ans.** $-4 + 8 - 16 + \cdots$

1. $\displaystyle\sum_{i=1}^{4} i^2$ 2. $\displaystyle\sum_{i=1}^{3} (3i - 2)$ 3. $\displaystyle\sum_{j=5}^{7} (j - 2)$

4. $\displaystyle\sum_{j=2}^{6} (j^2 + 1)$ 5. $\displaystyle\sum_{k=1}^{4} k(k + 1)$ 6. $\displaystyle\sum_{i=2}^{6} \frac{i}{2}(i + 1)$

7. $\displaystyle\sum_{i=1}^{4} \frac{(-1)^i}{2^i}$ 8. $\displaystyle\sum_{i=3}^{5} \frac{(-1)^{i+1}}{i - 2}$ 9. $\displaystyle\sum_{i=1}^{\infty} (2i - 1)$

10. $\displaystyle\sum_{j=1}^{\infty} \frac{1}{j}$ 11. $\displaystyle\sum_{k=0}^{\infty} \frac{1}{2^k}$ 12. $\displaystyle\sum_{k=0}^{\infty} \frac{k}{1 + k}$

13. $\displaystyle\sum_{i=1}^{n} (2i + 1)$ 14. $\displaystyle\sum_{j=0}^{n} \frac{(-1)^{j+1}}{2^j + 1}$ 15. $\displaystyle\sum_{k=1}^{n} \frac{k}{(k + 1)^k}$

Write in sigma notation.

Examples:

  a. $5 + 8 + 11 + 14$ b. $x^2 + x^4 + x^6 + \cdots + x^{2n}$

    Find a general term.

    $3i + 2$ x^{2i}

  Ans. $\displaystyle\sum_{i=1}^{4} (3i + 2)$ **Ans.** $\displaystyle\sum_{i=1}^{n} x^{2i}$

16. $1 + 2 + 3 + 4$ 17. $2 + 4 + 6 + 8$

18. $x + x^3 + x^5 + x^7$ 19. $x^3 + x^5 + x^7 + x^9 + x^{11}$

20. $1 + 4 + 9 + 16 + 25$ 21. $\frac{1}{3} + \frac{1}{9} + \frac{1}{27} + \frac{1}{81}$

22. $1 - 1 + 1 - 1 \cdots + (-1)^{n+1}$ 23. $0 + 1 + 2 + 3 + \cdots + n$

24. $-1 + 2 - 3 + 4 - 5 + \cdots + (-1)^n n$ 25. $\frac{1}{2} + \frac{1}{4} + \frac{1}{8} + \frac{1}{16} + \cdots + (\frac{1}{2})^n$

Write, in sigma notation, an infinite series whose first four terms are as given.

Examples:

  a. $3 + 6 + 9 + 12 + \cdots$ b. $\frac{3}{5} + \frac{5}{7} + \frac{7}{9} + \frac{9}{11} + \cdots$

    Find a general term.

    $3i$ $\dfrac{2i + 1}{2i + 3}$

    Ans. $\displaystyle\sum_{i=1}^{\infty} 3i$ **Ans.** $\displaystyle\sum_{i=1}^{\infty} \frac{2i + 1}{2i + 3}$

26. $1 \cdot 2 + 2 \cdot 3 + 3 \cdot 4 + 4 \cdot 5 + \cdots$ 27. $\frac{1}{2} + \frac{2}{3} + \frac{3}{4} + \frac{4}{5} + \cdots$

28. $\frac{2}{1} + \frac{3}{2} + \frac{4}{3} + \frac{5}{4} + \cdots$ 29. $\frac{1}{1} + \frac{2}{3} + \frac{3}{5} + \frac{4}{7} + \cdots$

30. $\frac{3}{1} + \frac{5}{3} + \frac{7}{5} + \frac{9}{7} + \cdots$ 31. $\frac{1}{1} + \frac{2}{2} + \frac{4}{3} + \frac{8}{4} + \cdots$

32. $\frac{1}{2} + \frac{3}{4} + \frac{9}{6} + \frac{27}{8} + \cdots$

33. Consider

$$S_n = \sum_{i=1}^{n} f(i).$$

    Explain why this equation defines a sequence function. What is the independent variable? What is the dependent variable?

10.3 Arithmetic Progressions

Any sequence whose general term is linear in n has the property that each term except the first can be obtained from the preceding term by adding a common number. Consider the sequence whose general term is

$$s_n = dn + g \tag{1}$$

where $d \neq 0$. The succeeding term is given by replacing n in (1) with $(n + 1)$, and we have

$$s_{n+1} = d(n + 1) + g. \tag{2}$$

By rewriting the right-hand member of (2),

$$s_{n+1} = dn + d + g$$
$$= (dn + g) + d,$$

we see that the $(n + 1)$st term is obtained from the nth term by adding the number d, called the **common difference**. For example, the sequence

$$2, 4, 6, 8, \cdots, \tag{3}$$

in which the nth term is given by

$$s_n = 2n,$$

has the property that each term is obtained by adding the number 2 to the preceding term. Similarly, the sequence

$$3, 7, 11, 15, \cdots \tag{4}$$

is generated (except for the first term) by adding 4 to a given term to obtain the succeeding term. (What is the general term in this sequence?) A sequence with this property is called an **arithmetic progression**, and we can state the definition for such a sequence symbolically:

$$s_1 = a,$$
$$s_{n+1} = s_n + d.$$

Definitions of this sort are called recursive definitions. It is customary to denote the first term in such a sequence by the letter a, the common difference between successive terms by d, the number of terms in the sequence (when finite) by n, and the nth term by s_n. Notice that when the nth term is given by an equation of the form (1), the coefficient of n is the common difference. Thus, in the arithmetic progression (4), a is 3, d is 4, the number of terms is indicated as infinite, and the nth term (for finite n) can be given by $s_n = 4n - 1$.

We can verify that a finite sequence is an arithmetic progression simply by subtracting each term from its successor and noting that the difference in each case is the same. For example,

$$7, 18, 29, 40$$

is an arithmetic progression because

$$18 - 7 = 11,$$
$$29 - 18 = 11,$$
$$40 - 29 = 11.$$

If at least two consecutive terms in an arithmetic progression are known, we can determine the common difference and generate as many terms as we wish. Furthermore, a linear expression can be found for the nth term. Consider the general arithmetic progression with first term a and common difference d. The

first term is a,
second term is $a + d$,
third term is $a + d + d = a + 2d$,
fourth term is $a + d + d + d = a + 3d$,

. . . .

nth term is $a + d + d + \cdots + d = a + (n - 1)d$.

Thus

$$s_n = a + (n - 1)d. \tag{5}$$

Here again we have used an informal inductive process to obtain expression (5). We shall assume its validity for all natural numbers n. For example, the twenty-third term of the sequence

$$4, 7, 10, \cdots$$

is given by

$$s_{23} = 4 + (23 - 1)3 = 70.$$

The problem of finding an explicit representation for the sum of n terms of a sequence in terms of n is, in general, very difficult; however, we can obtain such a representation for the sum of n terms in an arithmetic progression. Consider the series of n terms associated with the general arithmetic progression $a, (a + d), (a + 2d), \cdots, a + (n - 1)d$. That is,

$$S_n = a + (a + d) + (a + 2d) + \cdots + [a + (n - 1)d], \tag{6}$$

and then consider the same series written

$$S_n = s_n + (s_n - d) + (s_n - 2d) + \cdots + [s_n - (n - 1)d], \tag{7}$$

where the terms are written in reverse order. Adding (6) and (7) term by term, we have

$$S_n + S_n = (a + s_n) + (a + s_n) + (a + s_n) + \cdots + (a + s_n),$$

where the term $(a + s_n)$ occurs n times. Then

$$2S_n = n(a + s_n)$$

or

$$S_n = \frac{n}{2}(a + s_n). \tag{8}$$

$d =$ Common difference

If (8) is rewritten

$$S_n = n\left(\frac{a + s_n}{2}\right),$$

we observe that the sum is given by the product of the number of terms in the series and the average of the first and last terms.

An alternative form for (8) is obtained by substituting the value for s_n as given by (5) in (8) to obtain

$$S_n = \frac{n}{2}\left(a + [a + (n - 1)d]\right)$$

or

$$S_n = \frac{n}{2}\left[2a + (n - 1)d\right],$$

where the sum is now expressed in terms of a, n, and d.

EXERCISE 10.3

a.   Write the next three terms in each of the following arithmetic progressions.
b.   Find an expression for the general term.

Examples:

    a. $5, 9, \cdots$ b. $x, x - a, \cdots$

        Find the common difference and then continue the sequence.

    $d = 9 - 5 = 4$ $d = (x - a) - x = -a$

    Ans. 13, 17, 21   **Ans.** $x - 2a, x - 3a, x - 4a$

        Use $s_n = a + (n - 1)d$ to find an expression for the general term.

    $s_n = 5 + (n - 1)4$ $s_n = x + (n - 1)(-a)$

    Ans. $s_n = 4n + 1$ **Ans.** $s_n = x - a(n - 1)$

1. $3, 7, \cdots$ **2.** $-6, -1, \cdots$ **3.** $-1, -5, \cdots$

4. $-10, -20, \cdots$ **5.** $x, x + 1, \cdots$ **6.** $a, a + 5, \cdots$

7. $x + a, x + 3a, \cdots$ **8.** $y - 2b, y, \cdots$ **9.** $2x + 1, 2x + 4, \cdots$

10. $a + 2b, a - 2b, \cdots$ **11.** $x, 2x, \cdots$ **12.** $3a, 5a, \cdots$

Example: Find the fourteenth term of the arithmetic progression $-6, -1, 4, \cdots$.

    Find the common difference.

    $d = -1 - (-6) = 5$

       Use $s_n = a + (n - 1)d$.

    $s_{14} = -6 + (13)5 = 59$

    Ans. 59

13. Find the seventh term in the arithmetic progression $7, 11, 15, \cdots$.

14. Find the tenth term in the arithmetic progression $-3, -12, -21, \cdots$.

15. Find the twelfth term in the arithmetic progression $2, \frac{5}{2}, 3, \cdots$.

16. Find the seventeenth term in the arithmetic progression $-5, -2, 1, \cdots$.

17. Find the twentieth term in the arithmetic progression $3, -2, -7, \cdots$.

18. Find the tenth term in the arithmetic progression $\frac{3}{4}, 2, \frac{13}{4}, \cdots$.

Example: Find the first term in an arithmetic progression in which the third term is 7 and the eleventh term is 55.

Find a common difference by considering an arithmetic progression whose first term is 7 and whose ninth term is 55. Use $s_n = a + (n-1)d$.

$s_9 = 7 + (9 - 1)d$
$55 = 7 + 8d$
$d = 6$

Use this difference to find the first term in an arithmetic progression in which the third term is 7. Use $s_n = a + (n-1)d$.

$s_3 = a + (3 - 1)6$
$7 = a + 12$
$a = -5$

Ans. -5

Alternative Solution:

Use $s_n = a + (n-1)d$, with $s_3 = 7$.

$7 = a + (3 - 1)d$ or $7 = a + 2d$ $\qquad$ (1)

Use $s_n = a + (n-1)d$ with $s_{11} = 55$.

$55 = a + (11 - 1)d$ or $55 = a + 10d$ $\qquad$ (2)

Solve the system (1) and (2) to obtain $a = -5$.

Ans. -5

19. If the third term in an arithmetic progression is 7 and the eighth term is 17, find the common difference. What is the first term? What is the twentieth term?

20. If the fifth term of an arithmetic progression is -16 and the twentieth term is -46, what is the twelfth term?

21. What term in the arithmetic progression $4, 1, -2, \cdots$ is -77?

22. What is the twelfth term in an arithmetic progression in which the second term is x and the third term is y?

Find the sum of the finite series.

Example: $\displaystyle\sum_{i=1}^{12} (4i + 1)$

Write the first two or three terms in expanded form.

$5 + 9 + 13 + \cdots$

By inspection, the first term is 5 and the common difference is 4. Use $s_n = \dfrac{n}{2}[2a + (n - 1)d]$ with $n = 12$.

$s_{12} = \tfrac{12}{2}[2(5) + (12 - 1)4]$

Ans.   324

23. $\displaystyle\sum_{i=1}^{7} (2i + 1)$ **24.** $\displaystyle\sum_{i=1}^{21} (3i - 2)$ **25.** $\displaystyle\sum_{j=3}^{15} (7j - 1)$

26. $\displaystyle\sum_{j=10}^{20} (2j - 3)$ **27.** $\displaystyle\sum_{k=1}^{8} (\tfrac{1}{2}k - 3)$ **28.** $\displaystyle\sum_{k=1}^{100} k$

29. Find the sum of all even integers n, where $13 < n < 89$.

30. Find the sum of all integral multiples of 7 between 8 and 110.

31. How many bricks will there be in a pile one brick in thickness if there are 27 bricks in the first row, 25 in the second row, etc., and 1 in the top row?

32. If there are a total of 256 bricks in a pile arranged in the manner of those in Problem 31, how many bricks are there in the third row from the bottom of the pile?

33. Find a if $\displaystyle\sum_{j=1}^{5} aj = 14$.

34. Find p and q if $\displaystyle\sum_{i=1}^{4} (pi + q) = 28$ and $\displaystyle\sum_{i=2}^{5} (pi + q) = 44$.

35. Show that the sum of the first n odd natural numbers is n^2.

10.4   Geometric Progressions

Any sequence in which each term except the first is obtained by multiplying the preceding term by a common multiplier is called a **geometric progression** and is defined by the recursive equation

$$s_1 = a,$$

$$s_{n+1} = rs_n,$$

where r is the common multiplier. Thus,

$$3, 9, 27, 81, \cdots$$

is a geometric progression in which each term except the first is obtained by multiplying the preceding term by 3. Since the effect of multiplying the terms in this way is to produce a fixed ratio between any two successive terms, the multiplier, r, is called the **ratio**.

If the first term is designated by a,

the second term is $a \cdot r$,
the third term is $ar \cdot r = ar^2$,
the fourth term is $ar^2 \cdot r = ar^3$,

and it appears that the nth term will take the form

$$s_n = ar^{n-1}. \tag{1}$$

We assume the validity of this expression for all natural numbers n. The general geometric progression will appear as

$$a, ar, ar^2, ar^3, ar^4, \cdots, ar^{n-1}, \cdots.$$

For example, consider the geometric progression

$$2, 6, 18, \cdots.$$

By writing the ratio of any term to its predecessor, say $\frac{18}{6}$, we find that $r = 3$. A representation for s_n of this sequence can now be written in terms of n by substituting 2 for a and 3 for r in equation (1). Thus

$$s_n = 2(3)^{n-1}.$$

The sequence function that generates a geometric progression is an exponential function. We shall consider such functions in greater detail in Chapter 11.

To find an explicit representation for the sum of a given number of terms in a geometric progression in terms of a, r, and n, we employ a device somewhat similar to the one we used in finding the sum of an arithmetic progression. Consider the geometric series containing n terms (2), and the series (3) obtained by multiplying both members of (2) by r,

$$S_n = a + ar + ar^2 + ar^3 + \cdots + ar^{n-2} + ar^{n-1}, \tag{2}$$

$$rS_n = \quad ar + ar^2 + ar^3 + ar^4 + \cdots + ar^{n-1} + ar^n. \tag{3}$$

Subtracting (3) from (2), all terms in the right-hand member except the first term in (2) and the last term in (3) vanish, and

$$S_n - rS_n = a - ar^n.$$

Factoring S_n from the left-hand member yields

$$(1 - r)S_n = a - ar^n,$$

from which

$$S_n = \frac{a - ar^n}{1 - r} \quad (r \neq 1), \tag{4}$$

and we have a formula for the sum of n terms of a geometric progression. For the special case $r = 1$, $S_n = na$.

An alternative expression for (4) can be obtained by noting that (4) can be written

$$S_n = \frac{a - r(ar^{n-1})}{1 - r}$$

$$S_n = ar^{n-1}$$

and, since $s_n = ar^{n-1}$,

$$S_n = \frac{a - rs_n}{1 - r} \quad (r \neq 1),$$

where the sum is now given in terms of a, s_n, and r.

EXERCISE 10.4

Write the next three terms in each of the following geometric progressions. Find the general term.

Examples:

a. $3, 6, 12, \cdots$ b. $x, 2, \dfrac{4}{x}, \cdots$

     Find the common ratio.

$$r = \frac{6}{3} = 2 \qquad\qquad\qquad r = \frac{2}{x}$$

     Multiply each term by r to determine the following term.

Ans. $24, 48, 96$ **Ans.** $\dfrac{8}{x^2}, \dfrac{16}{x^3}, \dfrac{32}{x^4}$

     Use $s_n = ar^{n-1}$ to find the general term.

Ans. $s_n = 3(2)^{n-1}$ **Ans.** $s_n = x\left(\dfrac{2}{x}\right)^{n-1}$ or $\dfrac{2^{n-1}}{x^{n-2}}$

1. $2, 8, 32, \cdots$ 2. $4, 8, 16, \cdots$ 3. $\frac{2}{3}, \frac{4}{3}, \frac{8}{3}, \cdots$

4. $6, 3, \frac{3}{2}, \cdots$ 5. $4, -2, 1, \cdots$ 6. $\frac{1}{2}, -\frac{3}{2}, \frac{9}{2}, \cdots$

7. $\dfrac{a}{x}, -1, \dfrac{x}{a}, \cdots$ 8. $\dfrac{a}{b}, \dfrac{a}{bc}, \dfrac{a}{bc^2}, \cdots$

Example: Find the ninth term of the geometric progression $-24, 12, -6, \cdots$.

     Find the common ratio.

$$r = -\tfrac{12}{24} = -\tfrac{1}{2}$$

     Use $s_n = ar^{n-1}$.

$$s_9 = -24(-\tfrac{1}{2})^8$$

Ans. $-\tfrac{3}{32}$

9. Find the sixth term in the geometric progression $48, 96, 192, \cdots$.

10. Find the eighth term in the geometric progression $-3, \frac{3}{2}, -\frac{3}{4}, \cdots$.

11. Find the seventh term in the geometric progression $-\frac{1}{3}a^2, a^5, -3a^8, \cdots$.

12. Find the ninth term in the geometric progression $-81, -27, -9, \cdots$.

13. Find the first term of a geometric progression whose fifth term is 48 and whose ratio is 2.

14. Find a value for x so that $-\frac{3}{2}, x, -\frac{8}{27}$ will be in geometric progression.

Find each of the following sums.

Example: $\displaystyle\sum_{i=2}^{7} (\tfrac{1}{3})^i$

Write the first two or three terms in expanded form.

$(\tfrac{1}{3})^2 + (\tfrac{1}{3})^3 + \cdots$

By inspection, the first term is $\frac{1}{9}$, the ratio is $\frac{1}{3}$, and $n = 6$ (i takes on 6 values, 2, 3, 4, 5, 6, 7). Use $S_n = \dfrac{a - ar^n}{1 - r}$.

$$S_n = \frac{\frac{1}{9} - \frac{1}{9}(\tfrac{1}{3})^6}{1 - \frac{1}{3}}$$

$$= \frac{\frac{1}{9}(1 - \frac{1}{729})}{\frac{2}{3}}$$

$$= \tfrac{1}{9} \cdot \tfrac{728}{729} \cdot \tfrac{3}{2}$$

Ans. $\frac{364}{2187}$

15. $\displaystyle\sum_{i=1}^{6} 3^i$

16. $\displaystyle\sum_{j=1}^{4} (-2)^j$

17. $\displaystyle\sum_{k=3}^{7} (\tfrac{1}{2})^{k-2}$

18. $\displaystyle\sum_{i=3}^{12} (2)^{i-5}$

19. $\displaystyle\sum_{j=1}^{6} (\tfrac{1}{3})^j$

20. $\displaystyle\sum_{k=1}^{5} (\tfrac{1}{4})^k$

21. $\displaystyle\sum_{i=3}^{5} (2i + 2^i + 1)$

22. $\displaystyle\sum_{k=5}^{8} (3k + k^2 - 5)$

23. Find $\displaystyle\sum_{j=1}^{4} [3 + (2)^j]$. *Hint:* $\sum (a + b) = \sum a + \sum b$.

24. Find $\displaystyle\sum_{i=1}^{n} (\tfrac{1}{2})^i$ for $n = 2, 3, 4,$ and 5. What number do you think $\displaystyle\sum_{i=1}^{n} (\tfrac{1}{2})^i$ approaches as n becomes larger and larger?

10.5 Infinite Geometric Progressions

Recall from Section 10.4 that the sum of n terms of a geometric progression is given by

$$S_n = \frac{a - ar^n}{1 - r}. \tag{1}$$

If $|r| < 1$, that is, if $-1 < r < 1$, then r^n becomes smaller and smaller for increasingly large n. For example, if $r = \frac{1}{2}$,

$$r^2 = (\tfrac{1}{2})^2 = \tfrac{1}{4},$$
$$r^3 = (\tfrac{1}{2})^3 = \tfrac{1}{8},$$
$$r^4 = (\tfrac{1}{2})^4 = \tfrac{1}{16},$$

etc., and we can make $(\frac{1}{2})^n$ as small as we please by taking n sufficiently large. Writing (1) in the form

$$S_n = \frac{a}{1-r}(1 - r^n), \tag{2}$$

we see that the value of the factor $(1 - r^n)$ can be made as close as we please to 1 providing $|r| < 1$ and n is taken large enough. Since this asserts that the sum (2) can be made to approximate

$$\frac{a}{1-r}$$

as close as we please, we define the sum of an infinite geometric progression with $|r| < 1$ to be

$$S_\infty = \frac{a}{1-r}. \tag{3}$$

A sequence whose nth term (and all terms after the nth) can be made to approximate a fixed number L as closely as desired by simply taking n large enough is said to approach the limit L as n increases without bound. We can indicate this in terms of symbols

$$\lim_{n \to \infty} S_n = L,$$

where S_n is the nth term of the sequence. Thus (3) might be written

$$S_\infty = \lim_{n \to \infty} S_n = \frac{a}{1-r}.$$

If $|r| \geq 1$, then r^n in equation (2) does not approach 0 and $\lim_{n \to \infty} S_n$ does not exist.

An interesting application of this sum arises in connection with repeating decimals—that is, decimal numerals that, after a finite number of decimal places, have endlessly repeating groups of digits. For example,

$$0.212121\cdots,$$

$$0.3333\cdots,$$

$$0.172317231723\cdots,$$

$$0.818181\cdots,$$

$$0.138512512512\cdots,$$

are repeating decimals. Consider the problem of expressing such a decimal numeral as a fraction. We illustrate the process involved with the first example above:

$$0.212121\cdots. \tag{4}$$

This decimal can be written either as

$$0.21 + 0.0021 + 0.000021 + \cdots, \tag{5}$$

or

$$\frac{21}{100} + \frac{21}{10,000} + \frac{21}{1,000,000} + \cdots, \tag{6}$$

which are geometric progressions with ratio 0.01 (or 1/100). Since the ratio is less than 1 in absolute value, we can use (3) to find the sum of an infinite number of terms of (6). Thus

$$S_\infty = \frac{a}{1-r} = \frac{\dfrac{21}{100}}{1 - \dfrac{1}{100}}$$

$$= \frac{\dfrac{21}{100}}{\dfrac{99}{100}} = \frac{21}{99} = \frac{7}{33},$$

and the given decimal numeral is equivalent to 7/33.

EXERCISE 10.5

Find the sum of each of the following infinite geometric series. If the series has no sum, so state.

Examples:

a. $3 + 2 + \frac{4}{3} + \cdots$
    $r = \frac{2}{3}$; series has a sum since $|r| < 1$.

    $S = \dfrac{a}{1-r} = \dfrac{3}{1 - \frac{2}{3}}$

    Ans. The sum is 9.

b. $\frac{1}{81} - \frac{1}{54} + \frac{1}{36} + \cdots$
    $r = -\frac{1}{54} \div \frac{1}{81}$
      $= -\frac{3}{2}$

    Ans. Series does not have a sum since $|r| > 1$.

1. $12 + 6 + 3 + \cdots$

2. $2 + 1 + \frac{1}{2} + \cdots$

3. $\frac{1}{36} + \frac{1}{30} + \frac{1}{25} + \cdots$

4. $1 + \frac{2}{3} + \frac{4}{9} + \cdots$

5. $\frac{3}{4} - \frac{1}{2} + \frac{1}{3} + \cdots$

6. $\frac{1}{16} - \frac{1}{8} + \frac{1}{4} + \cdots$

7. $\frac{1}{49} + \frac{1}{56} + \frac{1}{64} + \cdots$

8. $2 - \frac{3}{2} + \frac{9}{8} + \cdots$

9. $\sum_{i=1}^{\infty} \left(\frac{2}{3}\right)^i$

10. $\sum_{i=1}^{\infty} \left(-\frac{1}{4}\right)^i$

Find a fraction equivalent to each of the given decimal numerals.

Example: $2.045045045\cdots$

    Rewrite as a series.

$2 + \frac{45}{1000} + \frac{45}{1,000,000} + \cdots$

    Find the common ratio: $r = \frac{1}{1000}$ for series beginning with $\frac{45}{1000}$.   Use

$S = \dfrac{a}{1 - r}.$

$S = \dfrac{\frac{45}{1000}}{1 - \frac{1}{1000}} = \dfrac{\frac{45}{1000}}{\frac{999}{1000}} = \dfrac{45}{999} = \dfrac{5}{11}.$

Ans. $\frac{227}{111}$ or $2\frac{5}{111}$

11. $0.33333\cdots$ **12.** $0.66666\cdots$

13. $0.313131\cdots$ **14.** $0.454545\cdots$

15. $2.410410\cdots$ **16.** $3.027027\cdots$

17. $0.128888\cdots$ **18.** $0.83333\cdots$

19. A force is applied to a particle moving in a straight line in such a fashion that each second it moves only one half of the distance it moved the preceding second. If the particle moves ten centimeters the first second, approximately how far will it move before coming to rest?

20. The arc length through which the bob on a pendulum moves is nine tenths of its preceding arc length. Approximately how far will the bob move before coming to rest if the first arc length is 12 inches?

21. A ball returns two thirds of its original height on each bounce. If the ball is dropped from a height of 6 feet, approximately what is the total distance the ball travels before coming to rest?

10.6   The Binomial Expansion

    There are situations, as in the binomial expansion below, in which it is necessary to write the product of consecutive positive integers. To facilitate writing products of this type we use a special symbol $n!$ (read "n factorial or factorial n"), which is defined by

$$n! = n(n - 1)(n - 2)\cdots(1).$$

Thus

           $5! = 5\cdot4\cdot3\cdot2\cdot1$ (read "five factorial"),

and

           $8! = 8\cdot7\cdot6\cdot5\cdot4\cdot3\cdot2\cdot1$ (read "eight factorial").

Factorial notation can also be used to represent the products of consecutive positive integers, beginning with integers different from 1. For example,

$$8\cdot7\cdot6\cdot5 = \frac{8!}{4!}$$

because

$$\frac{8!}{4!} = \frac{8 \cdot 7 \cdot 6 \cdot 5 \cdot 4 \cdot 3 \cdot 2 \cdot 1}{4 \cdot 3 \cdot 2 \cdot 1} = 8 \cdot 7 \cdot 6 \cdot 5.$$

Since

$$n! = n(n - 1)(n - 2)(n - 3) \cdots 5 \cdot 4 \cdot 3 \cdot 2 \cdot 1$$

and

$$(n - 1)! = (n - 1)(n - 2)(n - 3) \cdots 5 \cdot 4 \cdot 3 \cdot 2 \cdot 1,$$

we can write the recursive relationship

$$\boldsymbol{n! = n(n - 1)!}.$$

For example,

$$7! = 7 \cdot 6!,$$

$$27! = 27 \cdot 26!,$$

$$(n + 2)! = (n + 2)(n + 1)!.$$

If $n = 1$, we have

$$1! = 1 \cdot (1 - 1)!$$

or

$$1! = 1 \cdot 0!.$$

Therefore, for consistency, we shall define

$$\boldsymbol{0! = 1.}$$

The series obtained by expanding a binomial of the form

$$(a + b)^n$$

is particularly useful in certain branches of mathematics. Starting with familiar examples where n takes the value 1, 2, 3, 4, and 5 in turn, we can show by direct multiplication that

$$(a + b)^1 = a + b,$$

$$(a + b)^2 = a^2 + 2ab + b^2,$$

$$(a + b)^3 = a^3 + 3a^2b + 3ab^2 + b^3,$$

$$(a + b)^4 = a^4 + 4a^3b + 6a^2b^2 + 4ab^3 + b^4,$$

$$(a + b)^5 = a^5 + 5a^4b + 10a^3b^2 + 10a^2b^3 + 5ab^4 + b^5.$$

We observe that in each case where there is a sufficient number of terms:

1. The first term is a^n.

2. The variable factors of the second term are $a^{n-1}b^1$ and the coefficient is n or $n/(1!)$.

3. The variable factors of the third term are $a^{n-2}b^2$ and the coefficient is $\dfrac{n(n - 1)}{2!}$.

4. The variable factors of the fourth term are $a^{n-3}b^3$ and the coefficient is $\dfrac{n(n-1)(n-2)}{3!}$.

The results of these examples can be generalized to obtain the **binomial expansion**

$$(a + b)^n = a^n + \frac{na^{n-1}b}{1!} + \frac{n(n-1)a^{n-2}b^2}{2!} + \frac{n(n-1)(n-2)a^{n-3}b^3}{3!}$$

$$+ \cdots + \frac{n(n-1)(n-2)\cdots(n-r+2)a^{n-r+1}b^{r-1}}{(r-1)!}$$

$$+ \cdots + b^n,$$

where r is the number of the term. For example,

$$(x-2)^4 = x^4 + \frac{4x^3(-2)^1}{1!} + \frac{4\cdot3x^2(-2)^2}{2!} + \frac{4\cdot3\cdot2x(-2)^3}{3!} + \frac{4\cdot3\cdot2\cdot1(-2)^4}{4!}$$

$$= x^4 - 8x^3 + 24x^2 - 32x + 16.$$

In this case $a = x$ and $b = -2$ in the binomial expansion.

Observe that the rth term in a binomial expansion is given by

$$\frac{n(n-1)(n-2)\cdots(n-r+2)}{(r-1)!} a^{n-r+1}b^{r-1}. \tag{1}$$

For example, the seventh term of $(x-2)^{10}$ is

$$\frac{10\cdot9\cdot8\cdot7\cdot6\cdot5}{1\cdot2\cdot3\cdot4\cdot5\cdot6} x^4(-2)^6,$$

which simplifies to $13440x^4$.

EXERCISE 10.6

Write in expanded form and simplify.

Examples:

a. $\dfrac{4!\,6!}{8!}$ b. $\dfrac{(n-1)!}{(n-3)!}$ c. $\dfrac{12!}{13!-12!}$

$\dfrac{4\cdot3\cdot2\cdot1\cdot6!}{8\cdot7\cdot6!}$ $\dfrac{(n-1)(n-2)(n-3)!}{(n-3)!}$ $\dfrac{12!}{12!\,(13-1)}$

Ans. $\dfrac{3}{7}$ **Ans.** $(n-1)(n-2)$ **Ans.** $\dfrac{1}{12}$

1. $4!$ 2. $6!$ 3. $\dfrac{9!}{8!}$ 4. $\dfrac{13!}{10!}$

5. $\dfrac{5!\,7!}{8!}$ 6. $\dfrac{(12!)(8!)}{16!}$ 7. $\dfrac{(8-2)!}{(4+1)!}$ 8. $\dfrac{(10+3)!}{(12-1)!}$

9. $\dfrac{6!}{7! - 6!}$ 10. $\dfrac{3! + 4!}{4!}$ 11. $\dfrac{3! + 5!}{5! - 3!}$ 12. $\dfrac{n!}{(n - 1)!}$

13. $\dfrac{(n + 2)!}{n!}$ 14. $\dfrac{(n + 2)!}{(n - 1)!}$ 15. $\dfrac{(n + 1)(n + 2)!}{(n + 3)!}$

16. $\dfrac{(2n + 4)!}{(2n + 2)!}$ 17. $\dfrac{(2n)!\,(n - 2)!}{4(2n - 2)!\,(n)!}$ 18. $\dfrac{(2n + 1)!\,(2n - 1)!}{[(2n)!]^2}$

Write in factorial notation.

Examples:

   a. $1 \cdot 2 \cdot 3 \cdot 4 \cdot 5 \cdot 6$ b. $11 \cdot 12 \cdot 13 \cdot 14$ c. 150

   Ans. $6!$ **Ans.** $\dfrac{14!}{10!}$ **Ans.** $\dfrac{150!}{149!}$

19. $1 \cdot 2 \cdot 3$ **20.** $1 \cdot 2 \cdot 3 \cdot 4 \cdot 5$ **21.** $3 \cdot 4 \cdot 5 \cdot 6$

22. 7 **23.** $8 \cdot 7 \cdot 6$ **24.** $28 \cdot 27 \cdot 26 \cdot 25 \cdot 24$

Expand.

Example: $(a - 3b)^4$

$$(a - 3b)^4 = a^4 + 4a^3(-3b) + \frac{12}{2!} a^2(-3b)^2 + \frac{24}{3!} a(-3b)^3 + \frac{24}{4!} (-3b)^4$$

   Ans. $a^4 - 12a^3b + 54a^2b^2 - 108ab^3 + 81b^4$

25. $(x + 3)^5$ **26.** $(2x + y)^4$ **27.** $(x - 3)^4$ **28.** $(2x - 1)^5$

29. $\left(2x - \dfrac{y}{2}\right)^3$ **30.** $\left(\dfrac{x}{3} + 3\right)^5$ **31.** $\left(\dfrac{x}{2} + 2\right)^6$ **32.** $\left(\dfrac{2}{3} - a^2\right)^4$

Write the first four terms in the expansion.   Do not simplify the terms.

Example: $(x + 2y)^{15}$

   Ans. $(x + 2y)^{15} = x^{15} + 15x^{14}(2y) + \dfrac{15 \cdot 14}{2!} x^{13}(2y)^2$

$$+ \frac{15 \cdot 14 \cdot 13}{3!} x^{12}(2y)^3 + \cdots$$

33. $(x + y)^{20}$ **34.** $(x - y)^{15}$ **35.** $(a - 2b)^{12}$

36. $(2a - b)^{12}$ **37.** $(x - \sqrt{2})^{10}$ **38.** $\left(\dfrac{x}{2} + 2\right)^8$

Find to the nearest hundredth.

Example: $(0.97)^7$

$(0.97)^7 = (1 - 0.03)^7$

$$= 1^7 + \frac{7(1)^6(-0.03)^1}{1!} + \frac{7 \cdot 6(1)^5(-0.03)^2}{2!} + \frac{7 \cdot 6 \cdot 5(1)^4(-0.03)^3}{3!} + \cdots$$

$$= 1 - 0.21 + 0.0189 - 0.000945 + \cdots$$

$$= 0.987955^+$$

Ans. 0.99 (Only three terms were actually needed.)

39. $(1.02)^{10}$ *Hint:* $1.02 = (1 + 0.02)$

40. $(1.01)^{15}$ **41.** $(0.99)^8$ **42.** $(0.98)^8$

43. If an amount of money (P) is invested at 4% compounded annually, the amount (A) present at the end of (n) years is given by $A = P(1 + 0.04)^n$. Find the amount present (to the nearest cent) if $1000 was invested for 5 years.

44. In Problem 43, find the amount present at the end of 20 years.

Find the specified term.

Example: $(x - 2y)^{12}$, the seventh term.

In Formula (1), page 253, use $n = 12$, $r = 7$.

$$\frac{12 \cdot 11 \cdot 10 \cdot 9 \cdot 8 \cdot 7}{6!} x^6(-2y)^6$$

Ans. $59{,}136x^6y^6$

45. $(a - b)^{15}$, the sixth term.

46. $(x + 2)^{12}$, the fifth term.

47. $(x - 2y)^{10}$, the fifth term.

48. $(a^3 - b)^9$, the seventh term.

49. Given that the binomial formula holds for $(1 + x)^n$ where n is a negative integer:

(a) write the first four terms of $(1 + x)^{-1}$;

(b) find the first four terms of the quotient $1/(1 + x)$ by dividing $(1 + x)$ into 1.

Compare the results of (a) and (b).

50. Given that the binomial formula holds as an infinite "sum" for $(1 + x)^n$ where n is a rational number and $|x| < 1$, find to two decimal places:

(a) $\sqrt{1.02}$;

(b) $\sqrt{0.99}$.

CHAPTER REVIEW

1. Find the first four terms in a sequence whose general term is $s_n = \dfrac{(-1)^{n-1}}{n}$.

2. Find a general term for the sequence whose first four terms are $\frac{1}{1}, \frac{1}{3}, \frac{1}{7}, \frac{1}{15}, \cdots$.

3. Write $\displaystyle\sum_{k=2}^{5} k(k-1)$ in expanded form.

4. Write $x^2 + x^3 + x^4 + \cdots$ in sigma notation.

5. a. Find the twenty-third term of the arithmetic progression $-82, -74, -66, \cdots$.
    b. Find the sum of the first twenty-three terms.

6. Find the sum of the odd numbers between 22 and 112.

7. The first term of an arithmetic progression is 8 and the twenty-eighth term is 89. Find the twenty-first term.

8. Find x such that $\frac{2}{3}, x, \frac{7}{8}$ forms an arithmetic progression.

9. The first term of an arithmetic progression is x and the second term is y. Find the seventeenth term in terms of x and y.

10. a. Find the eighth term of the geometric progression $\frac{16}{27}, -\frac{8}{9}, \frac{4}{3}, \cdots$.
    b. Find the sum of the first eight terms.

11. The second term of a geometric progression is 3 and the fifth term is $\frac{81}{8}$. Find the seventh term.

12. Find x such that $-4, x, -49$ forms a geometric progression.

13. Find $\displaystyle\sum_{i=1}^{\infty} \left(\tfrac{1}{3}\right)^i$.

14. Simplify $\dfrac{(n+1)!}{n(n-2)!}$.

15. a. Write the first four terms of the binomial expansion of $(x - y)^9$.
    b. Find the seventh term.

11

EXPONENTIAL AND
LOGARITHMIC FUNCTIONS

11.1 The Exponential Function

In Chapter 2 powers b^x were defined for any real b, and x a natural number. In Chapter 4 the definition was extended to include x negative or zero, and then x a rational number p/q. For rational exponents, the base b was restricted to positive values to ensure that $b^{p/q}$ be real.

We now inquire whether we can interpret powers with irrational exponents, such as

$$b^\pi, \quad b^{\sqrt{2}}, \quad b^{-\sqrt{3}},$$

to be real numbers. In Section 4.6 it was observed that irrational numbers can be approximated by rational numbers to as great a degree of accuracy as desired. That is, $\sqrt{2} \approx 1.4$ or $\sqrt{2} \approx 1.414$, etc. Also, although we do not prove it here, if x and y are rational numbers and $x > y$, then if $b > 1$, $b^x > b^y$, and if $0 < b < 1, b^x < b^y$. Now because 2^x is defined for rational x, we can write the sequence of inequalities

$$2^1 < 2^{\sqrt{2}} < 2^2;$$
$$2^{1.4} < 2^{\sqrt{2}} < 2^{1.5};$$
$$2^{1.41} < 2^{\sqrt{2}} < 2^{1.42};$$
$$2^{1.414} < 2^{\sqrt{2}} < 2^{1.415};$$

etc., where $2^{\sqrt{2}}$ is a number lying between the number on the left and that on the right.   It is clear that this process can be continued indefinitely, and that the difference between the number on the left and that on the right can be made as small as we please.   This being the case, we assume that there is just one number, $2^{\sqrt{2}}$, that will satisfy this inequality no matter how long this process is carried on.   Since we can produce the same type of argument for any irrational exponent x, we shall assume that b^x ($b > 0$) is defined for all real values of x.

Since for each real x there is one and only one number b^x, the equation

$$f(x) = b^x \quad (b > 0) \tag{1}$$

defines a function.   Because $1^x = 1$ for all real values of x, (1) defines a constant function if $b = 1$.   If $b \neq 1$, we say that (1) defines an **exponential function**.

Exponential functions can perhaps be visualized more clearly by considering their graphs.   We illustrate two typical examples, in which $0 < b < 1$ and $b > 1$, respectively.   Assigning values to x in the equations

$$f(x) = (\tfrac{1}{2})^x \quad \text{and} \quad f(x) = (2)^x,$$

we find some ordered pairs in each function and sketch the graphs in Figure 11.1.

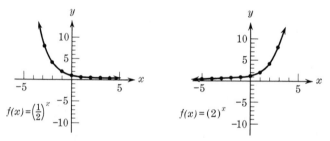

Fig. 11.1

Notice that a line parallel to the y-axis will not intersect the graphs at more than one point, and hence each equation defines a function.   Notice also that the graph of the function determined by $f(x) = (\tfrac{1}{2})^x$ goes *down* to the right, and the graph of the function determined by $f(x) = (2)^x$ goes *up* to the right.   For this reason, we say that the former function is a decreasing function and that the latter is an increasing function.   In either case, the domain is the set of real numbers and the range is the set of positive real numbers.

It may be observed in passing that if the domain of an exponential function is restricted to the set of natural numbers

$$y = b^x, \quad x \in \{1, 2, 3, \cdots\},$$

the function is a sequence function whose range can be viewed as a geometric progression.

EXERCISE 11.1

Find the second component of each of the ordered pairs that makes the pair a solution of the equation.

Example: $y = 2^x$; $(-3,\ )$, $(0,\ )$, $(3,\ )$, $(6,\ )$

For $x = -3$, $y = 2^{(-3)} = \frac{1}{8}$.

For $x = 0$, $y = 2^{(0)} = 1$.

For $x = 3$, $y = 2^{(3)} = 8$.

For $x = 6$, $y = 2^{(6)} = 64$.

Ans. $(-3, \frac{1}{8})$, $(0, 1)$, $(3, 8)$, $(6, 64)$

1. $y = 3^x$; $(0,\ )$, $(1,\ )$, $(2,\ )$, $(3,\ )$
2. $y = 4^x$; $(0,\ )$, $(1,\ )$, $(2,\ )$, $(3,\ )$
3. $y = 2^x$; $(-2,\ )$, $(0,\ )$, $(2,\ )$, $(4,\ )$
4. $y = 5^x$; $(-2,\ )$, $(0,\ )$, $(2,\ )$, $(4,\ )$
5. $f(x) = (\frac{1}{2})^x$; $(-3,\ )$, $(0,\ )$, $(3,\ )$, $(5,,\ )$
6. $f(x) = (\frac{1}{3})^x$; $(-3,\ )$, $(0,\ )$, $(3,\ )$, $(5,\ )$
7. $g(x) = (10)^x$; $(-3,\ )$, $(-2,\ )$, $(-1,\ )$, $(0,\ )$
8. $g(x) = (10)^x$; $(0,\ )$, $(1,\ )$, $(2,\ )$, $(3,\ )$

Graph the functions defined by each of the following exponential equations. Use selected integral values $-5 < x < 5$.

Example: $y = 3^x$

Arbitrarily select integral values of x, say, $(-2,\ )$, $(-1,\ )$, $(0,\ )$, $(1,\ )$, $(2,\ )$, $(3,\ )$.

Determine the y-components of each ordered pair.

$(-2, \frac{1}{9})$, $(-1, \frac{1}{3})$, $(0, 1)$, $(1, 3)$, $(2, 9)$, $(3, 27)$.

Plot the points and connect with a smooth curve.

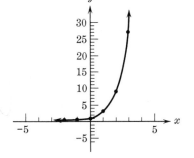

9. $y = 4^x$ 10. $y = 5^x$ 11. $y = 10^x$ 12. $y = 2^{-x}$
13. $y = 3^{-x}$ 14. $y = 2^{2x}$ 15. $y = 3^{2x}$ 16. $y = (\frac{1}{3})^x$
17. $y = (\frac{1}{4})^x$ 18. $y = (\frac{1}{10})^x$ 19. $y = (\frac{1}{2})^{-x}$ 20. $y = (\frac{1}{3})^{-x}$

11.2 The Inverse of a Relation

Before examining another function, one closely related to the exponential function, let us consider an extension of the relation concept in general. If the components of each ordered pair in a given relation are interchanged, the resulting relation and the given relation are called **inverses** of each other, and each is said to be the inverse of the other.   Thus,

$$\{(1, 2), (3, 4), (5, 6)\} \quad \text{and} \quad \{(2, 1), (4, 3), (6, 5)\}$$

are inverse relations.

The inverse of a relation R is denoted by R^{-1} (read "R inverse" or "the inverse of R").   It is evident from the definition of inverse relations that the domain and range of R^{-1} are the range and domain, respectively, of R. If $y = R(x)$ or $y < R(x)$ define a relation R, then $x = R(y)$ or $x < R(y)$ define the inverse of R.   For example, the inverse of the relation defined by

$$y = 4x - 3 \tag{1}$$

is defined by

$$x = 4y - 3 \tag{2}$$

or, when y is expressed in terms of x, by

$$y = \frac{1}{4}(x + 3). \tag{2'}$$

The equation $x = R(y)$ is equivalent to $y = R^{-1}(x)$.

The graphs of inverse relations are related in an interesting and useful way.   To see this, we first observe that the graphs of the ordered pairs (a, b) and (b, a) are always located symmetrically with respect to the graph of $y = x$ (Figure 11.2).   Therefore, because for every ordered pair (a, b) in

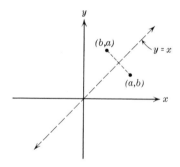

Fig. 11.2

R the ordered pair (b, a) is in R^{-1}, the graphs of $y = R^{-1}(x)$ and $y = R(x)$ are reflections of each other about the graph of $y = x$.   Figure 11.3 shows the graphs of

$$R = \{(x, y) \mid y = 4x - 3\}$$

and its inverse

$$R^{-1} = \{(x, y) \mid x = 4y - 3\} = \{(x, y) \mid y = \tfrac{1}{4}(x + 3)\}$$

together with the graph of $y = x$.

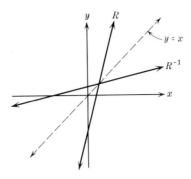

Fig. 11.3

Because every function is a relation, every function has an inverse, but the inverse is not always a function. For example, Figure 11.4 shows the graph of the function

$$F = \{(x, y) \mid y = x^2\},$$

together with the graph of its inverse

$$F^{-1} = \{(x, y) \mid x = y^2\} = \{(x, y) \mid y = \pm\sqrt{x}\}.$$

Since for all but one value in its domain F^{-1} associates two different y's with each x, F^{-1} is not a function.

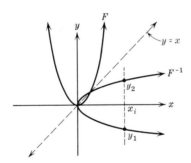

Fig. 11.4

In order for a function F to have an inverse that is a function, not only must each element in the domain of F be associated with just one element in its range, but, also, each element in its range must be associated with but one element in its domain. Such a function F is called a one-to-one function. Then if F and F^{-1} are both functions, and if F associates the number a with the *unique* number b, then F^{-1} associates the number b with the *unique* number a. Therefore, it must be true that, for every x in the domain of F,

$$F^{-1}[F(x)] = x$$

and, for every x in the domain of F^{-1},

$$F[F^{-1}(x)] = x.$$

Using example (1) above, we note that if F is defined by

$$F(x) = 4x - 3$$

then F is a one-to-one function.   Now F^{-1} is defined by

$$F^{-1}(x) = \tfrac{1}{4}(x + 3),$$

and we see that

$$F^{-1}[F(x)] = \tfrac{1}{4}[(4x - 3) + 3] = x$$

and

$$F[F^{-1}(x)] = 4[\tfrac{1}{4}(x + 3)] - 3 = x.$$

EXERCISE 11.2

In each Problem 1–12, each equation defines a relation in $R \times R$.
  a. Write the equation defining R^{-1}.
  b. Sketch the graphs of R and R^{-1} on the same set of axes.
  c. State whether R^{-1} is a function.

1. $2x + 4y = 7$ 2. $3x - 2y = 5$ 3. $y = x^2 - 4x$

4. $y = x^2 - 4$ 5. $x^2 + 4y^2 = 36$ 6. $x^2 + y^2 = 4$

7. $x^2 - y^2 = 3$ 8. $9x^2 + y^2 = 36$ 9. $y = \sqrt{4 + x^2}$

10. $y = -\sqrt{x^2 - 4}$ 11. $y = |x|$ 12. $y \le |x| + 1$

In each of Problems 13–18, the given equation defines a one-to-one function F in $R \times R$.   Find the equation defining F^{-1} and show that $F[F^{-1}(x)] = F^{-1}[F(x)] = x$.

13. $y = x$ 14. $y = -x$ 15. $2x + y = 4$

16. $x - 2y = 4$ 17. $3x - 4y = 12$ 18. $3x + 4y = 12$

19. The equation $y = x$ defines a function in $R \times R$.   Explain why this function is called the identity function.

20. Show that, if F is defined by an equation of the form $Ax + Ay = B$, where $A, B \in R$, then F is its own inverse.

21. Explain why every linear function has a function for an inverse.

22. The inverse of the function F in $R \times R$ defined by $y = ax^2 + bx + c$, where $a \ne 0$, is defined by $x = ay^2 + by + c$.   Explain why F^{-1} is not a function.   Sketch the graph of F^{-1}.

23. Consider the function F with domain $\{x \mid x \le 1\}$ defined by $y = x^2 - 2x + 1$ in $R \times R$.
  a. What is the range of F?
  b. Find the equation defining F^{-1} and state its domain.
  c. Is F^{-1} a function?

24. The equation $y = \sqrt{4 - x^2}$ defines a function F with domain $\{x \mid |x| \leq 2\}$.
    a. What is the range of F?
    b. Find the equation defining F^{-1} and state its domain.
    c. Is F^{-1} a function?

25. The equation $y = 2^x$ defines an exponential function F over $R \times R$.
    a. What is the domain of F?
    b. What is the range of F?
    c. Find an equation defining F^{-1}.
    d. Graph F and F^{-1} on the same set of axes.
    e. Is F^{-1} a function?

11.3 The Logarithmic Function

In the exponential function

$$\{(x, y) \mid y = b^x, b > 0, b \neq 1\}, \tag{1}$$

for $b = \frac{1}{2}$ and $b = 2$ (Figure 11.1), there is only one x associated with each y as well as only one y associated with each x. Therefore, the inverse of the function (1) is also a function, namely,

$$\{(x, y) \mid x = b^y, b > 0, b \neq 1\}. \tag{2}$$

Since the domain and range of (1) are the same as the range and domain of (2), respectively, we have for the domain of (2) $\{x \mid x > 0\}$, while the range of (2) is R, the set of real numbers.

The graphs of functions of the form (2) can be illustrated by the example

$$x = 10^y \quad (x > 0).$$

We assign arbitrary values to x, say, 0.01, 0.1, 1, 10, and 100, and obtain the ordered pairs which can be plotted and connected with a smooth curve as in Figure 11.5. Alternatively, we can reflect the graph of $y = 10^x$ (see Problem 11, Exercise 11.1) and obtain the same result.

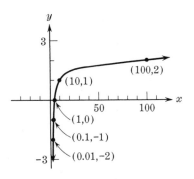

Fig. 11.5

It is always useful to be able to express the variable y explicitly in terms of the variable x. To do this in equations such as that defining (2), we use the notation

$$y = \log_b x \quad (x > 0, b > 0, b \neq 1), \tag{3}$$

where the symbolism $\log_b x$ is read "logarithm to the base b of x." The functions defined by such equations are called **logarithmic functions.**

It should be recognized that

$$x = b^y \quad \text{and} \quad y = \log_b x$$

are different forms of an equation defining the same function, in the same way that $x - y = 4$ and $y = x - 4$ define the same function, and we may use whichever equation suits our purpose. Thus, exponential statements may be written in logarithmic form—for example,

$$5^2 = 25 \text{ is equivalent to } \log_5 25 = 2,$$
$$8^{1/3} = 2 \text{ is equivalent to } \log_8 2 = \tfrac{1}{3},$$
$$3^{-2} = \tfrac{1}{9} \text{ is equivalent to } \log_3 \tfrac{1}{9} = -2,$$

etc. Also, logarithmic statements may be written in exponential form—for example,

$$\log_{10} 100 = 2 \text{ is equivalent to } 10^2 = 100,$$
$$\log_3 81 = 4 \text{ is equivalent to } 3^4 = 81,$$
$$\log_2 \tfrac{1}{2} = -1 \text{ is equivalent to } 2^{-1} = \tfrac{1}{2}, \text{ etc.}$$

The logarithmic function associates with each number x the exponent on b, such that the power is equal to x. In other words, we can think of $\log_b x$ as an exponent on b. Thus, we have the very important relationship,

$$b^{\log_b x} = x.$$

EXERCISE 11.3

Express in logarithmic notation.

Examples:

a. $3^2 = 9$ b. $16^{1/4} = 2$ c. $64^{-1/3} = \tfrac{1}{4}$

   Ans. $\log_3 9 = 2$ Ans. $\log_{16} 2 = \tfrac{1}{4}$ Ans. $\log_{64} \tfrac{1}{4} = -\tfrac{1}{3}$

1. $4^2 = 16$	2. $5^3 = 125$	3. $3^3 = 27$	4. $8^2 = 64$
5. $(\tfrac{1}{2})^2 = \tfrac{1}{4}$	6. $(\tfrac{1}{3})^2 = \tfrac{1}{9}$	7. $8^{-1/3} = \tfrac{1}{2}$	8. $64^{-1/6} = \tfrac{1}{2}$
9. $10^2 = 100$	10. $10^0 = 1$	11. $10^{-1} = 0.1$	12. $10^{-2} = 0.01$

Express in exponential notation.

Examples:

a. $\log_6 36 = 2$ b. $\log_{1/5} 125 = -3$ c. $\log_{10} 100 = 2$

   Ans. $6^2 = 36$ Ans. $(\tfrac{1}{5})^{-3} = 125$ Ans. $10^2 = 100$

13. $\log_2 64 = 6$	14. $\log_5 25 = 2$	15. $\log_3 9 = 2$
16. $\log_{16} 256 = 2$	17. $\log_{1/3} 9 = -2$	18. $\log_{1/2} 8 = -3$
19. $\log_{10} 1000 = 3$	20. $\log_{10} 1 = 0$	21. $\log_{10} (0.01) = -2$

Find the value of each of the following.

Example: $\log_3 81$

3 raised to what power equals 81?

Ans. 4

22. $\log_5 5$	**23.** $\log_7 49$	**24.** $\log_2 32$
25. $\log_4 64$	**26.** $\log_5 \sqrt{5}$	**27.** $\log_3 \sqrt{3}$
28. $\log_3 \frac{1}{3}$	**29.** $\log_5 \frac{1}{5}$	**30.** $\log_3 3$
31. $\log_2 2$	**32.** $\log_{10} 10$	**33.** $\log_{10} 100$
34. $\log_{10} 1$	**35.** $\log_{10} 0.1$	**36.** $\log_{10} 0.01$

Find an equivalent equation of the form $x = c$, $y = c$, or $b = c$, where c is a constant.

Examples:

a. $\log_2 x = 3$ b. $\log_b 2 = \frac{1}{2}$

    Write in exponential form.

    $2^3 = x$ $b^{1/2} = 2$

    Solve for the variable.

Ans. $x = 8$ $(b^{1/2})^2 = (2)^2$

                     Ans. $b = 4$

37. $\log_3 9 = y$	**38.** $\log_5 125 = y$	**39.** $\log_b 8 = 3$
40. $\log_b 625 = 4$	**41.** $\log_4 x = 3$	**42.** $\log_{1/2} x = -5$
43. $\log_2 (\frac{1}{8}) = y$	**44.** $\log_5 5 = y$	**45.** $\log_b 10 = \frac{1}{2}$
46. $\log_b 0.1 = -1$	**47.** $\log_2 x = 2$	**48.** $\log_{10} x = -3$

49. What is $\log_2 1$? $\log_7 1$? $\log_a 1$, for $a > 0$?

50. Graph the equation $y = \log_2 x$.

51. By examining the graph of $\log_2 x$, what can you assert about $\log_2 a$ and $\log_2 b$ if $a < b$?

52. Show that $\log_b b = 1$.   *Hint:* Consider the definition of $\log_b x$.

53. Show that $b^{\log_b z} = x$ for all real $x > 0$.   *Hint:* Consider the definition of $\log_b x$.

54. Show that $\log_b x^a = a \log_b x$ for $x, b > 0$.   *Hint:* Set $y = \log_b x^a$, so that $x^a = b^y$.

55. From Problem 54, show that $\log_b b^x = x$, for all $b > 0$.

11.4   Properties of Logarithms

Because by definition a logarithm is an exponent, it follows that for positive x_1 and x_2:

   1. $\log_b (x_1 x_2) = \log_b x_1 + \log_b x_2.$

The validity of this law can be shown as follows: Since

$$x_1 = b^{\log_b x_1} \quad \text{and} \quad x_2 = b^{\log_b x_2},$$

then

$$x_1 x_2 = b^{\log_b x_1} \cdot b^{\log_b x_2}$$
$$= b^{\log_b x_1 + \log_b x_2},$$

and, by the definition of a logarithm,

$$\log_b (x_1 x_2) = \log_b x_1 + \log_b x_2.$$

The validity of the following law can be established in a similar manner:

2. $\log_b \dfrac{x_2}{x_1} = \log_b x_2 - \log_b x_1.$

Another law, whose proof involves concepts not developed here, applies to powers with real-number exponents. Thus if $m \in R$,

3. $\log_b (x_1)^m = m \log_b x_1.$

Before illustrating the use of these laws, let us make three assumptions:

L–1   If $M = N$ $(M, N > 0)$, then $\log_b M = \log_b N$.

L–2   If $\log_b M = \log_b N$, then $M = N$.

L–3   If $M = N$, then $b^M = b^N$.

These assumptions should seem plausible because exponential and logarithmic functions are one-to-one.

EXERCISE 11.4

Express as the sum or difference of simpler logarithmic quantities. Assume that all variables denote positive real numbers.

Example: $\log_b \left(\dfrac{xy}{z} \right)^{1/2}$

Use the third law of logarithms.

$$\log_b \left(\frac{xy}{z} \right)^{1/2} = \tfrac{1}{2} \log_b \left(\frac{xy}{z} \right)$$

Use the first and second laws of logarithms.

$$\log_b \left(\frac{xy}{z} \right)^{1/2} = \tfrac{1}{2}[\log_b x + \log_b y - \log_b z]$$

Ans. $\tfrac{1}{2}[\log_b x + \log_b y - \log_b z]$

1. $\log_b (xy)$ **2.** $\log_b (xyz)$ **3.** $\log_b \left(\dfrac{x}{y} \right)$

4. $\log_b \left(\dfrac{xy}{z} \right)$ **5.** $\log_b x^5$ **6.** $\log_b x^{1/2}$

7. $\log_b \sqrt[3]{x}$ **8.** $\log_b \sqrt[3]{x^2}$ **9.** $\log_b x^2 y^3$

10. $\log_b \dfrac{x^{1/2}y}{z^2}$ **11.** $\log_b \sqrt{\dfrac{x}{z}}$ **12.** $\log_b \sqrt{xy}$

13. $\log_{10} \sqrt[3]{\dfrac{xy^2}{z}}$ **14.** $\log_{10} \sqrt[5]{\dfrac{x^2y}{z^3}}$ **15.** $\log_{10} \sqrt{x} \sqrt[3]{y^2}$

16. $\log_{10} \dfrac{\sqrt{x} \sqrt[4]{y^3}}{z^2}$ **17.** $\log_{10} \sqrt{x(x-y)}$ **18.** $\log_{10} \sqrt[3]{(x-y)^2(x+y)}$

19. $\log_{10} 2\pi \sqrt{\dfrac{l}{g}}$ **20.** $\log_{10} \sqrt{s(s-a)(s-b)(s-c)}$

Express as a single logarithm with a coefficient of 1.

Example: $\frac{1}{2}(\log_b x - \log_b y)$

By the second law of logarithms.

$$\frac{1}{2}(\log_b x - \log_b y) = \frac{1}{2} \log_b \left(\frac{x}{y} \right)$$

By the third law of logarithms.

$$\frac{1}{2}(\log_b x - \log_b y) = \log_b \left(\frac{x}{y} \right)^{1/2}$$

Ans. $\log_b \left(\dfrac{x}{y} \right)^{1/2}$

21. $\log_b x + \log_b y$ **22.** $\log_b x - \log_b y$

23. $-\log_b x$ **24.** $-\frac{1}{2} \log_b x$

25. $2 \log_b x + 3 \log_b y$ **26.** $\frac{1}{4} \log_b x - \frac{3}{4} \log_b y$

27. $3 \log_b x + \log_b y - 2 \log_b z$ **28.** $\frac{1}{3}(\log_b x + \log_b y - 2 \log_b z)$

29. $\log_{10} (x - 2) + \log_{10} x - 2 \log_{10} z$ **30.** $\frac{1}{2}(\log_{10} x - 3 \log_{10} y - 5 \log_{10} z)$

31. Show that $\frac{1}{4} \log_{10} 8 + \frac{1}{4} \log_{10} 2 = \log_{10} 2$.

32. Show that $4 \log_{10} 3 - 2 \log_{10} 3 + 1 = \log_{10} 90$.

33. Show that $10^{2 \log_{10} x} = x^2$.

34. Show that $a^{2 \log_a 3} + b^{3 \log_b 2} = 17$.

35. Show that $\log_{10} [\log_3 (\log_5 125)] = 0$.

11.5 Logarithms to the Base 10

There are two logarithmic functions of special interest in mathematics; one is defined by

$$y = \log_{10} x, \tag{1}$$

and the other by

$$y = \log_e x, \tag{2}$$

where e is an irrational number whose decimal approximation is 2.7182818 to eight digits. Because these functions possess similar properties, and because we are more familiar with the number 10, we shall, for the present, confine our attention to (1).

Values for $\log_{10} x$ are called **logarithms to the base 10** or **common logarithms**. From the definition of $\log_{10} x$,

$$10^{\log_{10} x} = x \quad (x > 0); \tag{3}$$

that is, $\log_{10} x$ is the exponent that must be placed on 10 so that the resulting power is x. The problem we are concerned with in this section is that of finding, for each positive x, $\log_{10} x$. First, $\log_{10} x$ can easily be determined for all values of x that are integral powers of 10:

$$\log_{10} 10 \quad = \log_{10} 10^1 = 1, \quad \text{since } 10^1 = 10;$$
$$\log_{10} 100 \quad = \log_{10} 10^2 = 2, \quad \text{since } 10^2 = 100;$$
$$\log_{10} 1000 = \log_{10} 10^3 = 3, \quad \text{since } 10^3 = 1000;$$

etc., and

$$\log_{10} 1 \quad = \log_{10} 10^0 = 0 \quad \text{since } 10^0 = 1;$$
$$\log_{10} 0.1 \quad = \log_{10} 10^{-1} = -1, \quad \text{since } 10^{-1} = 0.1;$$
$$\log_{10} 0.01 \quad = \log_{10} 10^{-2} = -2, \quad \text{since } 10^{-2} = 0.01;$$
$$\log_{10} 0.001 = \log_{10} 10^{-3} = -3, \quad \text{since } 10^{-3} = 0.001; \text{ etc.}$$

A table of logarithms is used to find $\log_{10} x$ where $1 \le x \le 10$ (see page 292). Consider the excerpt from this table shown in Figure 11.6. Each

x	0	1	2	3	4	5	6	7	8	9
3.8	.5798	.5809	.5821	.5832	.5843	.5855	.5866	.5877	.5888	.5899
3.9	.5911	.5922	.5933	.5944	.5955	.5966	.5977	.5988	.5999	.6010
4.0	.6021	.6031	.6042	.6053	.6064	.6075	.6085	.6096	.6107	.6117
4.1	.6128	.6138	.6149	.6160	.6170	.6180	.6191	.6201	.6212	.6222
4.2	.6232	.6243	.6253	.6263	.6274	.6284	.6294	.6304	.6314	.6325
4.3	.6335	.6345	.6355	.6365	.6375	.6385	.6395	.6405	.6415	.6425
4.4	.6435	.6444	.6454	.6464	.6474	.6484	.6493	.6503	.6513	.6522
4.5	.6532	.6542	.6551	.6561	.6571	.6580	.6590	.6599	.6609	.6618
4.6	.6628	.6637	.6646	.6656	.6665	.6675	.6684	.6693	.6702	.6712

Fig. 11.6

number in the column headed x represents the first two significant digits of the numeral for x, while each number in the row containing x contains the third significant digit of the numeral for x. The digits located at the intersection of a row and a column form the logarithm of x. For example, to find $\log_{10} 4.25$, we look at the intersection of the row containing 4.2 under x and the column containing 5 to the right of x. Thus

$$\log_{10} 4.25 = 0.6284.$$

Similarly,

$$\log_{10} 4.02 = 0.6042,$$
$$\log_{10} 4.49 = 0.6522,$$

etc. The equals sign is being used here in a very loose sense. More properly $\log_{10} 4.25 \approx 0.6284$, $\log_{10} 4.02 \approx 0.6042$, and $\log_{10} 4.49 \approx 0.6522$, because these numbers are irrational and cannot be precisely represented by a decimal numeral. However, we shall follow customary usage and write $=$ instead of $\approx$, and leave the intent to the context.

Now suppose we wish to find $\log_{10} x$ for values of x outside the range of the table—that is, for $0 < x < 1$ or $x > 10$. This can be done quite readily by first representing the number in scientific notation—that is, as the product of a number between 1 and 10 and a power of 10 and applying the first law of logarithms. For example,

$$\log_{10} 42.5 = \log_{10} (4.25 \times 10^1) = \log_{10} 4.25 + \log_{10} 10^1$$
$$= 0.6284 + 1$$
$$= 1.6284,$$

$$\log_{10} 425 = \log_{10} (4.25 \times 10^2) = \log_{10} 4.25 + \log_{10} 10^2$$
$$= 0.6284 + 2$$
$$= 2.6284,$$

$$\log_{10} 4250 = \log_{10} (4.25 \times 10^3) = \log_{10} 4.25 + \log_{10} 10^3$$
$$= 0.6284 + 3$$
$$= 3.6284.$$

Observe that the decimal portion of the logarithm is always 0.6284, and *the integral portion is just the exponent on 10 when the number is written in scientific notation.*

This process can be reduced to a mechanical one by considering $\log_{10} x$ to consist of two parts, an integral part (called the **characteristic**) and a nonnegative decimal fraction part (called the **mantissa**). Thus the table of values for $\log_{10} x$ for $1 < x < 10$ can be looked upon as a table of mantissas for $\log_{10} x$ for all $x > 0$.

To find $\log_{10} 4370$, we first write

$$\log_{10} 4370 = \log_{10} (4.37 \times 10^3).$$

Upon examining the table of logarithms, we find that $\log_{10} 4.37 = 0.6405$, so that

$$\log_{10} 43700 = 3.6405,$$

where we have prefixed the characteristic 3, the exponent on the base 10.

Now consider an example of the form $\log_{10} x$ for $0 < x < 1$. To find $\log_{10} 0.00402$, we write

$$\log_{10} 0.00402 = \log_{10} (4.02 \times 10^{-3}).$$

Examining the table, we find $\log_{10} 4.02$ is 0.6042. Upon adding 0.6042 to the characteristic -3, we obtain

$$\log_{10} 0.00402 = -2.3958,$$

where the decimal portion of the logarithm is no longer 0.6042 as it is in the case of all numbers $x > 1$ for which the first three significant digits of x are 402. To circumvent this situation, and thus provide access to the table, it is customary to write the logarithm in a form in which the fractional part is positive. In the foregoing example, we write

$$\log_{10} 0.00402 = 0.6042 - 3$$
$$= 0.6042 + (7 - 10)$$
$$= 7.6042 - 10,$$

and the fractional part is positive. The logarithms

$$6.6042 - 9,$$
$$12.6042 - 15,$$

etc. are equally valid representations, but $7.6042 - 10$ is customary in most cases.

It is possible to reverse the process described in this section and, being given $\log_{10} x$, to find x. In this event, x is referred to as the **antilogarithm** (antilog$_{10}$) of $\log_{10} x$. For example, antilog$_{10}$ 1.6395 can be obtained by locating the mantissa, 0.6395, in the body of the $\log_{10}$ tables and observing that the associated antilog$_{10}$ is 4.36. Thus

$$\text{antilog}_{10}\ 1.6395 = 4.36 \times 10^1 = 43.6.$$

If we seek the common logarithm of a number that is not an entry in the table (for example, $\log_{10} 3712$), or if we seek x when $\log_{10} x$ is not an entry in the table, it is customary to use a procedure called **linear interpolation**, which is discussed in the next section.

EXERCISE 11.5

Write the characteristic of each of the following.

Examples:

  a. $\log_{10} 248$ b. $\log_{10} 0.0057$

  Represent the number in scientific notation.

  $\log_{10} (2.48 \times 10^2)$ $\log_{10} (5.7 \times 10^{-3})$

  The exponent on the base 10 is the characteristic.

  Ans. 2   **Ans.** -3 or $7 - 10$

1. $\log_{10} 312$ **2.** $\log_{10} 8.12$ **3.** $\log_{10} 7912$

4. $\log_{10} 31$ **5.** $\log_{10} 0.02$ **6.** $\log_{10} 0.00851$

7. $\log_{10} 8.012$ **8.** $\log_{10} 752.31$ **9.** $\log_{10} 0.00031$

10. $\log_{10} 0.0004$ **11.** $\log_{10} (15 \times 10^3)$ **12.** $\log_{10} (820 \times 10^4)$

Find each logarithm.

Examples:

a. $\log_{10} 16.8$ b. $\log_{10} 0.043$

Represent the number in scientific notation.

$\log_{10} (1.68 \times 10^1)$ $\log_{10} (4.3 \times 10^{-2})$

Determine the mantissa from the table of logarithms.

0.2253   0.6335

Add the characteristic as determined by the exponent on the base 10.

Ans. 1.2253   **Ans.** $8.6335 - 10$

13. $\log_{10} 6.73$ **14.** $\log_{10} 891$ **15.** $\log_{10} 83.7$

16. $\log_{10} 21.4$ **17.** $\log_{10} 317$ **18.** $\log_{10} 219$

19. $\log_{10} 0.813$ **20.** $\log_{10} 0.00214$ **21.** $\log_{10} 0.08$

22. $\log_{10} 0.000413$ **23.** $\log_{10} (2.48 \times 10^2)$ **24.** $\log_{10} (5.39 \times 10^{-3})$

Find each antilogarithm.

Example: $\text{antilog}_{10} 2.7364$

Locate the mantissa in the body of the table of mantissas and determine the associated antilog_{10} (a number between 1 and 10); write the characteristic as an exponent on the base 10.

5.45×10^2

Write in standard form.

Ans. 545

25. $\text{antilog}_{10} 0.6128$ **26.** $\text{antilog}_{10} 0.2504$

27. $\text{antilog}_{10} 1.5647$ **28.** $\text{antilog}_{10} 3.9258$

29. $\text{antilog}_{10} (8.8075 - 10)$ **30.** $\text{antilog}_{10} (3.9722 - 5)$

31. $\text{antilog}_{10} 1.2041$ **32.** $\text{antilog}_{10} 2.6590$

33. $\text{antilog}_{10} 3.7388$ **34.** $\text{antilog}_{10} 2.0086$

35. $\text{antilog}_{10} (6.8561 - 10)$ **36.** $\text{antilog}_{10} (1.8156 - 4)$

Find each of the following by means of the table of logarithms to the base 10. *Hint:* Find the antilog of the exponent.

37. $10^{0.9590}$ **38.** $10^{0.8241}$ **39.** $10^{3.6990}$

40. $10^{2.3874}$ **41.** $10^{2.0531}$ **42.** $10^{1.7396}$

43. What is the characteristic of $\log_5 33$? Of $\log_2 33$? Of $\log_4 33$? Of $\log_{30} 33$?

44. What is the characteristic of $\log_2 \frac{1}{5}$? *Hint:* $\log_2 \frac{1}{4} = -2$ and $\log_2 \frac{1}{8} = -3$.

45. Would you expect the mantissa of $\log_2 33$ to be greater or less than the mantissa of $\log_3 33$? Why?

11.6 Linear Interpolation

We recall from Section 7.2 that a function is a set of ordered pairs. A table of common logarithms represents just such a set. For each number x there is an associated number $\log_{10} x$, and we have a set of ordered pairs $(x, \log_{10} x)$ displayed in convenient tabular form. Because of space limitations, only three digits for the number x and four for the number $\log_{10} x$ appear in the table. By means of a process called **linear interpolation,** however, the table can be used to find approximations to logarithms for numbers with four-digit numerals.

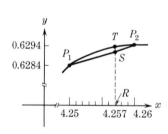

Let us examine geometrically the concepts involved. A portion of the graph of

$$y = \log_{10} x$$

Fig. 11.7

is shown in Figure 11.7. The curvature is exaggerated to illustrate the principle involved. We propose to use the straight line joining the points P_1 and P_2 as an approximation to the curve passing through the points. If a large graph of $y = \log_{10} x$ were available, the value of, say, $\log_{10} 4.257$, could be found by using the value of the ordinate (RT) to the curve for $x = 4.257$. Since there is no way to accomplish this with a table of values only, we shall instead use the value of the ordinate (RS) to the straight line as an approximation to the ordinate of the curve.

This can be accomplished directly from the set of numbers available in the table of logarithms. Consider Figure 11.8, where P_2P_3 and P_4P_5 are perpendicular to P_1P_3. From geometry, we have $\triangle P_1P_4P_5 \sim \triangle P_1P_2P_3$, where the corresponding sides are proportional, and hence

$$\frac{x}{X} = \frac{y}{Y}. \tag{1}$$

If we know any three of these numbers, the fourth can be determined. For the purpose of interpolation, we assume all of our members now have four-digit numerals; that is, we consider 4.250 instead of 4.25 and 4.260 instead of 4.26. We note that the number 4.257 falls on a point just $\frac{7}{10}$ of the distance between 4.250 and 4.260 and the distance Y (0.0010) is just the distance between the logarithms 0.6284 and 0.6294. It follows from (1) that

$$\frac{7}{10} = \frac{y}{0.0010}$$

and

$$y = \frac{7}{10}(0.0010) = 0.0007.$$

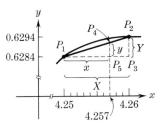

We can now add 0.0007 to 0.6284 and obtain a good approximation to the required logarithm. That is,

Fig. 11.8

$$\log_{10} 4.257 = 0.6291.$$

The first example in Exercise 11.6 shows a convenient arrangement for the calculations involved in the example presented here. The antilogarithm of a number can be found by a similar procedure. The second example in Exercise 11.6 illustrates the process. However, with practice, it is possible to interpolate mentally in both procedures.

EXERCISE 11.6

Find each logarithm.

Example: $\log_{10} 4.257$

$$10 \left\{ 7 \left\{ \begin{array}{c|c} x & \log_{10} x \\ \hline 4.250 & 0.6284 \\ 4.257 & ? \\ 4.260 & 0.6294 \end{array} \right\} y \right\} 0.0010$$

Set up proportion and solve for y.

$$\frac{7}{10} = \frac{y}{0.0010}; \quad y = 0.0007$$

Add this value of y to 0.6284.

$$\log_{10} 4.257 = 0.6284 + 0.0007 = 0.6291$$

Ans. 0.6291

1. $\log_{10} 4.213$	2. $\log_{10} 8.184$	3. $\log_{10} 6.219$
4. $\log_{10} 10.31$	5. $\log_{10} 1522$	6. $\log_{10} 203.4$
7. $\log_{10} 37110$	8. $\log_{10} 72.36$	9. $\log_{10} 0.5123$
10. $\log_{10} 0.09142$	11. $\log_{10} 0.008351$	12. $\log_{10} 0.03741$

Find each antilogarithm.

Example: antilog$_{10}$ 0.6446

$$0.0010\left\{0.0002\left\{\begin{matrix} x \\ 0.6444 \\ 0.6446 \\ 0.6454 \end{matrix}\quad\begin{matrix} \text{antilog}_{10}\,x \\ 4.410 \\ ? \\ 4.420 \end{matrix}\right\}y\right\}0.010$$

Set up proportion and solve for y.

$$\frac{0.0002}{0.0010} = \frac{y}{0.010}; \quad y = 0.002$$

Add this value of y to 4.410.

antilog$_{10}$ 0.6446 = 4.410 + 0.002 = 4.412

Ans.   4.412

13. antilog$_{10}$ 0.5085   **14.** antilog$_{10}$ 0.8087

15. antilog$_{10}$ 1.9512   **16.** antilog$_{10}$ 2.2620

17. antilog$_{10}$ 1.0220   **18.** antilog$_{10}$ 3.0759

19. antilog$_{10}$ (8.7055 − 10)   **20.** antilog$_{10}$ (3.6112 − 5)

21. antilog$_{10}$ ((9.8742 − 10)   **22.** antilog$_{10}$ (20.9979 − 22)

23. antilog$_{10}$ (2.8748 − 3)   **24.** antilog$_{10}$ (7.7397 − 10)

25. If we interpolate to find log$_{10}$ 3.751 and log$_{10}$ 3.755, which of the resulting approximations should we expect to be more nearly correct? Why?

26. If we interpolate to find log$_{10}$ 1.025 and log$_{10}$ 9.025, which of the resulting approximations should we expect to be more nearly correct? Why?

11.7   Computations with Logarithms

The use of the slide rule and the advent of high-speed computing devices have almost removed the need to perform routine numerical computations with pencil and paper by logarithms. Nevertheless, we introduce the techniques involved in making such computations because the writing of the logarithmic equations involved sheds light on the properties of the logarithmic function and on the usefulness of the laws of logarithms which we reproduce here using the base 10.

If x_1 and x_2 are positive real numbers, then

   1. $\log_{10}(x_1 x_2) = \log_{10} x_1 + \log_{10} x_2,$

   2. $\log_{10} \dfrac{x_2}{x_1} = \log_{10} x_2 - \log_{10} x_1,$

   3. $\log_{10}(x_1)^m = m \log_{10} x_1.$

We also restate the three assumptions made on page 266 using the base 10.

L–1   If $M = N\,(M, N > 0)$, then $\log_{10} M = \log_{10} N$.

L–2   If $\log_{10} M = \log_{10} N$, then $M = N$.

L–3   If $M = N$, then $10^M = 10^N$.

Now, consider the product
$$(3.825)(0.00729).$$
If we set
$$N = (3.825)(0.00729),$$
then by assumption L–1,
$$\log_{10} N = \log_{10} [(3.825)(0.00729)].$$
Now, by the first law of logarithms,
$$\log_{10} N = \log_{10} 3.825 + \log_{10} 0.00729,$$
and from the table,
$$\log_{10} 3.825 = 0.5826,$$
$$\log_{10} 0.00729 = 7.8627 - 10,$$
so that
$$\log_{10} N = (0.5826) + (7.8627 - 10)$$
$$= 8.4453 - 10.$$
The computation is completed by referring to the table for
$$N = \text{antilog}_{10} (8.4453 - 10) = 2.788 \times 10^{-2}$$
$$= 0.02788,$$
and
$$N = (3.825)(0.00729) = 0.02788.$$
Actual computation shows the product to be 0.02788425 so that the result obtained by use of logarithms is correct to four significant digits. Some error should be expected because we are using approximations to irrational numbers when we employ a table of logarithms.

Consider a more complicated example,
$$\frac{(8.21)^{1/2}(2.17)^{2/3}}{(3.14)^3}.$$
Setting
$$N = \frac{(8.21)^{1/2}(2.17)^{2/3}}{(3.14)^3},$$
we have
$$\log_{10} N = \log_{10} \frac{(8.21)^{1/2}(2.17)^{2/3}}{(3.14)^3}$$
$$= \log_{10} (8.21)^{1/2} + \log_{10} (2.17)^{2/3} - \log_{10} (3.14)^3,$$
$$\log_{10} N = \tfrac{1}{2} \log_{10} (8.21) + \tfrac{2}{3} \log_{10} (2.17) - 3 \log_{10} (3.14).$$

The table provides values for the logarithms involved here, and the remainder of the computation is routine. In order to avoid confusion in computations of this sort, a systematic approach of some kind is desirable (see example in Exercise 11.7).

EXERCISE 11.7

Compute by means of logarithms.

Example: $\sqrt{\dfrac{(23.4)(0.681)}{4.13}}$

     Let $P = \sqrt{\dfrac{(23.4)(0.681)}{4.13}}$,

then $\log_{10} P = \frac{1}{2}(\log_{10} 23.4 + \log_{10} 0.681 - \log_{10} 4.13)$.

$$\left.\begin{array}{rl} \log_{10} 23.4 = & 1.3692 \\ \log_{10} 0.681 = & 9.8331 - 10 \end{array}\right\}\text{add}$$

$$\left.\begin{array}{rl} \log_{10} (23.4)(0.681) = & 11.2023 - 10 \\ \log_{10} 4.13 = & 0.6160 \end{array}\right\}\text{subtract}$$

$$\log_{10} \frac{(23.4)(0.681)}{4.13} = 10.5863 - 10 = 0.5863$$

$$\frac{1}{2} \log_{10} \frac{(23.4)(0.681)}{4.13} = \frac{1}{2}(0.5863) = 0.2931$$

     $P = \text{antilog}_{10}\ 0.2931 = 1.964$

Ans. 1.964

1. $(2.32)(1.73)$ **2.** $(82.3)(6.12)$ **3.** $\dfrac{3.15}{1.37}$

4. $\dfrac{0.00214}{3.17}$ **5.** $(2.3)^5$ **6.** $(4.62)^3$

7. $\sqrt[3]{8.12}$ **8.** $\sqrt[5]{75}$ **9.** $(0.0128)^5$

10. $(0.0021)^6$ **11.** $\sqrt{0.0021}$ **12.** $\sqrt[6]{0.0471}$

13. $\dfrac{(8.12)(8.74)}{7.19}$ **14.** $\dfrac{(0.421)^2(84.3)}{\sqrt{21.7}}$ **15.** $\dfrac{(6.49)^2\sqrt[3]{8.21}}{17.9}$

16. $\dfrac{(2.61)^2(4.32)}{\sqrt{7.83}}$ **17.** $\dfrac{(0.3498)(27.16)}{6.814}$ **18.** $\dfrac{(4.813)^2(20.14)}{3.612}$

19. $\sqrt{\dfrac{(4.71)(0.00481)}{(0.0432)^2}}$ **20.** $\sqrt{\dfrac{(2.85)^3(0.97)}{(0.035)}}$

21. $\sqrt{25.1(25.1 - 18.7)(25.1 - 4.3)}$ **22.** $\sqrt{\dfrac{4.17^3(68.1 - 4.7)}{(68.1 - 52.9)}}$

23. $\dfrac{\sqrt{(23.4)^3(0.0064)}}{\sqrt[3]{69.1}}$ **24.** $\dfrac{\sqrt{38.7}\ \sqrt[3]{491}}{\sqrt[4]{9.21}}$

25. The period T of a simple pendulum is given by the formula $T = 2\pi\sqrt{L/g}$, where T is in seconds, L is the length of the pendulum in feet, and $g \approx 32$ ft/sec². Find the period of a pendulum 12 inches long.

26. The area A of a triangle in terms of the sides is given by the formula $A = \sqrt{s(s - a)(s - b)(s - c)}$, where a, b, and c are the lengths of the sides of the triangle and s equals one half of the perimeter. Find the area of a triangle in which the three sides are 2.314 inches, 4.217 inches, and 5.618 inches.

27. The pressure p and volume v of saturated steam are related by the expression $pv^{1.06} = c$, in which p is in pounds per square inch, v is in cubic feet, and c is a constant. If $v = 2.874$ cu ft when $p = 40$ lb/in.^{2}, find the volume when the pressure is doubled.

11.8 Exponential and Logarithmic Equations

An equation in which a variable occurs in an exponent is called an **exponential equation.** Solution sets of some such equations in one variable can be found by means of logarithms.

Consider the equation

$$5^x = 7.$$

Because $5^x > 0$ for all x, we can apply Assumption L–1 from the preceding section and write

$$\log_{10} 5^x = \log_{10} 7,$$

and from the third law of logarithms,

$$x \log_{10} 5 = \log_{10} 7.$$

Multiplying each member by $1/\log_{10} 5$,

$$x = \frac{\log_{10} 7}{\log_{10} 5} = \frac{0.8451}{0.6990},$$

and the solution set is then

$$\{1.209\}.$$

Note that in seeking a numerical approximation to this solution the logarithms are *divided*, not subtracted.

As another example, consider the equation

$$6^{3x-4} = 3.$$

We have, from L–1,

$$\log_{10} 6^{3x-4} = \log_{10} 3,$$

and, from the third law of logarithms,

$$(3x - 4) \log_{10} 6 = \log_{10} 3.$$

Multiplying each member by $1/\log_{10} 6$,

$$3x - 4 = \frac{\log_{10} 3}{\log_{10} 6}.$$

Then

$$3x = \frac{\log_{10} 3}{\log_{10} 6} + 4,$$

$$x = \frac{\log_{10} 3}{3 \log_{10} 6} + \frac{4}{3},$$

and the solution set is

$$\left\{ \frac{\log_{10} 3}{3 \log_{10} 6} + \frac{4}{3} \right\}.$$

We shall leave solutions in logarithmic notation as in the example above. A decimal numeral approximation can be obtained by using the logarithm tables and then rewriting the expression.

Solution sets can also be found for some equations in which the terms involve logarithms. For example, consider the equation

$$\log_{10} x + \log_{10} (x - 3) = 1. \tag{1}$$

From the first law of logarithms, (1) can be written

$$\log_{10} x(x - 3) = 1. \tag{2}$$

Rewriting (2) in exponential form, we have

$$x(x - 3) = 10^1. \tag{3}$$

This quadratic equation can be solved as follows:

$$x^2 - 3x = 10,$$
$$x^2 - 3x - 10 = 0,$$
$$(x - 5)(x + 2) = 0,$$
$$x = 5 \quad \text{and} \quad x = -2,$$

and the solution set of (3) is $\{5, -2\}$. Is this also the solution set of (1)? We have adopted the argument that if (1) has a solution, then it must be included in the solution set of (2), but the converse may very well not be true. To be careful about the matter, we should note that (2) follows from (1) only if $x > 3$, that is, x and $x - 3$ are positive. However, proceeding as we did in Section 6.4 with equations involving radicals, a suspected solution set can be found and then each member checked in the original equation. Checking each member of $\{5, -2\}$ in equation (1), we note that -2 does not satisfy the equation because $\log_{10} -2$ is not defined. The number 5, however, is a valid solution and the solution set is $\{5\}$.

EXERCISE 11.8

Solve. Leave solutions in logarithmic form—use the base 10.

Example: $3^{x-2} = 16$

Use assumption L–1.

$$\log_{10} 3^{x-2} = \log_{10} 16$$

Use the third law of logarithms.

$$(x - 2) \log_{10} 3 = \log_{10} 16$$

Multiply each member by $1/\log_{10} 3$.

$$x - 2 = \frac{\log_{10} 16}{\log_{10} 3}$$

$$x = \frac{\log_{10} 16}{\log_{10} 3} + 2$$

Ans. $\left\{ \dfrac{\log_{10} 16}{\log_{10} 3} + 2 \right\}$

1. $2^x = 7$ **2.** $3^x = 4$ **3.** $3^{x+1} = 8$ **4.** $2^{x-1} = 9$

5. $7^{2x-1} = 3$ **6.** $3^{x+2} = 10$ **7.** $4^{x^2} = 15$ **8.** $3^{x^2} = 21$

9. $3^{-x} = 10$ **10.** $2.13^{-x} = 8.1$ **11.** $3^{1-x} = 15$ **12.** $4^{2-x} = 10$

Solve. Leave the results in the form of an equation equivalent to the given equation.

13. $y = x^n$, for n **14.** $y = Cx^{-n}$, for n **15.** $y = e^{kt}$, for t

16. Solve Problem 15 using logarithms to the base e. Simplify.

Solve.

Example: $\log_{10} (x + 9) + \log_{10} (x) = 1$

Use the first law of logarithms.

$$\log_{10} (x + 9)(x) = 1$$

Write in exponential form.

$$x^2 + 9x = 10^1$$

Solve for x.

$$x^2 + 9x - 10 = 0$$
$$(x + 10)(x - 1) = 0$$
$$x = -10, \ x = 1$$

-10 does not satisfy the original equation.

Ans. $\{1\}$

17. $\log_{10} x + \log_{10} 2 = 3$ **18.** $\log_{10} (x - 1) - \log_{10} 4 = 2$

19. $\log_{10} x + \log_{10} (x + 21) = 2$ **20.** $\log_{10} (x + 3) + \log_{10} (x) = 1$

21. $\log_{10} (x + 2) + \log_{10} (x - 1) = 1$ **22.** $\log_{10} (x - 3) - \log_{10} (x + 1) = 1$

23. Solve for x: $3^{\log_3 x} = 7$ **24.** Solve for x: $5^{3 \log_5 x} = 8$

25. Show that the solution set of $3^x = 18$ is $\{\log_3 18\}$, and hence infer a means of finding $\log_a b$ in terms of $\log_{10} b$ by solving a similar equation, $a^{\log_a b} = b$.

26. Find a value for $\log_2 3$ using a table of logarithms to the base 10. *Hint:* Let $x = \log_2 3$ and write in exponential form, etc.

11.9 Changing the Base of a Logarithm—Log$_e$

The number e $(e \approx 2.7182818)$ mentioned in Section 11.5 is of great mathematical interest.   It has certain very useful properties of wide application in more advanced mathematics and in many practical situations.   For our purposes, we wish only to find a way to go from $\log_{10} x$ to $\log_e x$ or, in general, from $\log_a x$ to $\log_b x$.

First note that for $a, x > 0$ and $a \neq 1$,

$$x = a^{\log_a x}. \tag{1}$$

By applying Assumption L–1 from Section 11.4, we can equate the logarithms to the base b $(b > 0, b \neq 1)$ of each member of (1), yielding

$$\log_b x = \log_b a^{\log_a x}.$$

By the third law of logarithms,

$$\log_b x = \log_a x \cdot \log_b a \tag{2}$$

from which

$$\log_a x = \frac{\log_b x}{\log_b a}. \tag{3}$$

Equation (3) gives us a means of finding $\log_a x$ when we have a table of logarithms to the base b.   In particular, if $a = e$ and $b = 10$, we have

$$\log_e x = \frac{\log_{10} x}{\log_{10} e}. \tag{4}$$

Since $\log_{10} e \approx 0.4343$, (4) can be written as

$$\log_e x = \frac{\log_{10} x}{0.4343} \tag{5}$$

or

$$\log_e x = 2.303 \log_{10} x. \tag{6}$$

Equation (5) can also be written in the form

$$\log_{10} x = 0.4343 \log_e x. \tag{7}$$

[Note that in (5), (6), and (7) we are again using = for $\approx$.]

Another useful relationship can be obtained from (3) by setting $x = b$. This yields

$$\log_a b = \frac{\log_b b}{\log_b a}. \tag{8}$$

But, from the definition of a logarithm,

$$\log_b b = 1,$$

so that (8) becomes

$$\log_a b = \frac{1}{\log_b a}.$$

EXERCISE 11.9

Find each logarithm using Table II, page 292.

Examples:

a. $\log_e 14$

b. $\log_3 7$

Represent the number to the base 10.

$$\log_e 14 = \frac{\log_{10} 14}{\log_{10} e}$$

$$\log_3 7 = \frac{\log_{10} 7}{\log_{10} 3}$$

Use table of mantissas, base 10.

$$= \frac{1.1461}{0.4343}$$

$$= \frac{0.8451}{0.4771}$$

Divide.

Ans. 2.64

Ans. 1.77

1. $\log_e 3$	**2.** $\log_e 8$	**3.** $\log_e 17$	**4.** $\log_e 98$
5. $\log_e 327$	**6.** $\log_e 107$	**7.** $\log_e 24$	**8.** $\log_e 14$
9. $\log_2 10$	**10.** $\log_2 5$	**11.** $\log_5 240$	**12.** $\log_3 18$
13. $\log_7 8.1$	**14.** $\log_5 60$	**15.** $\log_{15} 8.1$	**16.** $\log_{20} 200$
17. $\log_{100} 38$	**18.** $\log_{1000} 240$		

Solve without using the table of logarithms.

19. If $\log_{10} 4 = 0.6021$, find $\log_4 10$.

20. If $\log_{10} 2 = 0.3010$, find $\log_2 10$.

21. If $\log_{10} 3 = 0.4771$, find $\log_3 10$.

22. If $\log_{10} e = 0.4343$, find $\log_e 10$.

23. If $\log_{10} 5 = 0.6990$, find $\log_5 100$.

24. If $\log_{10} 3 = 0.4771$, find $\log_3 100$.

25. Without using the table of logarithms, show that $\log_9 7 = \frac{1}{2} \log_3 7$. By a similar argument, show that for $a, b > 0$, $\log_{a^2} b = \frac{1}{2} \log_a b$. *Hint:* In the first case, $\log_9 7 = \frac{1}{\log_7 9}$, and $9 = 3^2$.

26. Explain why $y = \log_x x$ $(x > 0,\ x \neq 1)$ defines a function. What is its domain? What is its range? Graph the function.

27. Without using the table of logarithms, show that

$$(\log_{10} 4 - \log_{10} 2)\log_2 10 = 1.$$

28. Show that $(2 \log_2 3)(\log_9 2 + \log_9 4) = 3$.

11.10 Applications

Both exponential and logarithmic functions are of considerable importance in applied mathematics. In this section we will illustrate several applications.

One such application of logarithms is the computation of compound interest. The interest on a given amount of money over a definite period at a specified rate is called **simple interest** and can be computed by the familiar formula $I = Pr$. If, however, the interest accruing to an amount of money is added to the amount periodically, and, over the next period, this new total is earning interest, we say that the principal is earning **compound interest.** For example, if the sum of one dollar is earning interest at a rate r per year compounded annually, the amount present

after one year, $A = 1 + r$;

after two years, $A = (1 + r) + r(1 + r) = (1 + r)^2$;

after three years, $A = (1 + r)^2 + r(1 + r)^2 = (1 + r)^3$;

and, by informal mathematical induction, we have that

$$\text{after } n \text{ years, } A = (1 + r)^n. \tag{1}$$

For each dollar invested under such an arrangement, we have $(1 + r)^n$ dollars after n years, so that P dollars invested under the same arrangement, after n years, would amount to

$$A = P(1 + r)^n. \tag{2}$$

If the interest is compounded t times yearly, then the rate per period is r/t instead of r and the number of periods is increased to tn, so that (2) becomes

$$A = P\left(1 + \frac{r}{t}\right)^{tn}. \tag{3}$$

Specifically, if P dollars is compounded *semiannually* for n years at a yearly rate of interest r, the amount present is given by

$$A = P\left(1 + \frac{r}{2}\right)^{2n}, \tag{3a}$$

and when compounded *quarterly*,

$$A = P\left(1 + \frac{r}{4}\right)^{4n}. \tag{3b}$$

Although from a practical standpoint problems similar to the example following are handled by means of tables, for illustrative purposes we shall use logarithms in this example and in the exercise set.

What rate is necessary in order that \$2500 compounded quarterly will amount to \$4800 in twelve years? We have from (3b)

$$4800 = 2500\left(1 + \frac{r}{4}\right)^{48}$$

or

$$\left(1 + \frac{r}{4}\right)^{48} = 1.92,$$

and

$$\left(1 + \frac{r}{4}\right) = 1.92^{1/48}.$$

Solving for r by means of logarithms,

$$\log_{10}\left(1 + \frac{r}{4}\right) = \log_{10} 1.92^{1/48}$$

$$= \tfrac{1}{48}\log_{10} 1.92 = \tfrac{1}{48}(0.2833) = 0.0059,$$

$$\text{antilog}_{10}\ 0.0059 = 1 + \frac{r}{4} = 1.014.$$

Thus

$$r = 4(1.014 - 1) = 0.056.$$

The required rate of interest is about 5.6%.

A second interesting application of logarithms occurs in the field of chemistry. The chemist defines the pH (hydrogen potential) of a solution by

$$pH = \log_{10} \frac{1}{[H^+]} \tag{4}$$

$$= \log_{10} [H^+]^{-1},$$

$$pH = -\log_{10} [H^+] \tag{4a}$$

where $[H^+]$ is a numerical value for the concentration of hydrogen ions in aqueous solution in moles per liter. Now suppose we wish to find the pH of a solution where the concentration of hydrogen ions $[H^+]$ is 4.0×10^{-5}. We have from (4) that

$$pH = \log_{10} \frac{1}{4 \times 10^{-5}}$$

$$= \log_{10} (2.5 \times 10^4),$$

$$pH = 4.4.$$

pH values are generally stated to the nearest tenth.

Conversely, suppose we wish to find the hydrogen ion concentration $[H^+]$ of a solution whose pH is 5.6. From (4a),

$$-\log_{10} [H^+] = 5.6$$

and

$$\log_{10} [H^+] = -5.6.$$

To use the table of mantissas to find the antilog$_{10}$ -5.6, -5.6 is changed to $-6 + 0.4$ or $4.4 - 10$, a form in which the mantissa is positive. Thus

$$[H^+] = \text{antilog}_{10} (4.4 - 10)$$
$$= 2.5 \times 10^{-6},$$

and the hydrogen ion concentration is about 2.5×10^{-6}.

The hydrogen ion concentration in the example above can be determined by an alternative method. From (4),

$$\log_{10} \frac{1}{[H^+]} = 5.6,$$

$$\frac{1}{[H^+]} = \text{antilog}_{10} 5.6 = 3.98 \times 10^5,$$

$$[H^+] = \frac{1}{3.98 \times 10^5} = 0.25 \times 10^{-5} = 2.5 \times 10^{-6}.$$

As an example of the use of the exponential function, consider the disintegration of an isotope of radium in accordance with the relationship

$$y = y_0\, e^{-0.038t},$$

where t is the time in centuries, y is the amount present at any time t, and y_0 is the amount present at time $t = 0$. How long will it take 100 grams of radium to decompose to 50 grams? We have

$$50 = 100\, e^{-0.038t},$$

from which

$$e^{-0.038t} = \tfrac{1}{2}.$$

Now

$$\log_{10} e^{-0.038t} = \log_{10} \tfrac{1}{2},$$

$$-0.038t \log_{10} e = \log_{10} 1 - \log_{10} 2 = -\log_{10} 2.$$

From the tables, $\log_{10} e \approx 0.4343$ and $\log_{10} 2 \approx 0.3010$, so that this last equation becomes

$$-0.038t(0.4343) = -(0.3010)$$

or

$$t = 18.24.$$

Therefore, it will take approximately 18.24 centuries for the stated decomposition. Since half of the original quantity has decomposed, this period of time is called the half-life of the element.

EXERCISE 11.10

Solve for the variable n (nearest year), r (nearest $\frac{1}{2}\%$), or A (accuracy obtainable using 4-place table of mantissas).

Examples:

a. $(1 + r)^{12} = 1.127$

Equate $\log_{10}$ of each member and apply the third law of logarithms.

$12 \log_{10} (1 + r) = \log_{10} 1.127 = 0.0519$

Multiply each member by $\frac{1}{12}$.

$\log_{10} (1 + r) = \frac{1}{12}(0.0519) = 0.0043$

Determine antilog$_{10}$ 0.0043 and solve for r.

antilog$_{10}$ 0.0043 $= 1 + r = 1.01$

$r = 0.01$

Ans. $r = 1\%$

b. $40(1 + 0.02)^n = 51.74$

Multiply each member by $\frac{1}{40}$; equate $\log_{10}$ of each member and apply the second and third laws of logarithms. Solve for n.

$n \log_{10} (1.02) = \log_{10} 51.74 - \log_{10} 40$

$n(0.0086) = 1.7138 - 1.6021$

$$n = \frac{0.1117}{0.0086}$$

Ans. $n = 13$ years

1. $(1 + 0.03)^{10} = A$ **2.** $(1 + 0.04)^8 = A$ **3.** $(1 + r)^6 = 1.34$

4. $(1 + r)^{10} = 1.48$ **5.** $(1 + 0.04)^n = 2.19$ **6.** $(1 + 0.04)^n = 1.60$

7. $100\left(1 + \frac{r}{2}\right)^{10} = 113$ **8.** $40\left(1 + \frac{r}{4}\right)^{12} = 50.9$

9. $150(1 + 0.01)^{4n} = 240$ **10.** $60(1 + 0.02)^{2n} = 116$

11. Find the compounded amount of $5000 invested at 4% for 10 years when compounded annually. When compounded semiannually.

12. Two men, A and B, each invested $10,000 at 4% for 20 years with a bank that computed interest quarterly. A withdrew his interest at the end of each 3-month period but B let his investment be compounded. How much more did B earn over the period of 20 years?

Calculate the pH of a solution whose hydrogen ion concentration is as given.

Example: $[H^+] = 3.7 \times 10^{-6}$

Substitute 3.7×10^{-6} for $[H^+]$ in the relationship $pH = \log_{10} \dfrac{1}{[H^+]}$.

$$pH = \log_{10} \frac{1}{3.7 \times 10^{-6}}$$

Solve for pH.

$$pH = \log_{10}(2.7 \times 10^5) = 5.4$$

Ans. 5.4

13. $[H^+] = 10^{-7}$ **14.** $[H^+] = 4.0 \times 10^{-5}$ **15.** $[H^+] = 2.0 \times 10^{-8}$
16. $[H^+] = 8.5 \times 10^{-3}$ **17.** $[H^+] = 6.3 \times 10^{-7}$ **18.** $[H^+] = 5.7 \times 10^{-7}$

Calculate the hydrogen ion concentration $[H^+]$ of a solution whose pH is as given.

Example: $pH = 7.4$

Substitute 7.4 for pH in the relationship $pH = \log_{10} \dfrac{1}{[H^+]}$.

$$\log_{10} \frac{1}{[H^+]} = 7.4$$

Equate antilog$_{10}$ of each member and solve for $[H^+]$.

$$\frac{1}{[H^+]} = \text{antilog}_{10}\, 7.4 = 2.5 \times 10^7$$

$$[H^+] = \frac{1}{2.5 \times 10^7} = 0.4 \times 10^{-7}$$

Ans. 4×10^{-8}

19. $pH = 3.0$ **20.** $pH = 4.2$ **21.** $pH = 5.6$
22. $pH = 8.3$ **23.** $pH = 7.2$ **24.** $pH = 6.9$

The relationship between hydrogen ions and hydroxide ions $[OH^-]$ is expressed by $[H^+][OH^-] = 1 \times 10^{-14}$. Calculate the hydroxide ion concentration $[OH^-]$ of an aqueous solution whose pH is as given.

Example: $pH = 7.4$

Determine $[H^+]$ as in the preceding example.

$$[H^+] = 4 \times 10^{-8}$$

Substitute 4×10^{-8} for $[H^+]$ in the relationship $[H^+][OH^-] = 1 \times 10^{-14}$.

$$[OH^-] = \frac{1 \times 10^{-14}}{4 \times 10^{-8}} = 0.25 \times 10^{-6}$$

Ans. 2.5×10^{-7}

25. $pH = 5.0$ **26.** $pH = 4.0$ **27.** $pH = 8.4$
28. $pH = 6.2$ **29.** $pH = 11.3$ **30.** $pH = 12.7$

31. The amount of a radioactive element available at any time (t) is given by $y = y_0 e^{-0.4t}$, where t is in seconds and y_0 is the amount present initially. How much of the element would remain after three seconds if 40 grams were present initially?

32. The number of bacteria present in a culture is related to time by the formula $N = N_0 e^{0.04t}$, where N_0 is the amount of bacteria present at time $t = 0$, and t is time in hours. If 10,000 bacteria are present 10 hours after the beginning of the experiment, how many were present when $t = 0$?

33. The atmospheric pressure p, in inches of mercury, is given approximately by $p = 30.0(10)^{-0.09a}$, where a is the altitude in miles above sea level. What is the atmospheric pressure at sea level? At 3 miles above sea level?

34. The intensity I (in lumens) of a light beam after passing through a thickness t (in centimeters) of a medium having an absorption coefficient of 0.1 is given by $I = 1000 e^{-0.1t}$. How many centimeters of the material would reduce the illumination to 800 lumens?

35. For pure water $[H^+] = [OH^-]$. Show that the pH of pure water is 7.

CHAPTER REVIEW

1. Sketch the graph of
   a. $y = 5^x$
   b. $y = 5^{-x}$

2. State the inverse of the function $\{(x, y) \mid y = x^2 - 4x\}$ and whether the inverse is a function.

3. Graph $\{(x, y) \mid y = 4^x\}$ and its inverse on the same set of axes.

4. Write in logarithmic notation.
   a. $9^{3/2} = 27$
   b. $(\frac{4}{9})^{1/2} = \frac{2}{3}$

5. Write in exponential notation.
   a. $\log_5 625 = 4$
   b. $\log_{10} 0.0001 = -4$

6. Find a value for x.
   a. $\log_3 x = 3$
   b. $\log_x 3 = 3$

7. Find.
   a. $\log_{10} 0.713$
   b. $\log_{10} 1814$

8. Find.
   a. antilog$_{10}$ 8.1771 $-$ 10
   b. antilog$_{10}$ 3.7234

9. Express as the sum or difference of simpler logarithmic quantities.
   a. $\log_a 3x^2y$
   b. $\log_a \dfrac{y\sqrt{x}}{z^2}$

10. Compute by means of logarithms.
    a. $(3.17)(8.23)$
    b. $\dfrac{\sqrt{18.72}}{3.12}$

11. Solve.

  a. $3^x = 15$ b. $2^{x-4} = 10$

12. Find.

  a. $\log_e 7$ b. $\log_7 e$

13. What is the characteristic of $\log_7 54$?

14. For what values of x will $\log_{10} x < 5$?

15. Find the amount of \$4000 invested at 4% for 10 years when compounded semiannually.

APPENDIX

TABLE I

SQUARES, SQUARE ROOTS, AND PRIME FACTORS

No.	Sq.	Sq. Root	Prime Factors	No.	Sq.	Sq. Root	Prime Factors
1	1	1.000		41	1,681	6.403	41
2	4	1.414	2	42	1,764	6.481	$2 \cdot 3 \cdot 7$
3	9	1.732	3	43	1,849	6.557	43
4	16	2.000	2^2	44	1,936	6.633	$2^2 \cdot 11$
5	25	2.236	5	45	2,025	6.708	$3^2 \cdot 5$
6	36	2.449	$2 \cdot 3$	46	2,116	6.782	$2 \cdot 23$
7	49	2.646	7	47	2,209	6.856	47
8	64	2.828	2^3	48	2,304	6.928	$2^4 \cdot 3$
9	81	3.000	3^2	49	2,401	7.000	7^2
10	100	3.162	$2 \cdot 5$	50	2,500	7.071	$2 \cdot 5^2$
11	121	3.317	11	51	2,601	7.141	$3 \cdot 17$
12	144	3.464	$2^2 \cdot 3$	52	2,704	7.211	$2^2 \cdot 13$
13	169	3.606	13	53	2,809	7.280	53
14	196	3.742	$2 \cdot 7$	54	2,916	7.348	$2 \cdot 3^3$
15	225	3.873	$3 \cdot 5$	55	3,025	7.416	$5 \cdot 11$
16	256	4.000	2^4	56	3,136	7.483	$2^3 \cdot 7$
17	289	4.123	17	57	3,249	7.550	$3 \cdot 19$
18	324	4.243	$2 \cdot 3^2$	58	3,364	7.616	$2 \cdot 29$
19	361	4.359	19	59	3,481	7.681	59
20	400	4.472	$2^2 \cdot 5$	60	3,600	7.746	$2^2 \cdot 3 \cdot 5$
21	441	4.583	$3 \cdot 7$	61	3,721	7.810	61
22	484	4.690	$2 \cdot 11$	62	3,844	7.874	$2 \cdot 31$
23	529	4.796	23	63	3,969	7.937	$3^2 \cdot 7$
24	576	4.899	$2^3 \cdot 3$	64	4,096	8.000	2^6
25	625	5.000	5^2	65	4,225	8.062	$5 \cdot 13$
26	676	5.099	$2 \cdot 13$	66	4,356	8.124	$2 \cdot 3 \cdot 11$
27	729	5.196	3^3	67	4,489	8.185	67
28	784	5.292	$2^2 \cdot 7$	68	4,624	8.246	$2^2 \cdot 17$
29	841	5.385	29	69	4,761	8.307	$3 \cdot 23$
30	900	5.477	$2 \cdot 3 \cdot 5$	70	4,900	8.367	$2 \cdot 5 \cdot 7$
31	961	5.568	31	71	5,041	8.426	71
32	1,024	5.657	2^5	72	5,184	8.485	$2^3 \cdot 3^2$
33	1,089	5.745	$3 \cdot 11$	73	5,329	8.544	73
34	1,156	5.831	$2 \cdot 17$	74	5,476	8.602	$2 \cdot 37$
35	1,225	5.916	$5 \cdot 7$	75	5,625	8.660	$3 \cdot 5^2$
36	1,296	6.000	$2^2 \cdot 3^2$	76	5,776	8.718	$2^2 \cdot 19$
37	1,369	6.083	37	77	5,929	8.775	$7 \cdot 11$
38	1,444	6.164	$2 \cdot 19$	78	6,084	8.832	$2 \cdot 3 \cdot 13$
39	1,521	6.245	$3 \cdot 13$	79	6,241	8.888	79
40	1,600	6.325	$2^3 \cdot 5$	80	6,400	8.944	$2^4 \cdot 5$

No.	Sq.	Sq. Root	Prime Factors	No.	Sq.	Sq. Root	Prime Factors
81	6,561	9.000	3^4	91	8,281	9.539	$7 \cdot 13$
82	6,724	9.055	$2 \cdot 41$	92	8,464	9.592	$2^2 \cdot 23$
83	6,889	9.110	83	93	8,649	9.644	$3 \cdot 31$
84	7,056	9.165	$2^2 \cdot 3 \cdot 7$	94	8,836	9.695	$2 \cdot 47$
85	7,225	9.220	$5 \cdot 17$	95	9,025	9.747	$5 \cdot 19$
86	7,396	9.274	$2 \cdot 43$	96	9,216	9.798	$2^5 \cdot 3$
87	7,569	9.327	$3 \cdot 29$	97	9,409	9.849	97
88	7,744	9.381	$2^3 \cdot 11$	98	9,604	9.899	$2 \cdot 7^2$
89	7,921	9.434	89	99	9,801	9.950	$3^2 \cdot 11$
90	8,100	9.487	$2 \cdot 3^2 \cdot 5$	100	10,000	10.000	$2^2 \cdot 5^2$

TABLE II
COMMON LOGARITHMS

x	0	1	2	3	4	5	6	7	8	9
1.0	.0000	.0043	.0086	.0128	.0170	.0212	.0253	.0294	.0334	.0374
1.1	.0414	.0453	.0492	.0531	.0569	.0607	.0645	.0682	.0719	.0755
1.2	.0792	.0828	.0864	.0899	.0934	.0969	.1004	.1038	.1072	.1106
1.3	.1139	.1173	.1206	.1239	.1271	.1303	.1335	.1367	.1399	.1430
1.4	.1461	.1492	.1523	.1553	.1584	.1614	.1644	.1673	.1703	.1732
1.5	.1761	.1790	.1818	.1847	.1875	.1903	.1931	.1959	.1987	.2014
1.6	.2041	.2068	.2095	.2122	.2148	.2175	.2201	.2227	.2253	.2279
1.7	.2304	.2330	.2355	.2380	.2405	.2430	.2455	.2480	.2504	.2529
1.8	.2553	.2577	.2601	.2625	.2648	.2672	.2695	.2718	.2742	.2765
1.9	.2788	.2810	.2833	.2856	.2878	.2900	.2923	.2945	.2967	.2989
2.0	.3010	.3032	.3054	.3075	.3096	.3118	.3139	.3160	.3181	.3201
2.1	.3222	.3243	.3263	.3284	.3304	.3324	.3345	.3365	.3385	.3404
2.2	.3424	.3444	.3464	.3483	.3502	.3522	.3541	.3560	.3579	.3598
2.3	.3617	.3636	.3655	.3674	.3692	.3711	.3729	.3747	.3766	.3784
2.4	.3802	.3820	.3838	.3856	.3874	.3892	.3909	.3927	.3945	.3962
2.5	.3979	.3997	.4014	.4031	.4048	.4065	.4082	.4099	.4116	.4133
2.6	.4150	.4166	.4183	.4200	.4216	.4232	.4249	.4265	.4281	.4298
2.7	.4314	.4330	.4346	.4362	.4378	.4393	.4409	.4425	.4440	.4456
2.8	.4472	.4487	.4502	.4518	.4533	.4548	.4564	.4579	.4594	.4609
2.9	.4624	.4639	.4654	.4669	.4683	.4698	.4713	.4728	.4742	.4757
3.0	.4771	.4786	.4800	.4814	.4829	.4843	.4857	.4871	.4886	.4900
3.1	.4914	.4928	.4942	.4955	.4969	.4983	.4997	.5011	.5024	.5038
3.2	.5051	.5065	.5079	.5092	.5105	.5119	.5132	.5145	.5159	.5172
3.3	.5185	.5198	.5211	.5224	.5237	.5250	.5263	.5276	.5289	.5302
3.4	.5315	.5328	.5340	.5353	.5366	.5378	.5391	.5403	.5416	.5428
3.5	.5441	.5453	.5465	.5478	.5490	.5502	.5514	.5527	.5539	.5551
3.6	.5563	.5575	.5587	.5599	.5611	.5623	.5635	.5647	.5658	.5670
3.7	.5682	.5694	.5705	.5717	.5729	.5740	.5752	.5763	.5775	.5786
3.8	.5798	.5809	.5821	.5832	.5843	.5855	.5866	.5877	.5888	.5899
3.9	.5911	.5922	.5933	.5944	.5955	.5966	.5977	.5988	.5999	.6010
4.0	.6021	.6031	.6042	.6053	.6064	.6075	.6085	.6096	.6107	.6117
4.1	.6128	.6138	.6149	.6160	.6170	.6180	.6191	.6201	.6212	.6222
4.2	.6232	.6243	.6253	.6263	.6274	.6284	.6294	.6304	.6314	.6325
4.3	.6335	.6345	.6355	.6365	.6375	.6385	.6395	.6405	.6415	.6425
4.4	.6435	.6444	.6454	.6464	.6474	.6484	.6493	.6503	.6513	.6522
4.5	.6532	.6542	.6551	.6561	.6571	.6580	.6590	.6599	.6609	.6618
4.6	.6628	.6637	.6646	.6656	.6665	.6675	.6684	.6693	.6702	.6712
4.7	.6721	.6730	.6739	.6749	.6758	.6767	.6776	.6785	.6794	.6803
4.8	.6812	.6821	.6830	.6839	.6848	.6857	.6866	.6875	.6884	.6893
4.9	.6902	.6911	.6920	.6928	.6937	.6946	.6955	.6964	.6972	.6981
5.0	.6990	.6998	.7007	.7016	.7024	.7033	.7042	.7050	.7059	.7067
5.1	.7076	.7084	.7093	.7101	.7110	.7118	.7126	.7135	.7143	.7152
5.2	.7160	.7168	.7177	.7185	.7193	.7202	.7210	.7218	.7226	.7235
5.3	.7243	.7251	.7259	.7267	.7275	.7284	.7292	.7300	.7308	.7316
5.4	.7324	.7332	.7340	.7348	.7356	.7364	.7372	.7380	.7388	.7396
x	0	1	2	3	4	5	6	7	8	9

x	0	1	2	3	4	5	6	7	8	9
5.5	.7404	.7412	.7419	.7427	.7435	.7443	.7451	.7459	.7466	.7474
5.6	.7482	.7490	.7497	.7505	.7513	.7520	.7528	.7536	.7543	.7551
5.7	.7559	.7566	.7574	.7582	.7589	.7597	.7604	.7612	.7619	.7627
5.8	.7634	.7642	.7649	.7657	.7664	.7672	.7679	.7686	.7694	.7701
5.9	.7709	.7716	.7723	.7731	.7738	.7745	.7752	.7760	.7767	.7774
6.0	.7782	.7789	.7796	.7803	.7810	.7818	.7825	.7832	.7839	.7846
6.1	.7853	.7860	.7868	.7875	.7882	.7889	.7896	.7903	.7910	.7917
6.2	.7924	.7931	.7938	.7945	.7952	.7959	.7966	.7973	.7980	.7987
6.3	.7993	.8000	.8007	.8014	.8021	.8028	.8035	.8041	.8048	.8055
6.4	.8062	.8069	.8075	.8082	.8089	.8096	.8102	.8109	.8116	.8122
6.5	.8129	.8136	.8142	.8149	.8156	.8162	.8169	.8176	.8182	.8189
6.6	.8195	.8202	.8209	.8215	.8222	.8228	.8235	.8241	.8248	.8254
6.7	.8261	.8267	.8274	.8280	.8287	.8293	.8299	.8306	.8312	.8319
6.8	.8325	.8331	.8338	.8344	.8351	.8357	.8363	.8370	.8376	.8382
6.9	.8388	.8395	.8401	.8407	.8414	.8420	.8426	.8432	.8439	.8445
7.0	.8451	.8457	.8463	.8470	.8476	.8482	.8488	.8494	.8500	.8506
7.1	.8513	.8519	.8525	.8531	.8537	.8543	.8549	.8555	.8561	.8567
7.2	.8573	.8579	.8585	.8591	.8597	.8603	.8609	.8615	.8621	.8627
7.3	.8633	.8639	.8645	.8651	.8657	.8663	.8669	.8675	.8681	.8686
7.4	.8692	.8698	.8704	.8710	.8716	.8722	.8727	.8733	.8739	.8745
7.5	.8751	.8756	.8762	.8768	.8774	.8779	.8785	.8791	.8797	.8802
7.6	.8808	.8814	.8820	.8825	.8831	.8837	.8842	.8848	.8854	.8859
7.7	.8865	.8871	.8876	.8882	.8887	.8893	.8899	.8904	.8910	.8915
7.8	.8921	.8927	.8932	.8938	.8943	.8949	.8954	.8960	.8965	.8971
7.9	.8976	.8982	.8987	.8993	.8998	.9004	.9009	.9015	.9020	.9025
8.0	.9031	.9036	.9042	.9047	.9053	.9058	.9063	.9069	.9074	.9079
8.1	.9085	.9090	.9096	.9101	.9106	.9112	.9117	.9122	.9128	.9133
8.2	.9138	.9143	.9149	.9154	.9159	.9165	.9170	.9175	.9180	.9186
8.3	.9191	.9196	.9201	.9206	.9212	.9217	.9222	.9227	.9232	.9238
8.4	.9243	.9248	.9253	.9258	.9263	.9269	.9274	.9279	.9284	.9289
8.5	.9294	.9299	.9304	.9309	.9315	.9320	.9325	.9330	.9335	.9340
8.6	.9345	.9350	.9355	.9360	.9365	.9370	.9375	.9380	.9385	.9390
8.7	.9395	.9400	.9405	.9410	.9415	.9420	.9425	.9430	.9435	.9440
8.8	.9445	.9450	.9455	.9460	.9465	.9469	.9474	.9479	.9484	.9489
8.9	.9494	.9499	.9504	.9509	.9513	.9518	.9523	.9528	.9533	.9538
9.0	.9542	.9547	.9552	.9557	.9562	.9566	.9571	.9576	.9581	.9586
9.1	.9590	.9595	.9600	.9605	.9609	.9614	.9619	.9624	.9628	.9633
9.2	.9638	.9643	.9647	.9652	.9657	.9661	.9666	.9671	.9675	.9680
9.3	.9685	.9689	.9694	.9699	.9703	.9708	.9713	.9717	.9722	.9727
9.4	.9731	.9736	.9741	.9745	.9750	.9754	.9759	.9763	.9768	.9773
9.5	.9777	.9782	.9786	.9791	.9795	.9800	.9805	.9809	.9814	.9818
9.6	.9823	.9827	.9832	.9836	.9841	.9845	.9850	.9854	.9859	.9863
9.7	.9868	.9872	.9877	.9881	.9886	.9890	.9894	.9899	.9903	.9908
9.8	.9912	.9917	.9921	.9926	.9930	.9934	.9939	.9943	.9948	.9952
9.9	.9956	.9961	.9965	.9969	.9974	.9978	.9983	.9987	.9991	.9996
x	0	1	2	3	4	5	6	7	8	9

FORMULAS FROM GEOMETRY

Plane Figures:

1. Square with side (s).
   Perimeter: $P = 4s$
   Area: $A = s^2$

2. Rectangle with length (l) and width (w).
   Perimeter: $P = l + l + w + w$
   $$P = 2l + 2w$$
   Area: $A = lw$

3. Triangle with sides (a) and (c), base (b) and altitude (h).
   Perimeter: $P = a + b + c$
   Area: $A = \frac{1}{2}bh$
   Sum of interior angles: $\angle A + \angle B + \angle C = 180°$
   a) Isosceles triangle
      two equal sides: $a = c$
      two equal angles: $\angle A = \angle C$
   b) Equilateral triangle
      three equal sides: $a = b = c$
      three equal angles: $\angle A = \angle B = \angle C$
   c) Right triangle with hypotenuse (c)
      Theorem of Pythagoras: $c^2 = a^2 + b^2$

4. Circle with radius (r).
   Diameter: $d = 2r$
   Circumference: $C = 2\pi r$ or πd
   Area: $A = \pi r^2$

Solid Figures:

1. Rectangular Prism with length (l), width (w), and height (h).
   Volume: $V = lwh$

2. Right circular cylinder with height (h) and radius of base (r).
   Volume: $V = \pi r^2 h$
   Lateral Area: $S = 2\pi rh$

ANSWERS

Exercise 1.1 (Page 4)

1. $\{1, 2, 3, 4, 5\}$

3. $\{1, 3, 5, 7, \cdots\}$

5. $\{5, 7, 9, 11\}$

7. $\{3, 6, 9, 12\}$

9. $\{6, -3, 0, -5\}$

11. $\{\sqrt{7}, -\sqrt{3}, \sqrt{5}\}$

13. $\{6\}$

15. $\emptyset, \{1\}, \{1, 2\}, \{1, 2, 3\},$
$\{2\}, \{1, 3\},$
$\{3\}, \{2, 3\}$

17. Infinite   **19.** Finite   **21.** Infinite   **23.** Variable

25. Variable   **27.** Constant   **29.** $\in$ **31.** $\subset$ or $\subseteq$

33. $\subset$ or $\subseteq$ **35.** $\subset$ **37.** $\not\subset$ **39.** $\in$

41. $\notin$ **45.** $J \subseteq Q$ **47.** $H \subseteq R$

Exercise 1.2 (Page 6)

1. $\{1, 3, 5\}$

3. $\{2, 4, 6, 7, 8, 9, 10\}$

5. $\{6, 8, 10\}$

7. $\{1, 2, 3, 4, 5, 6, 7, 8, 9, 10\}$

9. $\{2, 4, 6, 8, 10\}$

11. $\{1, 2, 3, 4, 5\}$

13. $\emptyset$

15. $\{1, 3, 5, 7, 9\}$

17. $\{1, 2, 3, 4, 5\}$

19. $\{6, 8, 10\}$

21. $\{1, 2, 3, 4, 5, 6, 7, 8, 9, 10\}$

23. Yes   **25.** Yes   **27.** $G = \emptyset$ and $H = \emptyset$

29. $G \subseteq H$ **31.** $G = \emptyset$ **35.** 11 members

37. 10 members

Exercise 1.3 (Page 10)

1. Symmetric law   **3.** Transitive law   **5.** Substitution law

7. Reflexive law   **9.** Substitution law   **29.** $7 > 3$

31. $-4 < -3$ **33.** $-1 < 0 < 1$ **35.** $x \not< y$

37. $3 < x < 5$ **39.** $3x \not< 5$ **41.** $-2 < 5$

43. $-7 < -1$ **45.** $-5 < -2$ **47.** $1\frac{1}{2} = \frac{3}{2}$

49. $3 < 5 < 7$ **51.** $3 = \frac{12}{4} > 2$ **53.** 5

55. $-\frac{1}{2}$ **57.** 0   **59.** 2

61. $2 < 5$ **63.** $7 < 8$ **65.** $x \geq y$

67. $x > 0$ or $x \nleq 0$ **69.** $x \geq 0$ or $x \nless 0$

Exercise 1.4 (Page 16)

1. Commutative law of addition

3. Commutative law of multiplication

5. Negative or additive inverse axiom

7. Closure for multiplication

9. Associative law of multiplication

11. Distributive law

13. Commutative law of multiplication

15. Associative law of addition

17. Commutative law of multiplication

19. Commutative law of addition

21. Commutative law of multiplication

23. Distributive law

25. Negative or additive inverse axiom

27. Positive

29. Positive

31. Addition law for equality

33. Double negative law

35. Cancellation law for multiplication

37. Zero factor law   **39.** Cancellation law for addition

41. No; yes   **43.** No; no

Exercise 1.5 (Page 21)

1. 5   **3.** -6 **5.** -36 **7.** 1   **9.** 27

11. 0   **13.** 1   **15.** 7   **17.** 1   **19.** 6

21. $b - a > 0$

23. No; if b is negative, $a + b < 0$.

25. No; if a and b are both negative, $a - b < 0$ only if $|a| > |b|$.

Exercise 1.6 (Page 24)

1. -6 **3.** 48   **5.** -36 **7.** 0   **9.** -64

11. -24 **13.** 4   **15.** 9   **17.** 0   **19.** Meaningless

21. $-32 = (-8)(4)$ **23.** $21 = (-7)(-3)$

25. $56 = (-7)(-8)$ **27.** $7(\frac{1}{8})$

29. $3(\frac{1}{8})$ **31.** $82(\frac{1}{11})$ **33.** $7(\frac{1}{100})$

35. $\frac{3}{2}$ **37.** $\frac{2}{7}$ **39.** $\frac{5}{8}$

41. $\frac{9}{2}$ **43.** $(2)(2)(2)$ **45.** $(7)(7)$

47. Prime   **49.** $-1(2)(2)(3)$ **51.** $(2)(2)(2)(7)$

53. $-1(2)(19)$ **55.** $(2)(2)(5)$ **57.** $(2)(53)$

Chapter 1 Review (Page 26)

1. a. $\{3, -2, 0\}$ **2.** a. $\{-1, 3, 5, 7, 9, 11\}$

   b. $\{3\}$ b. $\{3, 7\}$

3. $\{1, 3, 5\}, \{1, 2, 3, 5\}, \{1, 3, 4, 5\}, \{1, 2, 3, 4, 5\}$

4. 5 members   **5.** Identity element for addition

6. Reciprocal or multiplicative inverse axiom

7. Commutative law of multiplication

8. Negative or additive inverse axiom

9. Addition law of equality

10. Zero factor law

11. Multiplication law of equality or cancellation law of multiplication

12. Double negative law

13. $a < c$ **14.** $a < b < c$

15. $2 \cdot 2 \cdot 2 \cdot 2 \cdot 2 \cdot 3$ **16.** $a \geq b$

17. $2x \cdot \dfrac{1}{2y}$

Exercise 2.1 (Page 29)

1. x^3 **3.** $-5ab^3$ **5.** $-2x^2y^3$

7. $-r^2 + rs^2$ **9.** $x^3 + y^3$ **11.** $3a^2c - ab^2c^2$

13. $xxxxyyy$ **15.** $-aaabb$ **17.** $(-x)(-x)(-x)$

19. $-yyx$ **21.** $-xxx(-y)(-y)$ **23.** $aabbb - abbbb$

25. Trinomial; degree 2 in y

27. Binomial; degree 4 in x and y, 3 in x, 2 in y

29. Trinomial; degree 5 in x, y, and z, 1 in x, 2 in y, 3 in z, 3 in xy, 3 in xz, 4 in yz

31. 1   **33.** 2   **35.** 1   **37.** $-1, -21, 1$

39. 1, 1, 0   **41.** $-4, 60, 16$ **43.** 19, 7   **45.** 37, 11

47. 5, 5   **49.** 0, 15

Exercise 2.2 (Page 33)

1. $5a$	**3.** x	**5.** $-3x$
7. $2b - 2a$	**9.** $x^2y + 3xy$	**11.** $3x + 3y$
13. $4x - 1$	**15.** $-x^2 + 5x - 1$	**17.** $-2b$
19. $-3x^2 + 4x - 6$	**21.** $a - b + 2c - 3$	**23.** $2x^2 + 3x + 2$
25. $-2y - 1$	**27.** $2 - x$	**29.** $x - 1$
31. $-x^2 - 3x - 1$	**33.** $x - 2y$	**35.** $2x - y$

Exercise 2.3 (Page 36)

1. $5a^2$	**3.** $-15a^3$	**5.** $-2x^2y^3$
7. abc^2	**9.** x^{2n}	**11.** a^{2n}
13. x^{4n}	**15.** $-2a^2 + 2ab$	**17.** $-x^2 - x + 2$

19. $a^2bc - ab^2c + abc^2$ **21.** $a^3b - a^2b^2 + ab^3$

23. $a^{2n} - a^n$ **25.** $a^n + a^{2n-1}$

27. $x^2 + 2x - 3$ **29.** $x^2 - ax - 2a^2$

31. $x^2 + 2xy + y^2$ **33.** $10x^2 + 17x + 3$

35. $9a^2 - 6a + 1$ **37.** $4x^2 - 25$

39. $2x^2 + 3ax - 2a^2$ **41.** $4a^2 + 12ab + 9b^2$

43. $x^3 + 6x^2 + 7x - 4$ **45.** $\frac{1}{8}x^2 + \frac{3}{4}xy - 2y^2$

47. $\frac{3}{4}x^2 + \frac{1}{8}xy - \frac{1}{4}y^2$ **49.** $6x^3 + 16x^2 + 6x - 4$

51. $1 - a^{2n}$ **53.** $a^{5n} - a^{3n} + 2a^{2n} - 2$

55. $2a^{2n} + 5a^nb^n - 3b^{2n}$ **57.** $-2x^3 - 12x^2 - 18x$

59. $9x^4 - 33x^3 + 30x^2$ **61.** $-2ac + 6ad + bc - 3bd$

63. $a^3 - b^3$ **65.** 6 **67.** $-2a^2 - 2a$

69. $4a + 4$ **71.** $4a + 4$ **73.** $-4x^2 - 11x$

75. $20x^2 + 4x$ **81.** $-a$ $(a, b \neq 0)$

83. $2a^2b$ $(a \neq 0)$ **85.** $2(x - 2)$ $(x \neq 2)$

87. $2xy^2$ $(x, z \neq 0)$ **89.** x^n $(x \neq 0)$

91. a^n $(a \neq 0)$ **93.** x^{2n+4} $(x \neq 0)$

95. $x^{n-1}y^n$ $(x, y \neq 0)$ **97.** a^nb^n $(a, b \neq 0)$

99. a^{n^2} $(a \neq 0)$

Exercise 2.4 (Page 40)

1. $2(x + 3)$ **3.** $4x(x + 2)$

5. $3x(x - y + 1)$ **7.** $6(4a^2 + 2a - 1)$

9. $2x(x^3 - 2x + 4)$ **11.** $xz(xy^2z + 2y - 1)$

13. $x^n(x^{2n} + 1)$

15. $a^n(a^{2n} - a^n - 1)$

17. $x^n(x^2 + 1)$

19. $-2(x - 1)$

21. $-a(b + c)$

23. $-xy(1 + x)$

25. $-x(1 - x + x^2)$

27. $-x^n(x^n + 1)$

29. $x^a(x + 1)$

Exercise 2.5 (Page 42)

1. $(x - 6)(x - 2)$

3. $(2 - a)(3 + a)$

5. $(x + 5y)(x + y)$

7. $(x - 1)(x + 1)$

9. $(2 - b)(2 + b)$

11. $(ab - 1)(ab + 1)$

13. $(x^2 - 3)(x^2 + 3)$

15. $(a - 4b)(a + 4b)$

17. $(a^n - 2)(a^n + 2)$

19. $(x^n - y^n)(x^n + y^n)$

21. $[(ab)^n - 1][(ab)^n + 1]$

23. $(3x + 1)(x + 1)$

25. $(3x + 1)(3x - 8)$

27. $(3x - a)(x - 2a)$

29. $(3x - y)(3x + y)$

31. $(2x + 3)(2x + 3)$

33. $(1 - 4xy)(1 + 4xy)$

35. $3(x + 2)(x + 2)$

37. $2a(a - 5)(a + 1)$

39. $4(a - b)(a - b)$

41. $4y(x - 3)(x + 3)$

43. $x(4 + x)(3 - x)$

45. $x^2y^2(x - 1)(x + 1)$

47. $(y^2 + 1)(y^2 + 2)$

49. $(3x^2 + 1)(x^2 + 2)$

51. $(x^2 + 4)(x - 1)(x + 1)$

53. $(x - 2)(x + 2)(x - 1)(x + 1)$

55. $(2a^2 + 1)(a - 1)(a + 1)$

57. $(x^2 + 2a^2)(x - a)(x + a)$

59. $(x^n - 1)(x^n + 1)(x^{2n} + 1)$

61. $(x^{2n} + y^{2n})(x^n + y^n)(x^n - y^n)$

63. $(3x^{2n} - 1)(x^{2n} - 3)$

65. $0, 2$

67. $1, 2$

Exercise 2.6 (Page 44)

1. $(ax + 1)(x + 1)$

3. $(ax + 1)(x + a)$

5. $(x + a)(x + y)$

7. $(3a - c)(b - d)$

9. $(3x + y)(1 - 2x)$

11. $(a^2 + 2b^2)(a - 2b)$

13. $(x + 2y)(x - 1)$

15. $(2a^2 - 1)(b + 3)$

17. $(x^3 - 3)(y^2 + 1)$

19. $(x - 1)(x^2 + x + 1)$

21. $(2x + y)(4x^2 - 2xy + y^2)$

23. $(a - 2b)(a^2 + 2ab + 4b^2)$

25. $(xy - 1)(x^2y^2 + xy + 1)$

27. $(3a + 4b)(9a^2 - 12ab + 16b^2)$

29. $(2x - y)(x^2 - xy + y^2)$

31. $(x + y)(x - y)(x^2 + xy + y^2)(x^2 - xy + y^2)$

33. $2(3x^2 + 1)$

35. $\left(\dfrac{1}{y} - \dfrac{x^2}{2}\right)\left(\dfrac{1}{y^2} + \dfrac{x^2}{2y} + \dfrac{x^4}{4}\right)$

39. $(x + y)(x + 5y)$

Chapter 2 Review (Page 46)

1. a. $-b - 2c$ **2. a.** $18x^4y^5$ **3. a.** $-8xz$

    b. $2x - 3$ **b.** $6x^2 + 15x - 18$ **b.** $4x^2y^2$

4. a. a^{3n+1} **5. a.** $(2x - 3)(x + 7)$

    b. $x^{n+1}y^{n-1}$ **b.** $2x(x^2 - 2x + 3)$

6. a. $(a - 3b)(a - 4b)$

    b. $(x - 2a)(x^2 + 2ax + 4a^2)$

7. a. $(2x + 1)(y + x)$ **8. a.** $3x^n(2x^{2n} + 1)$

    b. $(3x^2 - yz)(3x^2 + yz)$ **b.** $x^{n+1}(x^n + 2)$

9. a. 22   **10. a.** 12

    b. $3x^2 + 2x + 1$ **b.** 109

11. Distributive law

12. Closure for multiplication

13. Distributive law and commutative law of multiplication

14. Negative or additive inverse axiom and identity element for addition

15. Closure for addition

Exercise 3.1 (Page 50)

1. $\dfrac{-3}{5}$ **3.** $\dfrac{4}{7}$

5. $\dfrac{-4x}{y}$ $(y \neq 0)$ **7.** $\dfrac{2}{x}$ $(x \neq 0)$

9. $\dfrac{-3x}{2y^2}$ $(y \neq 0)$ **11.** $\dfrac{-(2 + x)}{x}$ $(x \neq 0)$

13. $\dfrac{4}{y - 3}$ $(y \neq 3)$ **15.** $\dfrac{-1}{y - x}$ $(x \neq y)$

17. $\dfrac{2 - x}{x - 3}$ $(x \neq 3)$ **19.** $\dfrac{x}{y - x}$ $(x \neq y)$

21. $\dfrac{1}{y - x}$ $(x \neq y)$ **23.** $\dfrac{a}{3a + b}$ $(3a \neq -b)$

Exercise 3.2 (Page 54)

1. $\dfrac{a}{b}$ $(a, b, c \neq 0)$ **3.** $\dfrac{1}{3a^2b^2c}$ $(a, b, c \neq 0)$

5. 2 $(x \neq -y)$ **7.** -1 $(b \neq a)$

9. $b - a$ $(b \neq a)$ **11.** $-x - 1$ $(x \neq 1)$

13. $2x - 3$ **15.** $y - 1$ $(a \neq 0)$

17. $a^2 - 3a + 2$ $(a \neq 0)$ **19.** $y + 7$ $(y \neq 2)$

21. $y - 2$ $(y \neq -1)$

23. $4y^2 + 6y + 9$ $(y \neq \frac{3}{2})$

25. $x + y$ $(x \neq -a)$

27. $4a^2 + 2a + \frac{1}{4}$

29. $x^2 - 2x - \frac{3}{2}$ $(x \neq 0)$

31. $2y + 5$ $(y \neq -\frac{1}{2})$

33. $2y - 3 - \dfrac{2}{2y + 1}$ $(y \neq -\frac{1}{2})$

Exercise 3.3 (Page 58)

1. $x - 2$ $(x \neq 6)$

3. $x + 2$ $(x \neq -2)$

5. $x^3 - x^2 - \dfrac{1}{x - 2}$ $(x \neq 2)$

7. $2x^2 - 2x + 3 - \dfrac{8}{x + 1}$ $(x \neq -1)$

9. $2x^3 + 10x^2 + 50x + 249 + \dfrac{1251}{x - 5}$ $(x \neq 5)$ $3a \, (\, 9a + 1 \,)$

11. $x^2 + 2x - 3 + \dfrac{4}{x + 2}$ $(x \neq -2)$

13. $x^5 + x^4 + 2x^3 + 2x^2 + 2x + 1 + \dfrac{1}{x - 1}$ $(x \neq 1)$

15. $x^4 + x^3 + x^2 + x + 1$ $(x \neq 1)$

17. $x^5 + x^4 + x^3 + x^2 + x + 1$ $(x \neq 1)$

Exercise 3.4 (Page 59)

1. $\dfrac{9}{12}$

3. $\dfrac{-48}{15}$

5. $\dfrac{48}{12}$

7. $\dfrac{4}{12x}$ $(x \neq 0)$

9. $\dfrac{-3a^2b}{3b^3}$ $(b \neq 0)$

11. $\dfrac{xy^2}{xy}$ $(x, y \neq 0)$

13. $\dfrac{x + y}{3(x + y)}$ $(x \neq -y)$

15. $\dfrac{3x^2 - 3}{9(x + 1)}$ $(x \neq -1)$

17. $\dfrac{27a^2 + 27a}{9(a + 1)}$ $(a \neq -1)$ $9a +$

19. $\dfrac{3a + 3b}{a^2 - b^2}$ $(a \neq b, -b)$

21. $\dfrac{3xy - 9x}{y^2 - y - 6}$ $(y = -2, 3)$

23. $\dfrac{-2x - 4}{x^2 + 3x + 2}$ $(x \neq -2, -1)$

25. $\dfrac{-2b - 2a}{b^2 - a^2}$ $(b \neq a, -a)$

27. $\dfrac{-x^2 + x}{x^2 - 3x + 2}$ $(x \neq 1, 2)$

29. $\dfrac{3(a^2 - 3a + 9)}{a^3 + 27}$ $(a \neq -3)$

31. $\dfrac{-2(x^2 - y^2)}{x^4 - y^4}$ $(x \neq y, -y)$

33. $\dfrac{x(y + 3)}{xy + 3x - 2y - 6}$ $(x \neq 2; y \neq -3)$

Exercise 3.5 (Page 62)

1. 60

3. 120

5. 252

7. $6ab^2$

9. $24x^2y^2$

11. $a(a - b)^2$

13. $(a - b)(a + b)$ **15.** $(a + 4)(a + 1)^2$ **17.** $(x + 4)(x - 1)^2$

19. $x(x - 1)^3$ **21.** $4(a + 1)(a - 1)^2$ **23.** $x^3(x - 1)^2$

25. $\dfrac{x - 3}{2}$ **27.** $\dfrac{a + b - c}{6}$ **29.** $\dfrac{2x - 1}{2y}$ $(y \neq 0)$

31. $\dfrac{1 - 2x}{x + 2y}$ $(x \neq -2y)$ **33.** $\dfrac{6 - 2a}{a^2 - 2a + 1}$ $(a \neq 1)$

35. $\dfrac{2 - 2a}{ax}$ $(a, x \neq 0)$ **37.** $\dfrac{-a - 4}{6}$

39. $\dfrac{2x^2 + xy + 2y^2}{2xy}$ $(x, y \neq 0)$ **41.** $\dfrac{-4}{15(x - 2)}$ $(x \neq 2)$

43. $\dfrac{-x + 33}{2(x - 3)(x + 3)}$ $(x \neq 3, -3)$ **45.** $\dfrac{4}{r - 3}$ $(r \neq 3)$

47. $\dfrac{-a(2x + 3)}{(3x + 2)(x - 1)}$ $(x \neq 1, -\frac{2}{3})$

49. $\dfrac{-2(4x^2 - xy - 3y^2)}{(3x + y)(2x - y)}$ $(3x \neq -y, 2x \neq y)$

51. $\dfrac{-r^2 - 4rs + 3s^2}{(r + s)(r - s)}$ $(r \neq -s, s)$

53. $\dfrac{-6y - 4}{(y - 4)(y + 4)(y - 1)}$ $(y \neq 4, -4, 1)$

55. $\dfrac{x^3 - 2x^2 + 2x - 2}{(x - 1)^2}$ $(x \neq 1)$

57. 0 $(a \neq b, c; b \neq c)$

Exercise 3.6 (Page 66)

1. $\dfrac{2}{3}$ **3.** $\dfrac{7}{10}$ **5.** $\dfrac{10}{3}$ **7.** $\dfrac{-b^2}{a}$ $(a, b, c \neq 0)$

9. $\dfrac{3c}{35ab}$ $(a, b, c \neq 0)$ **11.** $\dfrac{5}{ab}$ $(a, b \neq 0)$

13. 5 $(x \neq 0, -5)$ **15.** $\dfrac{a(2a - 1)}{a + 4}$ $(a \neq 4, -4, -\frac{1}{2})$

17. $\dfrac{x + 3}{x - 5}$ $(x \neq 5, -4, -3)$ **19.** $\dfrac{3 - a}{a + 1}$ $(a \neq -2, -1, 2)$

21. $\dfrac{4}{3}$ **23.** $\dfrac{1}{ax^2y}$ $(a, b, x, y \neq 0)$

25. $\dfrac{28y}{9a}$ $(a, b, x, y \neq 0)$ **27.** $\dfrac{x}{2}$ $(x, y \neq 0, x \neq y)$

29. $\dfrac{5}{2}$ $(x \neq -3, 2)$ **31.** $\dfrac{a - 5}{a - 2}$ $(a \neq 5, -5, 2, -2, 3)$

33. $3(x^2 - xy + y^2)$ $(x \neq 0, -y)$

35. $(b - 1)(b + 1)$ $(b \neq -3, -1; b^2 + b + 1 \neq 0)$

37. $(x + 2)(y - 3)$ $(x \neq 2, -2, -1)$

39. $\dfrac{a - 1}{a - 3}$ $(a \neq 4, -4, 0, -1, 3)$

Exercise 3.7 (Page 69)

1. $\dfrac{3}{2}$ **3.** 20 **5.** $\dfrac{a}{bc}$ $(a, b, c \neq 0)$

7. $\dfrac{4y}{3}$ $(xy \neq 0)$ **9.** $\dfrac{1}{5}$ **11.** $\dfrac{1}{10}$

13. $\dfrac{7}{2(5a + 1)}$ $(a \neq 0, -\tfrac{1}{5})$ **15.** x $(y \neq -1, 0)$

17. $\dfrac{10}{7}$ **19.** $\dfrac{a(4a - 3)}{4a + 1}$ $(a \neq -\tfrac{1}{4})$

21. $\dfrac{-1}{y - 3}$ $(y \neq 2, 3)$ **23.** $-\dfrac{2b - a}{2b + a}$ $\left(b \neq 0, -\dfrac{a}{2}; a \neq b \right)$

25. $\dfrac{a + 6}{a - 1}$ $(a \neq -3, 1)$ **27.** 1 $(a, b, c \neq 0; 2a + 3b + c \neq 0)$

29. $\dfrac{-(a^2 + b^2)}{4ab}$ $(a, b, \neq 0; a \neq b, -b)$ **31.** $\dfrac{70}{29}$

Chapter 3 Review (Page 71)

1. a. $\dfrac{-1}{-(a - b)}, \ \dfrac{-1}{b - a}, \ -\dfrac{-1}{a - b}, \ -\dfrac{-1}{-(b - a)}, \ -\dfrac{1}{-(a - b)}, \ -\dfrac{1}{b - a}$

   b. $\dfrac{1}{a - b}$ is a positive number if $a > b$ and a negative number if $a < b$.

2. a. Yes   **3. a.** $4x$ $(x \neq 0, 2)$

   b. 2

                             b. $\dfrac{4x^2 - 2xy + y^2}{2x - y}$ $(y \neq -2x, 2x)$

4. $3x - 4 + \dfrac{25}{2x + 3}$ $(x \neq -\tfrac{3}{2})$ **5.** $y^2 + 2y - 4$ $(y \neq -1)$

6. $y^6 + y^5 + y^4 + y^3 + y^2 + y + 1$ $(y \neq 1)$

7. a. $\dfrac{x - 3}{(x + 1)(x + 3)}$ $(x \neq 0, 1, -1, -3)$

   b. $\dfrac{9x^2y - 3x^2y^2}{2x + 1}$ $(x \neq \tfrac{1}{2}, -\tfrac{1}{2}; y \neq 0, 3)$

8. a. 1 $(y \neq 3, -2x)$

   b. $\dfrac{1}{1 - a}$ $(a \neq 0, 1, b)$

9. a. $\dfrac{3(y - x)}{4xy}$ $(x, y \neq 0)$

 b. $\dfrac{-6y - 4}{(y - 4)(y + 4)(y - 1)}$ $(y \neq 1, 4, -4)$

10. a. $\dfrac{a^2}{a^3 + 1}$ $(a \neq 0, 1, -1)$

 b. 1 $(x \neq y, -y)$

11. a. $\dfrac{-2ab + b^2}{(a - b)^2}$ $(a \neq b)$

 b. 0 $(b \neq 0, b \neq a)$

12. $x^2 + 1$ $(x \neq 0, x \neq 1)$ **13.** 3

14. $x = y$ or $x = -y$ **15.** a and b

16. a   **17.** d and c

18. a and b   **19.** a

20. d, c, and a

Exercise 4.1 (Page 75)

1. Law IV   **3.** Law IIa   **5.** Law II   **7.** Law II

9. Law I   **11.** Law IV   **13.** Law II; Law IIa; Law V

15. Law IV; Law III   **17.** Law I; Law IV; Law III

19. x^5 **21.** y^7 **23.** x^3 $(x \neq 0)$

25. x^2y^3 $(x, y \neq 0)$ **27.** x^8 **29.** x^8

31. x^6y^9 **33.** $x^6y^4z^2$ **35.** $\dfrac{x^6}{y^9}$ $(y \neq 0)$

37. $\dfrac{81y^4}{x^8}$ $(x \neq 0)$ **39.** $\dfrac{-8x^3}{125y^6}$ $(y \neq 0)$ **41.** $108x^7$

43. $4x^7y^6$ **45.** $\dfrac{16}{x}$ $(x \neq 0)$ **47.** $\dfrac{y^4}{x}$ $(x, y \neq 0)$

49. x^4y $(x, y \neq 0)$ **51.** $\dfrac{8x}{9y^2}$ $(x, y \neq 0)$ **53.** $36y^2$ $(y \neq 0)$

55. x^{2n} **57.** x^{3n} $(x \neq 0)$ **59.** x^{2n} $(x \neq 0)$

Exercise 4.2 (Page 78)

1. 3   **3.** 2   **5.** -3 **7.** 9   **9.** 27

11. 16   **13.** $\frac{1}{32}$ **15.** $\frac{8}{27}$ **17.** Law II; Law III

19. Law V; Law III   **21.** Law V; Law IV; Law III

23. $x^{2/3}$ **25.** $x^{1/3}$ **27.** $n^{3/2}$ **29.** $m^{1/2}$

31. $a^{1/3}b^{1/2}$ **33.** $\dfrac{a^4}{c^2}$ **35.** $x^{3n/2}$ **37.** $x^{3n/2}$

39. $x^{5n/2}y^{3m/2+1}$ **41.** $x^{n/3}y^{n}$ **43.** $\dfrac{x^3y^2}{z^{1/n}}$ **45.** 5

47. $2|x|$ **49.** $\dfrac{2}{|x|(x+5)^{1/2}}$ $(x > -5, x \neq 0)$

Exercise 4.3 (Page 82)

1. $\dfrac{1}{2}$ **3.** $\dfrac{5}{3}$ **5.** 9   **7.** $\dfrac{-1}{2}$ **9.** $\dfrac{82}{9}$

11. $-\dfrac{7}{4}$ **13.** x **15.** x^7 **17.** $\dfrac{1}{x^6}$ **19.** $\dfrac{1}{x^{3/2}}$

21. $\dfrac{y^{1/2}}{x}$ **23.** 1   **25.** $\dfrac{y}{x}$ **27.** $\dfrac{a^2y^2}{b^2x^3}$ **29.** $4x^5y^2$

31. $\dfrac{4x^2}{y^{16}}$ **33.** $\dfrac{a^9b^9}{c^9}$ **35.** $\dfrac{b^2+a^2}{a^2b^2}$ **37.** $\dfrac{r^2s^2+1}{rs}$

39. $\dfrac{1}{(a-b)^2}$ **41.** $\dfrac{y^2-x^2}{xy}$ **43.** $\dfrac{a^2b+b}{a}$ **45.** $\dfrac{y+x}{y-x}$

47. a^{3-n} **49.** a^{2-2n} **51.** $b^{-1}c^{-1}$ **53.** x^{-1}

Exercise 4.4 (Page 85)

1. 3.4×10^4 **3.** 2.1×10 **5.** 8.372×10^6

7. 1.4×10^{-3} **9.** 6×10^{-7} **11.** -2.3×10^{-5}

13. 1600   **15.** 600,000   **17.** 19,500

19. 0.00000023   **21.** 12,340   **23.** 10^{-5}

25. 1   **27.** 6×10^{-3} **29.** 10^4

31. 2.5

Exercise 4.5 (Page 86)

1. x **3.** $x^{-1/3}$ **5.** $x^{4/3}$

7. $x^{3/2}+x$ **9.** $x-x^{2/3}$ **11.** $x^{-1}+1$

13. $x-x^{1/2}+4x^{-1/2}$ **15.** $(x+y)-(x+y)^{3/2}$ **17.** $x^{1/5}(x^{2/5})$

19. $x^{-2/3}(x^{1/3})$ **21.** $x(x^{-2/3})$ **23.** $x(x^{1/2}+1)$

25. $x^{1/3}(x^{2/3}-x^{1/3})$ **27.** $x^{3/2}(x^{-1}+1)$ **29.** $x^{-1/2}(x^{-1}+1)$

31. $(x+1)^{-1/2}(x)$ **33.** $(y+2)^{-2/3}(y+1)$ **35.** $x^{n/2}(x^{3n/2}+1)$

37. $(x^{1/2}-y^{1/2})(x^{1/2}+y^{1/2})$

Exercise 4.6 (Page 88)

1. $\sqrt{3}$ **3.** $\sqrt{x^3}$ **5.** $3\sqrt[3]{x}$ **7.** $-6x\sqrt{y}$

9. $\sqrt{xy}$ **11.** $-2\sqrt[5]{ab^2}$ **13.** $\sqrt{x+2y}$ **15.** $\sqrt[3]{(x-y)^2}$

17. $\sqrt{x} - \sqrt{y}$ **19.** $\dfrac{1}{\sqrt[3]{4}}$ **21.** $\dfrac{1}{\sqrt[3]{x^2}}$ **23.** $\dfrac{1}{\sqrt{x^2 - y^2}}$

25. $3^{1/2}$ **27.** $x^{2/3}$ **29.** $(xy)^{1/3}$ **31.** $4x^{1/2}$

33. $2^{1/3}x^{1/3}y^{2/3}$ **35.** $ax^{2/5}y^{3/5}$ **37.** $(x - y)^{1/2}$ **39.** $3(x^2 - y)^{1/3}$

41. $x^{1/2} - 2y^{1/2}$ **43.** $\dfrac{1}{x^{1/2}}$ **45.** $\dfrac{x}{y^{1/3}}$ **47.** $\dfrac{2}{(x + y)^{1/2}}$

49. 4   **51.** -5 **53.** 3   **55.** -4

57. -2 **59.** x^2 **61.** $2y^2$ **63.** $-x^2y^3$

65. $\frac{2}{3}xy^4$ **67.** $\dfrac{-2}{5}x$ **69.** $2|x|$

71. $|x + 1|$ **73.** $\dfrac{2}{|x + y|}$ $(x + y \neq 0)$

Exercise 4.7 (Page 93)

1. 3   **3.** $-10\sqrt{2}$ **5.** x^2 **7.** $-x\sqrt{x}$

9. $2x^2\sqrt{x}$ **11.** $-2x^3\sqrt{2}$ **13.** 4   **15.** $-2x^2$

17. $x\sqrt[4]{x}$ **19.** $x^2\sqrt[5]{xy}$ **21.** 6   **23.** x^3y

25. 2   **27.** x **29.** $10\sqrt{3}$ **31.** $100\sqrt{6}$

33. $\dfrac{\sqrt{3}}{100}$ **35.** $\dfrac{\sqrt{42}}{1000}$ **37.** $\dfrac{\sqrt{5}}{5}$ **39.** $\dfrac{-\sqrt{2}}{2}$

41. $\dfrac{\sqrt{2x}}{2}$ **43.** $\dfrac{-\sqrt{xy}}{x}$ **45.** $\sqrt{x}$ **47.** $-x\sqrt{y}$

49. $\dfrac{-\sqrt[3]{4x^2y}}{2x}$ **51.** $\dfrac{\sqrt[4]{2}}{2}$ **53.** a^2b **55.** ab^2

57. $\dfrac{1}{\sqrt{3}}$ **59.** $\dfrac{x}{\sqrt{xy}}$ **61.** $\sqrt{3}$ **63.** $\sqrt{3}$

65. $\sqrt[3]{9}$ **67.** $2\sqrt{x}$ **69.** $\sqrt{2x}$ **71.** $y\sqrt{x}$

73. $\sqrt[6]{72}$ **75.** $\sqrt[4]{20}$ **77.** $\sqrt[10]{y^7}$ **79.** $\sqrt[12]{16x^7y^9}$

Exercise 4.8 (Page 96)

1. $3\sqrt{3}$ **3.** $5\sqrt{3}$ **5.** $12\sqrt{2x}$

7. $4\sqrt{xy}$ **9.** $5\sqrt[3]{2}$ **11.** $9\sqrt[3]{2x}$

13. $\dfrac{2 + \sqrt{2}}{3}$ **15.** $\dfrac{3 + \sqrt{3}}{6}$ **17.** $\dfrac{4\sqrt{3} - 3\sqrt{2}}{6}$

19. $6 - 2\sqrt{5}$ **21.** $3\sqrt{2} + \sqrt{6}$ **23.** $1 - \sqrt{5}$

25. $x - 9$ **27.** $x - 6\sqrt{x} + 9$ **29.** $-4 + \sqrt{6}$

31. $7 - 2\sqrt{10}$ **33.** b **35.** $4 - 2\sqrt[3]{2}$

37. $2(1 + \sqrt{3})$ **39.** $6(\sqrt{3} + 1)$ **41.** $4(1 + \sqrt{y})$

43. $\sqrt{3}(y - x)$ **45.** $\sqrt{2}(1 - \sqrt{3})$ **47.** $\sqrt{x}(1 + \sqrt{3})$

49. $1 + \sqrt{3}$ **51.** $1 + \sqrt{2}$ **53.** $1 - \sqrt{x}$

55. $x - y$ **57.** $2 - 2\sqrt{3}$ **59.** $\dfrac{2(\sqrt{7} + 2)}{3}$

61. $\dfrac{4(1 - \sqrt{x})}{1 - x}$ $(x \neq 1)$ **63.** $\dfrac{x(\sqrt{x} + 3)}{x - 9}$ $(x \neq 9)$

65. $\dfrac{\sqrt{x}(\sqrt{x} + \sqrt{y})}{x - y}$ $(x \neq y)$ **67.** $\dfrac{x + 2\sqrt{xy} + y}{x - y}$ $(x \neq y)$

69. $\dfrac{\sqrt{x + 1}}{x + 1}$ **71.** $\dfrac{-\sqrt{x^2 + 1}}{x(x^2 + 1)}$ $(x \neq 0)$

73. $\dfrac{-1}{2(1 + \sqrt{2})}$ **75.** $\dfrac{x - 1}{3(\sqrt{x} + 1)}$ **77.** $\dfrac{x - y}{x(\sqrt{x} + \sqrt{y})}$

Exercise 4.9 (Page 101)

1. $3i$ **3.** $6i$ **5.** $16i\sqrt{2}$ **7.** $2i$

9. $1 - i$ **11.** $-1 - i\sqrt{2}$ **13.** $5 - i$ **15.** $-5 - 5i$

17. $2 - 12i$ **19.** -6 **21.** $6 + 3i$ **23.** $12 - 6i$

25. 13 **27.** $8 + 6i$ **29.** $-2 - 6i$ **31.** $10 + 2i$

33. $2i$ **35.** $-2 + i\sqrt{2}$ **37.** $22 + 4i\sqrt{3}$ **39.** 14

41. $-i$ **43.** $\frac{3}{2}i$ **45.** $-1 - i$ **47.** $\frac{9}{13} - \frac{6}{13}i$

49. $\frac{3}{13} + \frac{2}{13}i$ **51.** i **53.** $x \geq 3$ **55.** a. -1 b. 1 c. $-i$

57. a. $-i$ b. -1 c. i d. 1 e. $-i$

Chapter 4 Review (Page 103)

1. a. 9

  b. $\dfrac{a}{b^2 d^3}$ $(a, b, c, d \neq 0)$

2. a. x^2 $(x \neq 0)$

  b. x^{n+2} $(x \neq 0)$

3. a. 50

  b. 10^7

4. a. $\dfrac{x^2 y^3}{x^2 + y^3}$ $(x^2 + y^3 \neq 0)$

  b. $\frac{7}{3}$

5. a. $-3xy\sqrt[3]{x}$

  b. $\frac{1}{5}\sqrt[6]{5^4}$

6. a. $y\sqrt{2x}$

  b. $\dfrac{\sqrt{ab}}{b}$ $(a, b \neq 0)$

7. a. $4a\sqrt{3a}$

  b. $\sqrt{a} - \sqrt{b}$

8. a. $-1 + 5i$

  b. $10 + 5i$

9. a. $5 + i$

    b. $\dfrac{1}{3} + \dfrac{\sqrt{2}}{3} i$

10. a. $\dfrac{1}{\sqrt{3}}$

    b. $\dfrac{1}{2(\sqrt{x + 1} + \sqrt{x})}$

11. 8

12. $x \geq 4$

13. -1 and 7

14. $|x| \sqrt{2}$

15. a. Law V   b. Law III   c. Laws II, IIa, V and III

Exercise 5.1 (Page 107)

1. No   **3.** No   **5.** Yes   **7.** No   **9.** Yes

11. No   **13.** No   **15.** No   **17.** a   **19.** c

21. b   **23.** d   **25.** a

Exercise 5.2 (Page 111)

1. $\{3\}$ **3.** $\{3\}$ **5.** $\{4\}$ **7.** $\{-\frac{2}{3}\}$ **9.** $\{3\}$

11. $\{5\}$ **13.** $\{-2\}$ **15.** $\{-\frac{1}{3}\}$ **17.** $\{6\}$ **19.** $\{3\}$

21. $\{1\}$ **23.** $\{6\}$ **25.** $\{-\frac{5}{2}\}$ **27.** $\{4\}$ **29.** $\{3\}$

31. $\{-7\}$ **33.** $\emptyset$ **35.** $\{13\}$ **37.** $\emptyset$ **39.** $\{3, -3\}$

41. $\{3, 9\}$ **43.** $\{\frac{1}{4}, \frac{5}{4}\}$ **45.** $\{-\frac{8}{3}, -2\}$ **47.** $\{-\frac{1}{3}, -1\}$

49. $\{-\frac{1}{12}, \frac{1}{4}\}$ **53.** $|2x - 5|$ is always positive.   **55.** -7

Exercise 5.3 (Page 114)

1. $y = b$ **3.** $x = \dfrac{-6}{b}$ $(a, b \neq 0)$ **5.** $z = \dfrac{-b^2}{c}$ $(c \neq 0)$

7. $y = \dfrac{-bc}{a}$ $(a, b \neq 0)$ **9.** $x = \dfrac{c}{c + 1}$ $(c \neq -1)$

11. $x = a + b$ **13.** $x = \dfrac{3a + 6}{a + 3}$ $(a \neq -3)$

15. $x = \dfrac{a}{6a - 1}$ $(x, a \neq 0; a \neq \frac{1}{6})$ **17.** $x = \dfrac{ab}{a + b}$ $(a, b, x \neq 0; a \neq -b)$

19. $x = \dfrac{4b}{2a - 1}$ $(b, x \neq 0; a \neq \frac{1}{2})$ **21.** $k = v - gt$

23. $m = \dfrac{f}{a}$ $(a \neq 0)$ **25.** $v = \dfrac{K}{p}$ $(p \neq 0)$

27. $a = \dfrac{2s}{t^2}$ $(t \neq 0)$ **29.** $t = \dfrac{v - k}{g}$ $(g \neq 0)$

31. $h = \dfrac{V}{lw}$ $(l, w \neq 0)$ **33.** $B = 180 - A - C$

35. $c = \dfrac{2A - hb}{h}$ $(h \neq 0)$

37. $d = \dfrac{s - 5\pi D}{3\pi}$

39. $n = \dfrac{l - a + d}{d}$ $(d \neq 0)$

41. $x_1 = \dfrac{x_4}{x_2 - 2x_3}$ $(x_2 \neq 2x_3)$

43. $y' = \dfrac{1 + 3x}{x^2 - 2y^3}$ $(x^2 \neq 2y^3)$

Exercise 5.4 (Page 117)

23. Identity   **25.** $\emptyset$ **27.** $\{\frac{5}{3}\}$ **29.** $\{7\}$

Exercise 5.5 (Page 122)

1. $\{x \mid x < 2\}$

3. $\{x \mid x \leq 12\}$

5. $\{x \mid x > 3\}$

7. $\{x \mid x > 3\}$

9. $\{x \mid x < -6\}$

11. $\{x \mid x \geq -\frac{14}{3}\}$

13. $\{x \mid x < -\frac{6}{7}\}$

15. $\{x \mid x \leq -4\}$

17. $\{x \mid x \leq -\frac{9}{2}\}$

19. $\{x \mid -1 < x \leq 0\}$

21. $\{x \mid -\frac{7}{2} \leq x \leq \frac{5}{2}\}$

23. $\{x \mid -2 < x < 2\}$

25. $\{x \mid -7 < x < 1\}$

27. $\{x \mid 1 < x < 4\}$

29. $\{x \mid -4 \leq x \leq 12\}$

31. $\{x \mid x < -3\} \cup \{x \mid x > 3\}$

33. $\{x \mid x < -3\} \cup \{x \mid x > 7\}$

35. $\{x \mid x \leq -5\} \cup \{x \mid x \geq 2\}$

37. $\{x \mid 1 < x < 2\}$

Exercise 5.6 (Page 125)

1. a. $x + x + 2 + x + 4 = 78$

  b. 24, 26, 28

3. a. $\dfrac{x}{x + 6} = \dfrac{2}{3}$

  b. 12

5. a. $2w + 2(w + 10) = 168$

  b. width: 37 ft; length: 47 ft

7. a. $(s + 5)^2 = s^2 + 85$

  b. 6 inches

9. a. $5x + 10(x + 3) = 180$

  b. 10 nickels and 13 dimes

11. a. $150x + 85(82 - x) = 9310$

  b. 36 adults and 46 children

13. a. $0.30x + 0.12(40) = 0.20(x + 40)$

  b. 32 gal

15. a. $1.00x + 0.45(12) = 0.60(x + 12)$

   b. $4\frac{1}{2}$ oz

17. a. $0.03x + 0.04(2000 - x) = 66$

   b. \$1400 at 3%; \$600 at 4%

19. a. $0.05A + 0.03(3A) = 1680$

   b. \$12,000 in stocks; \$36,000 in bonds

21. a. $\dfrac{420}{r} = \dfrac{1260}{r + 120}$

   b. Rate of automobile: 60 mph; rate of airplane: 180 mph

23. a. $\dfrac{d}{40} = \dfrac{d}{80} + 3$

   b. 240 miles

25. a. $80 \leq \dfrac{78 + 64 + 88 + 76 + x}{5} \leq 90$

   b. grade $\geq 94\%$

Chapter 5 Review (Page 129)

1. $\{-4\}$ **2.** $\{\frac{5}{2}\}$ **3.** $y = -\dfrac{x}{5}$ **5. a.** any $x < 1$

                                                      b. $x \geq 1$

6. $\{x \mid x \leq 27\}$ **7.** $\{3, -4\}$ **8.** $\{x \mid -3 < x < 7\}$

9. $\{x \mid x \leq -3\} \cup \{x \mid x \geq 2\}$ **11.** $\emptyset$

12. 4 in.   **13.** \$2 per ft; \$3 per ft

14. Rate of slower train: 18 mph; rate of faster train: 24 mph   **15.** 26 games

Exercise 6.1 (Page 133)

1. $\{2, 3\}$ **3.** $\{0, \frac{3}{2}, -2\}$ **5.** $\{1, -\frac{5}{2}\}$

7. $\{a\}$ **9.** $\{a/2, 2a\}$ **11.** $\{3, -2\}$

13. $\{\frac{3}{2}, -1\}$ **15.** $\{-\frac{1}{2}, 3\}$ **17.** $\{a, -2a\}$

19. $\{0, -2\}$ **21.** $\{0, 6\}$ **23.** $\{3, -3\}$

25. $\{\frac{2}{3}, -\frac{2}{3}\}$ **27.** $\{\frac{5}{2}, -\frac{5}{2}\}$ **29.** $\{0, b\}$

31. $\{4, -1\}$ **33.** $\{2, -7\}$ **35.** $\{1\}$

37. $\{\frac{1}{2}, 1\}$ **39.** $\{3, -2\}$ **41.** $\{2a\}$

43. $\{\frac{3}{2}, -2\}$ **45.** $\{1, -3\}$ **47.** $\{1, -\frac{10}{3}\}$

49. $\{2, 13\}$ **51.** $x^2 - 5x + 6 = 0$ **53.** $2x^2 - 5x - 3 = 0$

55. $8x^2 - 10x + 3 = 0$ **57.** $x^2 - a^2 = 0$ **59.** $x^2 + 1 = 0$

61. $x^2 - 4x + 5 = 0$ **63.** $\{0, 2, 3\}$ **65.** $\{-2, -1, 1\}$

67. $\{-2, 1, 4\}$ **69.** $\{-3, 0, 2, 4\}$

Exercise 6.2 (Page 138)

1. $\{2, -2\}$ **3.** $\{2, -2\}$ **5.** $\{\frac{10}{3}, -\frac{10}{3}\}$

7. $\{\sqrt{5}, -\sqrt{5}\}$ **9.** $\{2\sqrt{3}, -2\sqrt{3}\}$ **11.** $\{\sqrt{c}, -\sqrt{c}\}$

13. $\{\sqrt{ab}, -\sqrt{ab}\}$ **15.** $\{3, -1\}$ **17.** $\{-1, -4\}$

19. $\{6 + \sqrt{5}, 6 - \sqrt{5}\}$ **21.** $\{2 + \sqrt{3}, 2 - \sqrt{3}\}$ **23.** $\{a + 2, a - 2\}$

25. $\left\{\dfrac{4 - b}{a}, \dfrac{-4 - b}{a}\right\}$ **27.** $\{c + b, c - b\}$ **29. a.** 1

  b. $(x + 1)^2$

31. a. 9   **33. a.** $\frac{9}{4}$ **35. a.** $\frac{49}{4}$

  b. $(x - 3)^2$ **b.** $(x + \frac{3}{2})^2$ **b.** $(x - \frac{7}{2})^2$

37. a. $\frac{1}{4}$ **39. a.** $\frac{1}{16}$ **41.** $\{2, -6\}$

  b. $(x - \frac{1}{2})^2$ **b.** $(x + \frac{1}{4})^2$

43. $\{1\}$ **45.** $\{-5, -4\}$ **47.** $\{1 + \sqrt{2}, 1 - \sqrt{2}\}$

49. $\left\{\dfrac{-3 + \sqrt{41}}{4}, \dfrac{-3 - \sqrt{41}}{4}\right\}$ **51.** $\left\{\dfrac{-2 + i\sqrt{2}}{2}, \dfrac{-2 - i\sqrt{2}}{2}\right\}$

53. $y = (x + 1)^2 + 2$ **55.** $y = (x - 4)^2 - 14$

57. $y = (x - \frac{3}{2})^2 - \frac{13}{4}$ **59.** $(x - 2)^2 + (y - 2)^2 = 5^2$

61. $(x + 3)^2 + (y - 1)^2 = 2^2$ **63.** $(x - 1)^2 + (y + 4)^2 = (\sqrt{2})^2$

65. $\left\{\dfrac{-b + \sqrt{b^2 - 4ac}}{2a}, \dfrac{-b - \sqrt{b^2 - 4ac}}{2a}\right\}$

Exercise 6.3 (Page 142)

1. $\{1, 2\}$; rational and unequal

3. $\{1\}$; rational and equal

5. $\left\{\dfrac{-1 + \sqrt{5}}{2}, \dfrac{-1 - \sqrt{5}}{2}\right\}$; irrational and unequal

7. $\{2, \frac{3}{2}\}$; rational and unequal

9. $\left\{\dfrac{1 + i\sqrt{7}}{4}, \dfrac{1 - i\sqrt{7}}{4}\right\}$; imaginary

11. $\{\frac{3}{2}, -\frac{5}{2}\}$; rational and unequal

13. $\{3, -\frac{3}{2}\}$; rational and unequal

15. $x = 2k$; $x = -k$ **17.** $x = \dfrac{1 \pm \sqrt{1 - 4ac}}{2a}$ $(a \neq 0)$

19. $x = -1 \pm \sqrt{1 + y}$ **21.** $x = \dfrac{1 \pm \sqrt{17 - 8y}}{4}$

23. $x = y \pm \sqrt{y^2 + 3y + 2}$

25. $x = \dfrac{-y \pm \sqrt{24 - 11y^2}}{6}$

27. $y = \dfrac{-x \pm \sqrt{8 - 11x^2}}{2}$

29. Rational and unequal

31. Irrational and unequal

33. Rational and equal

35. Imaginary

37. Imaginary

39. Irrational and unequal

41. $-5; -2$

43. $\frac{3}{2}; \frac{1}{4}$

45. 6; 1

47. $k = 4$

49. $\{k \mid k \le -2\}$

51. $\{k \mid k < 0\}$

Exercise 6.4 (Page 144)

1. $\{64\}$ **3.** $\{-7\}$ **5.** $\{4\}$ **7.** $\{13\}$

9. $\{5\}$ **11.** $\{0\}$ **13.** $\{4\}$ **15.** $\{1, 3\}$

17. $A = \pi r^2 \quad (r \ge 0)$ **19.** $y = \dfrac{1}{x^3} \quad (x > 0)$

21. $y = \pm \sqrt{a^2 - x^2} \quad (x \ge 0; \mid x \mid \le \mid a \mid)$

23. $x - 4$ cannot be negative.

Exercise 6.5 (Page 147)

1. $\{25\}$ **3.** $\left\{ \dfrac{1}{\sqrt{2}}, \dfrac{-1}{\sqrt{2}}, 3i, -3i \right\}$ **5.** $\{2, -7, -3, -2\}$

7. $\{64, -8\}$ **9.** $\{\frac{1}{4}, -\frac{1}{3}\}$ **11.** $\{626\}$

Exercise 6.6 (Page 150)

1. $\{x \mid x < -1 \text{ or } x > 2\}$ **3.** $\{x \mid 0 \le x \le 2\}$

5. $\{x \mid x < -1 \text{ or } x > 4\}$ **7.** $\{x \mid -\sqrt{5} < x < \sqrt{5}\}$

9. $\{x \mid x \in R\}$ **11.** $\{x \mid x \le 0 \text{ or } x \ge \frac{1}{2}\}$

13. $\{x \mid -\frac{8}{3} < x < -2\}$ **15.** $\{x \mid x < 0 \text{ or } 2 < x \le 4\}$

17. $\{x \mid -3 < x < 0 \text{ or } x > 2\}$

Exercise 6.7 (Page 151)

1. 9 and 4   **3.** 7 and 8; -8 and -7

5. 6 and 7   **7.** 4 or $\frac{1}{4}$

9. $\sqrt{185}$ in.   **11.** Width: 40 in.; length: 80 in.

13. 12 in.   **15.** $\frac{5}{2}$ sec; $\dfrac{5\sqrt{6}}{4}$

17. Rate riding: 3 mph; rate walking: 1 mph

19. 36 people

Chapter 6 Review (Page 152)

1. a. $\{0, \frac{3}{2}\}$

   b. $\{5, -3\}$

3. a. $\{0, b\}$

   b. $\left\{ \dfrac{-b + \sqrt{b^2 - 4ac}}{2c}, \dfrac{-b - \sqrt{b^2 - 4ac}}{2c} \right\}$ $(c \neq 0)$

4. a. $\{4, 1\}$

   b. $\{8\}$

6. $x^4 - 5x^2 - 36 = 0$

8. a. $\frac{2}{3}$;   **b.** $\frac{1}{3}$

10. $\{x \mid -3 \leq x \leq -2\}$

12. 40 mph

14. $x - 2 \geq 0$

2. a. $\left\{ \dfrac{5 + \sqrt{5}}{2}, \dfrac{5 - \sqrt{5}}{2} \right\}$

   b. $\{i\sqrt{3}, -i\sqrt{3}\}$

5. a. $\{2, -2, i, -i\}$

   b. $\{1, \frac{1}{4}\}$

7. $y = \dfrac{-3x \pm |x|\sqrt{5}}{2}$

9. $\{c\}$

11. Altitude: 4 in.; base: 9 in.

13. Imaginary coefficients

15. No restrictions

Exercise 7.1 (Page 156)

1. $\{(1, 1), (1, 2), (2, 1), (2, 2), (3, 1), (3, 2)\}$

3. $\{(1, 8), (1, 9), (1, 10), (2, 8), (2, 9), (2, 10), (3, 8), (3, 9), (3, 10)\}$

5. $\{(1, 1), (1, 2), (1, 3), (1, 4), (2, 1), (2, 2), (2, 3), (2, 4), (3, 1), (3, 2), (3, 3),$
   $(3, 4), (4, 1), (4, 2), (4, 3), (4, 4)\}$

7. a. $(0, 7)$ **b.** $(2, 9)$ **c.** $(-2, 5)$

9. a. $(0, -\frac{3}{2})$ **b.** $(2, 0)$ **c.** $(-5, -\frac{21}{4})$

11. $y = \dfrac{2 + x}{x}$ $(x \neq 0)$ **13.** $y = \dfrac{4}{x - 1}$ $(x \neq 1)$

15. $y > \dfrac{x^2 - 7}{4}$ **17.** $y = \pm\sqrt{\dfrac{1}{x} + 2}$ $(x \neq 0, y \neq \pm\sqrt{2})$

19. $y \leq \dfrac{3x^2 - 4}{4}$ **21.** $\{(-2, 1), (0, 0), (2, -1)\}$

23. $\{(-2, -1), (-2, 0), (-2, 1), (-2, 2), (-1, 0), (-1, 1), (-1, 2), (0, 1), (0, 2),$
   $(1, 2)\}$

25. $\{(-1, 1), (0, 0), (1, 1)\}$

27. $\{(-1, 0), (-1, 1), (-1, 2), (0, -1), (0, 0), (0, 1), (0, 2), (1, 0), (1, 1), (1, 2)\}$

29. mn

Exercise 7.2 (Page 159)

1. Relation is a function.

3. Relation is not a function.

5. Relation is a function.

7. Relation is not a function.

9. Relation is a function.

11. Prob. 1: domain, $\{0, 1, 2\}$; range, $\{0, 1, 2\}$

13. Prob. 3: domain, $\{1, 2\}$; range, $\{0, 1\}$

15. Prob. 5: domain, $\{-2, -1, 0, 1, 2\}$; range, $\{0, 1, 4\}$

17. Prob. 7: domain, $\{0, 1, 2\}$; range, $\{0, 1, 2\}$

19. Prob. 9: domain, $\{-2, -1, 0, 1, 2\}$; range, $\{0, 1, 2\}$

21. a. $3x + 3h - 4$ b. $3h$ c. 3

23. a. $x^2 + 2xh + h^2 - 3x - 3h + 5$ b. $2xh + h^2 - 3h$ c. $2x + h - 3$

25. a. $\dfrac{1}{x + h}$ $(x \neq -h)$ b. $\dfrac{-h}{x(x + h)}$ $(x \neq 0, -h)$

     c. $\dfrac{-1}{x(x + h)}$ $(x \neq 0, -h)$ **27.** $\dfrac{\sqrt{x} - \sqrt{x + h}}{h\sqrt{x}\sqrt{x + h}}$ $(h, x, x + h \neq 0)$

Exercise 7.3 (Page 165)

29. $C = 2\pi r, \{r \mid r > 0\}$ **31.** $P = 10 + 2w, \{w \mid w > 0\}$

Exercise 7.4 (Page 170)

1. Distance: 5; slope: $\frac{4}{3}$ **3.** Distance: 13; slope: $\frac{12}{5}$

5. Distance: $\sqrt{2}$; slope: 1   **7.** Distance: $3\sqrt{5}$; slope: $\frac{1}{2}$

9. Distance: 5; slope: 0   **11.** Distance: 10; slope: not defined

13. $7, 2\sqrt{17}, \sqrt{89}$ **15.** 10, 21, 17

Exercise 7.5 (Page 172)

1. $4x - y - 7 = 0$ **3.** $x + y - 10 = 0$

5. $3x - y = 0$ **7.** $x + 2y + 2 = 0$

9. $3x + 4y + 14 = 0$ **11.** $y - 2 = 0$

13. $y = -x + 3$
slope: -1
y-intercept: 3

15. $y = \frac{-3}{2}x + \frac{1}{2}$
slope: $\frac{-3}{2}$
y-intercept: $\frac{1}{2}$

17. $y = \frac{1}{3}x - \frac{2}{3}$
slope: $\frac{1}{3}$
y-intercept: $\frac{-2}{3}$

19. $y = \frac{8}{3}x$
slope: $\frac{8}{3}$
y-intercept: 0

21. $y = \frac{-2}{3}x + \frac{5}{3}$
slope: $\frac{-2}{3}$
y-intercept: $\frac{5}{3}$

23. $3x - 2y + 10 = 0$

25. a. $2x + 3y - 7 = 0$ b. $y = 0$ c. $3x + 5y + 1 = 0$ d. $x - y = 0$

Chapter 7 Review (Page 176)

1. $\{(a, x), (a, y), (b, x), (b, y), (c, x), (c, y)\}$

2. $\{(-1, -1), (2, 1)\}$

3. a. 9   b. $4x + 2h - 3$

4. Domain: $\{2, 3, 4\}$; range: $\{1, 2, 3\}$

5. x-intercept: 9; y-intercept: -6

6. 0

7. a. $\sqrt{178}$ b. $\frac{13}{3}$

8. $2x - y - 1 = 0$

9. $2x + 5y - 31 = 0$

10. $y = -\frac{2}{3}x + 2$;
    slope: $-\frac{2}{3}$;
    y-intercept: 2

11. $2x + 3y - 1 = 0$

Exercise 8.1 (Page 180)

17. a. 1 and 2
    b. minimum point: $(\frac{3}{2}, -\frac{1}{4})$

19. a. 1 and 2
    b. maximum point: $(\frac{3}{2}, \frac{1}{4})$

21. a. 1 and -9
    b. maximum point: $(-4, 25)$

23. a. 0 and -4
    b. maximum point: $(-2, 2)$

25. a. 0 and $-\frac{3}{2}$
    b. minimum point: $(-\frac{3}{4}, -\frac{9}{16})$

35. 4 and 4

37. 625 sq. in.

39. No; for each value of x, there are two values of y.

41. $f(x) = x^2, f(x) = \sqrt{x^2 + 1}$, and $f(x) = |x|$

Exercise 8.2 (Page 186)

1. a. $y = \pm\sqrt{4 - x^2}$
   b. $y = \sqrt{4 - x^2}$
      $y = -\sqrt{4 - x^2}$
   c. Domain: $\{x \mid -2 \le x \le 2\}$

3. a. $y = \pm 3\sqrt{4 - x^2}$
   b. $y = 3\sqrt{4 - x^2}$
      $y = -3\sqrt{4 - x^2}$
   c. Domain: $\{x \mid -2 \le x \le 2\}$

5. a. $y = \pm\frac{1}{2}\sqrt{16 - x^2}$
   b. $y = \frac{1}{2}\sqrt{16 - x^2}$
      $y = -\frac{1}{2}\sqrt{16 - x^2}$
   c. Domain: $\{x \mid -4 \le x \le 4\}$

7. a. $y = \pm\sqrt{x^2 - 1}$
   b. $y = \sqrt{x^2 - 1}$
      $y = -\sqrt{x^2 - 1}$
   c. Domain: $\{x \mid x \le -1 \text{ or } x \ge 1\}$

9. a. $y = \pm\sqrt{x^2 + 9}$
   b. $y = \sqrt{x^2 + 9}$
      $y = -\sqrt{x^2 + 9}$
   c. Domain: $\{x \mid x \in R\}$

11. a. $y = \pm\sqrt{\dfrac{24 - 2x^2}{3}}$
    b. $y = \sqrt{\dfrac{24 - 2x^2}{3}}$
       $y = -\sqrt{\dfrac{24 - 2x^2}{3}}$
    c. Domain: $\{x \mid -2\sqrt{3} \le x \le 2\sqrt{3}\}$

Exercise 8.3 (Page 189)

1. Circle   **3.** Parabola   **5.** Ellipse   **7.** Hyperbola

9. Two intersecting lines   **11.** Parabola   **13.** Circle

15. Ellipse   **17.** Parabola   **19.** Parabola

Exercise 8.4 (Page 193)

1. $d = kt$ **3.** $I = \dfrac{k}{R}$ **5.** $V = klw$

7. 3   **9.** 200   **11.** 2

13. 16   **15.** 400 ft   **17.** 160 lbs/sq ft

19. 3375/2 lbs

Chapter 8 Review (Page 197)

1. $(3, -4)$ **3.** $y = \frac{1}{3}\sqrt{26 - x}$

$y = -\frac{1}{3}\sqrt{26 - x}$

Domain of each: $\{x \mid x \le 26\}$

4. a. Hyperbola   **b.** Circle   **c.** Parabola   **d.** Ellipse

7. $\frac{3}{4}$ **10.** 9   **11.** $\frac{12800}{81}$ lbs

Exercise 9.1 (Page 204)

1. $\{(3, 2)\}$ **3.** $\{(2, 1)\}$ **5.** $\{(-5, 4)\}$

7. $\{(0, \frac{3}{2})\}$ **9.** $\{(\frac{2}{3}, -1)\}$ **11.** $\{(1, 2)\}$

13. $\{(-\frac{19}{5}, -\frac{18}{5})\}$ **15.** $\{(\frac{1}{5}, \frac{1}{4})\}$ **17.** $\{(-5, 3)\}$

19. $\{\frac{1}{6}, \frac{1}{2}\}$ **21.** 12

23. Length: 47 ft, width: 37 ft

25. 13 dimes, 10 nickels

27. \$1400 at 3%, \$600 at 4%

29. \$36,000 in bonds, \$12,000 in stocks

31. Airplane: 180 mph; car: 60 mph

33. $a = 1, b = -1$ **35.** $10x + 3y = 6$ **37.** $F = \frac{9}{5}C + 32$

Exercise 9.2 (Page 209)

1. 1   **3.** 0   **5.** 2

7. $-\frac{254}{225}$ **9.** $\{(1, 1)\}$ **11.** $\{(2, 2)\}$

13. $\{(6, 4)\}$ **15.** Inconsistent, $\emptyset$ **17.** $\{(4, 1)\}$

19. $\left\{\left(\dfrac{1}{a + b}, \dfrac{1}{a + b}\right)\right\}$

Exercise 9.3 (Page 212)

1. $\{(1, 2, -1)\}$ **3.** $\{(2, -2, 0)\}$ **5.** $\{(2, 2, 1)\}$

7. Dependent, infinitely many solutions

9. $\{(3, -1, 1)\}$ **11.** $\{(4, -2, 2)\}$ **13.** 3, 6, 6

15. 60 nickels, **17.** 24 ten-dollar bills,
20 dimes, 34 five-dollar bills,
5 quarters 36 one-dollar bills

19. $x^2 + y^2 + 2x + 2y - 23 = 0$

Exercise 9.4 (Page 216)

1. 3 **3.** 9 **5.** 0 **7.** -1 **9.** -5

11. 0 **13.** x^3 **15.** 0 **17.** $-2ab^2$ **19.** $\{3\}$

21. $\{2, -\frac{17}{7}\}$ **27.** 5 **29.** 6

Exercise 9.5 (Page 220)

1. $\{(1, 1, 1)\}$ **3.** $\{(1, 1, 0)\}$ **5.** $\{(1, -2, 3)\}$

7. $\{(3, -1, -2)\}$ **9.** $\emptyset$ **11.** $\{(1, -\frac{1}{3}, \frac{1}{2})\}$

13. $\{(-5, 3, 2)\}$ **15.** $\{(\frac{13}{2}, 0, -11)\}$ **17.** $\{(2, -1, 1, 0)\}$

Exercise 9.6 (Page 224)

1. Prop. 1 **3.** Prop. 3 **5.** Prop. 4 and Prop. 3

7. Prop. 2 **9.** Prop. 4 **11.** Prop. 4

13. Prop. 4 (twice) **15.** Prop. 5 **17.** Prop. 6

19. Prop. 6 **21.** Prop. 6

23. $\begin{vmatrix} 1 & 3 \\ 0 & -4 \end{vmatrix}$

25. $\begin{vmatrix} 1 & -2 & 1 \\ 0 & 7 & 1 \\ 0 & 2 & 1 \end{vmatrix}$

27. $\begin{vmatrix} 0 & 1 & -3 & -2 \\ 0 & 2 & 1 & 2 \\ 1 & 1 & 2 & 3 \\ 0 & 1 & 1 & 1 \end{vmatrix}$

29. $\begin{vmatrix} 1 & 1 & 2 & 1 \\ 2 & -2 & -1 & 2 \\ 3 & -2 & 1 & 1 \\ 0 & 0 & 0 & 1 \end{vmatrix}$

31. $-1 \begin{vmatrix} 2 & 1 \\ -1 & 2 \end{vmatrix} = -5$

33. $\begin{vmatrix} -1 & -5 \\ 2 & -2 \end{vmatrix} = 12$

35. $\begin{vmatrix} 4 & 4 \\ 3 & 7 \end{vmatrix} = 16$

37. $\begin{vmatrix} 1 & 3 \\ 15 & 10 \end{vmatrix} = -35$

39. $\begin{vmatrix} 6 & 1 \\ 0 & 3 \end{vmatrix} = 18$

Exercise 9.7 (Page 228)

  1. $\{(-1, -4), (5, 20)\}$ **3.** $\{(2, 3), (3, 2)\}$

  5. $\{(-3, 4), (4, -3)\}$ **7.** $\{(2, 2), (-2, -2)\}$

  9. $\{(i\sqrt{7}, 4), (-i\sqrt{7}, 4)\}$ **11.** $\{(3, 1), (2, 0)\}$

  13. $\{(-1, -3)\}$ **15.** $\left\{(0, -1), \left(\dfrac{30}{13}, \dfrac{7}{13}\right)\right\}$

  17. $2, 3$ **19.** Length: 12 in., width: 1 in.

  21. Length: 7 ft, width: 2 ft

  23. Pressure: 6 lbs/sq in., volume: 5 cu in.

  25. $\{(2, 2), (-2, -2)\}$

Exercise 9.8 (Page 232)

  1. $\{(1, 3), (-1, 3), (1, -3), (-1, -3)\}$

  3. $\{(1, 2), (-1, 2), (1, -2), (-1, -2)\}$

  5. $\{(3, \sqrt{2}), (-3, \sqrt{2}), (3, -\sqrt{2}), (-3, -\sqrt{2})\}$

  7. $\{(2, 1), (-2, 1), (2, -1), (-2, -1)\}$

  9. $\{(\sqrt{3}, 4), (-\sqrt{3}, 4), (\sqrt{3}, -4)(-\sqrt{3}, -4)\}$

  11. $\{(1, -2), (-1, 2), (2, -1), (-2, 1)\}$

  13. $\{(2, -2), (-2, 2), (2i\sqrt{2}, i\sqrt{2}), (-2i\sqrt{2}, -i\sqrt{2})\}$

  15. $\{(1, -1), (-1, 1), (i, i), (-i, -i)\}$

  17. $\{(3, 1), (-3, -1), (2\sqrt{7}, -\sqrt{7}), (-2\sqrt{7}, \sqrt{7})\}$

  19. a. 1   b. 2   c. 4

Chapter 9 Review (Page 233)

  1. $\{(\tfrac{1}{2}, \tfrac{7}{2})\}$ **2.** $\{(1, 2)\}$ **3.** $\{(-4, 3, -2)\}$ **4.** $\{(2, 1, -1)\}$

  5. $\{(4, -13), (1, 2)\}$ **6.** $\{(3, -2), (-2, 0)\}$

  7. $\{(2, 3), (2, -3), (-2, 3), (-2, -3)\}$

  8. $\{(2, 1), (-2, -1), (1, 2), (-1, -2)\}$

  9. -13 **10.** -2 **11.** $\{-7, 4\}$ **12.** $\{2, -1, 3\}$

  13. a. consistent and independent   b. dependent   c. inconsistent

  14. Property 4   **15.** Property 1   **16.** Property 6

  17. Properties 4 and 3   **19.** 31   **20.** $D = 0$

Exercise 10.1 (Page 237)

  1. $-4, -3, -2, -1$ **3.** $-\tfrac{1}{2}, 1, \tfrac{7}{2}, 7$

  5. $2, \tfrac{3}{2}, \tfrac{4}{3}, \tfrac{5}{4}$ **7.** $0, 1, 3, 6$

9. $-1, 1, -1, 1$

11. $1, 0, -\frac{1}{3}, \frac{1}{2}$

13. $4n$

15. $3n - 1$

17. $(-1)^n$

19. $(-1)^n(2n + 1)$

21. $\dfrac{n}{n + 1}$

23. $n^2 + 1$

25. x^{n+1}

27. $(-1)^n x^{2n-1}$

29. 40 bacteria,
160 bacteria,
$10(2)^n$ bacteria

31. 25 grams,
$6\frac{1}{4}$ grams

Exercise 10.2 (Page 239)

1. $1 + 4 + 9 + 16$

3. $3 + 4 + 5$

5. $2 + 6 + 12 + 20$

7. $-\frac{1}{2} + \frac{1}{4} - \frac{1}{8} + \frac{1}{16}$

9. $1 + 3 + 5 + \cdots$

11. $1 + \frac{1}{2} + \frac{1}{4} + \cdots$

13. $3 + 5 + 7 + \cdots + (2n + 1)$

15. $\dfrac{1}{2} + \dfrac{2}{9} + \dfrac{3}{64} + \cdots + \dfrac{n}{(n + 1)^n}$

17. $\displaystyle\sum_{i=1}^{4} 2i$

19. $\displaystyle\sum_{i=1}^{5} x^{(2i+1)}$

21. $\displaystyle\sum_{i=1}^{4} \frac{1}{3^i}$

23. $\displaystyle\sum_{i=0}^{n} i$

25. $\displaystyle\sum_{i=1}^{n} \frac{1}{2^i}$

27. $\displaystyle\sum_{i=1}^{\infty} \frac{i}{i + 1}$

29. $\displaystyle\sum_{i=1}^{\infty} \frac{i}{2i - 1}$

31. $\displaystyle\sum_{i=1}^{\infty} \frac{2^{i-1}}{i}$

33. For each n, there is one value for S_n; n; S_n

Exercise 10.3 (Page 243)

1. 11, 15, 19
$s_n = 4n - 1$

3. $-9, -13, -17$
$s_n = 3 - 4n$

5. $x + 2, x + 3, x + 4$
$s_n = x + n - 1$

7. $x + 5a, x + 7a, x + 9a$
$s_n = x + 2an - a$

9. $2x + 7, 2x + 10, 2x + 13$
$s_n = 2x + 3n - 2$

11. $3x, 4x, 5x$
$s_n = nx$

13. 31

15. $\frac{15}{2}$

17. -92

19. $2; 3, 41$

21. 28th term

23. 63

25. 806

27. -6

29. 1938

31. 196 bricks

33. $\frac{14}{15}$

Exercise 10.4 (Page 247)

1. 128, 512, 2048
$s_n = 2(4)^{n-1}$

3. $\frac{16}{3}, \frac{32}{3}, \frac{64}{3}$
$s_n = \frac{2}{3}(2)^{n-1}$

5. $-\frac{1}{2}, \frac{1}{4}, -\frac{1}{8}$

$s_n = 4(-\frac{1}{2})^{n-1}$

7. $-\frac{x^2}{a^2}, \frac{x^3}{a^3}, -\frac{x^4}{a^4}$

$s_n = \frac{a}{x}\left(-\frac{x}{a}\right)^{n-1}$

9. 1536

11. $-243a^{20}$

13. 3

15. 1092

17. $\frac{31}{32}$

19. $\frac{364}{729}$

21. 83

23. 42

Exercise 10.5 (Page 250)

1. 24

3. Does not exist

5. $\frac{9}{20}$

7. $\frac{8}{49}$

9. 2

11. $\frac{1}{3}$

13. $\frac{31}{99}$

15. $2\frac{410}{999}$

17. $\frac{29}{225}$

19. 20 cm

21. 30 ft

Exercise 10.6 (Page 253)

1. 24

3. 9

5. 15

7. 6

9. $\frac{1}{6}$

11. $\frac{21}{19}$

13. $(n+2)(n+1)$

15. $\frac{n+1}{n+3}$

17. $\frac{2n-1}{2(n-1)}$

19. $3!$

21. $\frac{6!}{2!}$

23. $\frac{8!}{5!}$

25. $x^5 + 15x^4 + 90x^3 + 270x^2 + 405x + 243$

27. $x^4 - 12x^3 + 54x^2 - 108x + 81$

29. $8x^3 - 6x^2y + \frac{3}{2}xy^2 - \frac{1}{8}y^3$

31. $\frac{1}{64}x^6 + \frac{3}{8}x^5 + \frac{15}{4}x^4 + 20x^3 + 60x^2 + 96x + 64$

33. $x^{20} + 20x^{19}y + \frac{20\cdot19}{2!}x^{18}y^2 + \frac{20\cdot19\cdot18}{3!}x^{17}y^3 + \cdots$

35. $a^{12} + 12a^{11}(-2b) + \frac{12\cdot11a^{10}}{2!}(-2b)^2 + \frac{12\cdot11\cdot10a^9}{3!}(-2b)^3 + \cdots$

37. $x^{10} + 10x^9(-\sqrt{2}) + \frac{10\cdot9x^8}{2!}(-\sqrt{2})^2 + \frac{10\cdot9\cdot8x^7}{3!}(-\sqrt{2})^3 + \cdots$

39. 1.22

41. 0.92

43. $1216.64

45. $-3003a^{10}b^5$

47. $3360x^6y^4$

49. a. $1 - x + x^2 - x^3 + \cdots$

     b. $1 - x + x^2 - x^3 + \cdots$

Chapter 10 Review (Page 255)

1. $1, -\frac{1}{2}, \frac{1}{3}, -\frac{1}{4}$

2. $\dfrac{1}{2^n - 1}$

3. $2 + 6 + 12 + 20$

4. $\displaystyle\sum_{i=2}^{\infty} x^i$

5. a. 94
   b. 138

6. 3015

7. 68

8. $\frac{37}{48}$

9. $-15x + 16y$

10. a. $\frac{-81}{8}$
   $\frac{-1261}{216}$

11. $\frac{739}{32}$

12. $14, -14$

13. $\frac{1}{2}$

14. $(n + 1)(n - 1)$

15. a. $x^9 - 9x^8y + \dfrac{9 \cdot 8 x^7 y^2}{2} - \dfrac{9 \cdot 8 \cdot 7 x^6 y^3}{3 \cdot 2}$
   b. $84x^3y^6$

Exercise 11.1 (Page 259)

1. $(0, 1), (1, 3), (2, 9), (3, 27)$

3. $(-2, \frac{1}{4}), (0, 1), (2, 4), (4, 16)$

5. $(-3, 8), (0, 1), (3, \frac{1}{8}), (5, \frac{1}{32})$

7. $(-3, \frac{1}{1000}), (-2, \frac{1}{100}), (-1, \frac{1}{10}), (0, 1)$

Exercise 11.2 (Page 262)

1. $2y + 4x = 7$; defines a function

3. $x = y^2 - 4y$; does not define a function

5. $y^2 + 4x^2 = 36$; does not define a function

7. $y^2 - x^2 = 3$; does not define a function

9. $x = \sqrt{4 + y^2}$; does not define a function

11. $x = |y|$; does not define a function

13. $F^{-1}: y = x$

15. $F^{-1}: y = \dfrac{4 - x}{2}$

17. $F^{-1}: y = \dfrac{4x + 12}{3}$

23. $\{y \mid y \geq 0\}$; $F^{-1}: x = y^2 - 2y + 1$ or $y = 1 \pm \sqrt{x}$, $\{x \mid x \geq 0\}$

25. $\{x \mid x \in R\}$; $\{y \mid y > 0\}$; $F^{-1}: x = 2^y$; F^{-1} is a function

Exercise 11.3 (Page 264)

1. $\log_4 16 = 2$
3. $\log_3 27 = 3$
5. $\log_{1/2} \frac{1}{4} = 2$
7. $\log_8 \frac{1}{2} = -\frac{1}{3}$
9. $\log_{10} 100 = 2$
11. $\log_{10} 0.1 = -1$
13. $2^6 = 64$
15. $3^2 = 9$
17. $(\frac{1}{3})^{-2} = 9$
19. $(10)^3 = 1000$
21. $(10)^{-2} = 0.01$
23. 2
25. 3
27. $\frac{1}{2}$
29. -1
31. 1
33. 2
35. -1
37. 2
39. 2
41. 64
43. -3
45. 100
47. 4
49. 0, 0, 0

Exercise 11.4 (Page 266)

1. $\log_b x + \log_b y$
3. $\log_b x - \log_b y$
5. $5 \log_b x$
7. $\frac{1}{3} \log_b x$
9. $2 \log_b x + 3 \log_b y$
11. $\frac{1}{2}(\log_b x - \log_b z)$
13. $\frac{1}{3} \log_{10} x + \frac{2}{3} \log_{10} y - \frac{1}{3} \log_{10} z$
15. $\frac{1}{2} \log_{10} x + \frac{2}{3} \log_{10} y$
17. $\frac{1}{2} \log_{10} x + \frac{1}{2} \log_{10} (x - y)$
19. $\log_{10} 2 + \log_{10} \pi + \frac{1}{2} \log_{10} l - \frac{1}{2} \log_{10} g$

21. $\log_b (xy)$
23. $\log_b \left(\dfrac{1}{x}\right)$
25. $\log_b (x^2 y^3)$

27. $\log_b \left(\dfrac{x^3 y}{z^2}\right)$
29. $\log_{10} \dfrac{x(x - 2)}{z^2}$

Exercise 11.5 (Page 270)

1. 2
3. 3
5. -2 or $8 - 10$
7. 0
9. -4 or $6 - 10$
11. 4
13. 0.8280
15. 1.9227
17. 2.5011
19. $9.9101 - 10$
21. $8.9031 - 10$
23. 2.3945
25. 4.10
27. 36.7
29. 0.0642
31. 16.0
33. 5480
35. 0.000718
37. 9.10
39. 5000
41. 113
43. 2; 5; 2; 1

Exercise 11.6 (Page 273)

1. 0.6246
3. 0.7937
5. 3.1824
7. 4.5695
9. $9.7095 - 10$
11. $7.9218 - 10$
13. 3.225
15. 89.38
17. 10.52
19. 0.05076
21. 0.7485
23. 0.7495
25. $\log_{10} 3.751$; it is closer to a tabulated value.

Exercise 11.7 (Page 276)

1. 4.014	**3.** 2.299	**5.** 64.34
7. 2.010	**9.** 3.436×10^{-10}	**11.** 0.04582
13. 9.872	**15.** 4.746	**17.** 1.394
19. 3.483	**21.** 57.81	**23.** 2.206
25. 1.11 sec.	**27.** 1.49 cu. ft.	

Exercise 11.8 (Page 278)

1. $\left\{ \dfrac{\log_{10} 7}{\log_{10} 2} \right\}$

3. $\left\{ \dfrac{\log_{10} 8}{\log_{10} 3} - 1 \right\}$

5. $\left\{ \dfrac{\log_{10} 3}{2 \log_{10} 7} + \dfrac{1}{2} \right\}$

7. $\left\{ \sqrt{\dfrac{\log_{10} 15}{\log_{10} 4}}, \ -\sqrt{\dfrac{\log_{10} 15}{\log_{10} 4}} \right\}$

9. $\left\{ -\dfrac{1}{\log_{10} 3} \right\}$

11. $\left\{ 1 - \dfrac{\log_{10} 15}{\log_{10} 3} \right\}$

13. $n = \dfrac{\log_{10} y}{\log_{10} x}$

15. $t = \dfrac{\log_{10} y}{k \log_{10} e}$

17. {500} **19.** {4} **21.** {3} **23.** {7}

Exercise 11.9 (Page 281)

All answers are given to the nearest hundredth.

1. 1.10	**3.** 2.83	**5.** 5.79	**7.** 3.18
9. 3.32	**11.** 3.41	**13.** 1.08	**15.** 0.77
17. 0.79	**19.** 1.66	**21.** 2.10	**23.** 2.86

Exercise 11.10 (Page 285)

Certain of the following answers are approximate values. They are consistent with the given data and the use of four-place tables.

1. 1.34	**3.** 5%	**5.** 20 yrs
7. 2.5%	**9.** 12 yrs	**11.** $7396, $7430
13. 7	**15.** 7.7	**17.** 6.2
19. 1.0×10^{-3}	**21.** 2.5×10^{-6}	**23.** 6.3×10^{-8}
25. 1.0×10^{-9}	**27.** 2.5×10^{-6}	**29.** 2.0×10^{-3}
31. 12 grams	**33.** 30 in. of mercury, 16.1 in. of mercury	

Chapter 11 Review (Page 287)

2. $\{(x, y) \mid x = y^2 - 4y\}$ or $\{(x, y) \mid y = 2 \pm \sqrt{4 + x}\}$; inverse is not a function.

4. a. $\log_9 27 = \frac{3}{2}$
  b. $\log_{4/9} \frac{2}{3} = \frac{1}{2}$

5. a. $5^4 = 625$
  b. $10^{-4} = 0.0001$

6. a. 27

  b. $\sqrt[3]{3}$

8. a. 0.01503

  b. 5289

10. a. 26.09

  b. 1.387

12. a. 1.95

  b. 0.51

14. $\{x \mid x < 10^5\}$

7. a. $9.8531 - 10$

  b. 3.2587

9. a. $\log_a 3 + 2 \log_a x + \log_a y$

  b. $\frac{1}{2} \log_a x + \log_a y - 2 \log_a z$

11. a. $\left\{ \dfrac{\log_{10} 15}{\log_{10} 3} \right\}$

  b. $\left\{ \dfrac{1}{\log_{10} 2} + 4 \right\}$

13. 2

15. \$5944

INDEX

INDEX